Annals of the DEEP SKY

A Survey of Galactic and Extragalactic Objects

Volume 6

Chamaeleon
Circinus
Columba
Coma Berenices
Corona Australis

Jeff Kanipe
Dennis Webb

Willmann-Bell, Inc. ™

P.O. Box 35025 • Richmond, VA 23235 • TOLL FREE 1 (800) 825-7827 • (804) 320-7016 • FAX (804) 272-5920
www.willbell.com

Annals of the Deep Sky® is a Registered Trademark of Willmann-Bell, Inc.
Copyright © 2018 Jeff Kanipe and Dennis Webb
Published by Willmann-Bell, Inc., P.O. Box 35025, Richmond, Virginia 23235

Without limiting the rights under copyright reserved above, no part of this publication may be reproduced, stored in or introduced into a retrieval system, or transmitted, in any form or by any means (electronic, mechanical, photocopying, recording or otherwise) without prior written permission of both the copyright owner and the above publisher of this book.

The scanning, uploading, and distribution of this book via the Internet or via any other means without the permission of the publisher is illegal and punishable by law.

Printed in the United States of America
First Printing, September 2018

Library of Congress Cataloging in Publication Data
Annals of the deep sky : a survey of galactic and extragalactic objects / [edited] by Jeff Kanipe and Dennis Webb.
    volumes cm
 Includes bibliographical references and index.
 Contents: volume 1. Andromeda, Antlia, Apus, and Aquarius
 ISBN 978-1-942675-00-6 (vol. 1 : alk. paper) -- ISBN 978-1-942675-01-3 (vol. 2 : alk. paper) 1. Astronomy--Encyclopedias. 2. Astronomy--Observers' manuals. 3. Constellations--Encyclopedias. I. Kanipe, Jeff, 1953- II. Webb, Dennis (Dennis J.)
 QB143.A56 2015
 523.802'16--dc23
                        2015001109
Volume 3 ISBN 978-1-942675-04-4
Volume 4 ISBN 978-1-942675-05-1
Volume 5 ISBN 978-1-942675-09-9
Volume 6 ISBN 978-1-942675-11-2

The following trademarks are hereby acknowledged:
Telrad

About the photograph on the cover: M64, the "Black Eye" or "Evil Eye" galaxy, is a product of the collision of two galaxies a billion years ago that has endowed the disk with a spectacular band of absorbing dust in front of the galaxy's bright nucleus, as well as unusual internal motions. In most galaxies, all stars rotate in the same direction, in this case clockwise. Research conducted in the 1990s, however, found that gas in the outer regions of M64 rotates in the opposite direction. Young, hot stars have sprung up in the shear region and appear as chains of blue stars near pink star forming regions of ionized hydrogen gas. This Hubble Space Telescope image was made using the Wide Field Planetary Camera 2. Credits: NASA and the Hubble Heritage Team (AURA/STScI); Acknowledgment: S. Smartt (Institute of Astronomy) and D. Richstone (University of Michigan).

Table of Contents

Dedicated to Ernst Johannes Hartung, author *of Astronomical Objects for Southern Telescopes*. After a long career teaching chemistry and leading research at the University of Melbourne, E. J. Hartung (1893–1970) retired to the countryside, built an observatory with a 30-cm telescope, and recorded observations of 4,000 southern objects. In 1968, Melbourne University Press published his comprehensive observer's guide, still in print and a singular amateur reference. Hartung's circa 1935 portrait reflects his curiosity and discipline. (Courtesy University of Melbourne, Colin Sach Collection, University of Melbourne Archives, 1985.0025.00011.)

Acknowledgments

Annals of the Deep Sky would not be possible without the help, advice, wisdom, evaluation, and services of the following individuals, organizations, and institutions, for which we are sincerely grateful.

Our reviewers — Harold Corwin, Paul Downing, Sue French, John D. Koester, and Brian Skiff — lent their keen eyes to review draft copy and figures. William I. Hartkopf of the U. S. Naval Observatory helped us disentangle multiple stars. Owen Brazell of the Webb Deep-Sky Society provided scanned versions of all *Deep-Sky Observer* journals. Dennis Crabtree of the National Research Council's Dominion Astrophysical Observatory, in Canada, discussed historical astronomy and the role of John Brashear, and provided a photograph. Bart Fried, founder and past-president of the Antique Telescope Society who provided a photograph, and Walter Stephani, specialist in the history of European astronomy, supplied telescope and historical scholarship concerning John Brashear and Max Wolf. Stephani was a great help in licensing Heidelberg Observatory photographs and plates. Daniel Mounsey and the good folks at Woodland Hills Camera and Telescopes, in California, provided sound telescope advice. Connor Ward built a database of constellations harboring known exoplanets, while Elisa Quintana of the Goddard Space Flight Center supplied additional perspective on exoplanets. Once again, we give Carolyn Chappell a big hug for compiling and managing image and figure permissions and credits. And a big thank you to Alexandra Witze for her text reviews and copyediting skills.

We wish to thank the following online data services: SIMBAD, VizieR, and the ALADIN interactive sky atlas offered by Centre de Données Astronomiques de Strasbourg; the NASA/IPAC Extragalactic Database (NED); the Smithsonian Astrophysical Observatory/NASA Astrophysics Data System (ADS); the Washington Double Star Catalog (WDS) maintained by the U. S. Naval Observatory; the Variable Star Index, Variable Star Plotter, and Light Curve Generator provided by the American Association of Variable Star Observers (AAVSO); the WEBDA open cluster database maintained by the Department of Theoretical Physics and Astrophysics of Masaryk University; the globular cluster catalog of parameters compiled by William E. Harris; the HyperLeda database of galaxies; James B. Kaler and his expansive website "Stars"; the downloadable database of Wolfgang Steinicke's *Revised New General Catalogue* and *Index Catalogue*; and WikiSky.org. We further acknowledge the analog databases found in the *Uranometria 2000.0 Deep Sky Field Guide* by Murray Cragin and Emil Bonanno, as well as Brent A. Archinal and Steven J. Hynes' *Star Clusters*, both published by Willmann-Bell. Another W-B product we salute is *MegaStar5* by Emil Bonanno, for helping us determine precise angular sizes and position angles.

Thanks again to Robert Hurt, visualization scientist for Spitzer and *GALEX*, for allowing us to use his rendering of the Milky Way's possible face-on appearance, which appears many times in this series.

Many thanks to our amateur colleagues for sharing their images, drawings, observing notes, and helpful critiques, specifically Bertrand Laville, Uwe Glahn, Richard Miller, Steve Crouch, and George Robert Kepple. We also thank the imagers of Astronomischer Arbeitskreis Salzkammergut for generously sharing their massive and ever expanding collection known as ccdguide.com.

We are grateful for individuals and institutions who shared their historical and recent photographs, including Silvia Torres-Peimbert and Elsa Recellas for their imagery related to Marie Pismis; Caltech archives for the Owen Wilson portrait; Philip Nagy for permitting our use of a photograph from the Edward Emerson Barnard Papers, Vanderbilt University Special Collections and University Archives; Bill Keel for a recent photograph of a historic telescope in Mexico; Barry Madore for his generous licensing of Halton Arp's *Atlas of Peculiar Galaxies* images; the University of Toronto and Pieter von Dokkum for the image of the Dragonfly array and team; the University of Heidelberg for photographs and plate scans associated with Max Wolf; and the Carnegie Library in Pittsburgh, and John D.

Koester, for photographs about John Brashear.

We are especially grateful to the professional journals of the American Astronomical Society, which publishes through IOP Science the *Astronomical Journal*, the *Astrophysical Journal*, and its *Supplements* and *Letters*. We are also grateful to the European Southern Observatory, which publishes *Astronomy & Astrophysics* through EDP Sciences.

A sincere thanks is also owed to the images and data freely provided by a number of NASA-supported orbiting observatories, including the *Hubble Space Telescope* under the auspices of the Space Telescope Science Institute (STScI) — including the Hubble Legacy Archive and the *Galaxy Evolution Explorer* (*GALEX*) archive, GALEXVIEW, provided by the Mikulski Archive for Space Telescopes (MAST). Similar thanks to the *Spitzer Space Telescope* and the *Wide-Field Infrared Survey Explorer* (*WISE*) infrared imaging sources offered by the NASA/IPAC Infrared Science Archive (IRSA), hosted by Caltech.

We additionally wish to thank the individuals overseeing the first and second generation of the STScI Digitized Sky Survey (DSS) images derived from scans of previous sky surveys, specifically the National Geographic Society Palomar Observatory Sky Survey (POSS I) and the Southern Sky Atlas and its Equatorial Extension (collectively known as SERC-J) made with the UK Schmidt Telescope at the Anglo-Australian Observatory, now called the Australian Astronomical Observatory. Lynn Kosloski, Brian McLean, and Fred Watson supported our use of these images.

We also appreciate the generous image-release policies of several organizations: STScI and its Hubble Heritage Program, offered by MAST; ESA/Hubble (the European Space Agency's significant role in the *Hubble Space Telescope*); the European Southern Observatory; *Chandra X-ray Observatory* images, released by the Chandra X-ray Center (CXC) at the Smithsonian Astrophysical Observatory (SAO), in partnership with NASA; and *The Carnegie-Irvine Galaxy Survey*, 2011, with generous support by Luis Ho. We especially appreciate the recent release of Sloan Digital Sky Survey (SDSS) imagery to the public domain, and we are grateful for their generous previous licensing of their images.

Jeff Kanipe, left, and Dennis Webb at the Texas Star Party 2018. Jeff was award-ed the Texas Star Party's Lone Star Gazer Award for his individual observation skills, an award Dennis earned in 2003 for his work on the Arp galaxies before their book on the subject. Photo courtesy Ann Webb.

Introduction

A WONDER LIKE NO OTHER

In her book *The Edge of the Sea* (1955), conservationist and author Rachel Carson referred to the countless grains of sand on a beach as both "beautiful" and "mysterious." Each grain, she wrote, "is the result of processes that go back into the shadowy beginnings of life, or of the earth itself."

Instead of sand, Carson might have been writing about stars, since they, too, are countless and the result of processes that extend back to the beginning of the universe. Astronomers, both amateur and professional, are often keenly aware of the enormity of their subject, although approaching it from the scientific perspective can sometimes make it a clinical exercise. Still, we are compelled to occasionally set aside our wired-up telescopes bristling with lenses, filter arrays, cameras, autoguiders, and hand controls, and simply gaze up at the universe *in situ*, as it were. It's as if we have a need to take it directly into our eyes without intervening optical apparatuses, where we may internalize it as a song, a poem, or ineffable meditation. When I asked a friend at a recent star party what she felt when she looked up at the stars, I was struck by her reply: "I feel a wonder like no other."

That is well said. Such sentiments express how we as compilers of *Annals of the Deep Sky* often feel — a singular wonder not only at the physical scale of the universe (and our smallness in it), but also its beauty and mystery. These attributes, after all, are what attract us to chasing stellar flickers and shadows between the stars, to pursue and celebrate what we may not be able to understand, but can certainly appreciate. Stars and galaxies, like grains of beach sand, each have their own evolutionary story that can be traced back to the primordial universe. Toward that end, we are pleased to present for your consideration volume 6, which abounds in through-the-looking-glass examples of stars and deep-sky objects.

Take Alpha Chamaeleontis for example, a star that is not what it appears. Its spectrum resembles an old giant, but its luminosity and temperature indicate that it's a younger dwarf. Epsilon Cha is also enigmatic in that it not only harbors an unknown number of companions, but it also may be a member of an entire association of comoving stars.

Consider another denizen of Chamaeleon, NGC 2915. Optical observations show it to be a modest-size galaxy with a nucleus that exhibits coarse star streams. Radio observations, however, reveal that the galaxy is immersed in a vast pool of neutral hydrogen with a radius at least a dozen times that of the visible disk.

Curiouser and curiouser are the objects we find in the other constellations featured in this volume. The Circinus Galaxy (ESO 97-13) exhibits both Seyfert 1 and Seyfert 2 characteristics (broad and narrow emission lines), while its ratio of infrared to nonthermal radio luminosity resembles that of the starburst galaxy M82 in Ursa Major. It apparently harbors an active galactic nucleus cloaked in a dusty torus that has produced a bipolar radio lobe.

Columba, too, has its cabinet of curiosities. The star Mu Columbae appears to be a runaway that originated in a double-star system in Orion some 2.5 million years ago. Its former stellar "partner" now resides in Auriga as AE Aurigae, 65° (1,600 light-years) to the north. Ensconced in the constellation's southwestern corner, the bright globular cluster NGC 1851 may have a secret identity: its huge halo suggests that it may have once been a dwarf galaxy. How a globular cluster or dwarf galaxy can retain such a large halo remains a mystery. And just looking at the image of another galaxy in that constellation, NGC 2188, one wonders how it came to look like a bar in a barred galaxy, but without a surrounding disk.

It was once theorized that this galaxy was not a disk system, per se, but a spinning rod!

There is simply no end to stellar and nonstellar curios in Coma Berenices, beginning with its alpha star Diadem, a close binary that is seen virtually edge-on. Because the components are so close in brightness, making it difficult to differentiate the primary from the secondary, it took years before a period was determined. Then we have FK Comae Berenices, which rotates at a dizzying speed of 160 kilometers per second. It is known as a "flip-flop" yellow giant because its concentrated active region periodically flips from one longitude to its opposite, where it remains for a little over 6 years before returning to its original longitude. The star may also be the product of a partially coalesced binary system. In any case, FK is not your typical rotational variable star.

Coma's Galactic *Wunderkammer* features such objects as NGC 5053, a globular cluster that may have been plucked by our galaxy from the Sagittarius dwarf spheroidal galaxy, and M53, a first-generation globular cluster, i.e., one of the oldest known in our galaxy: age, 12.7 billion years.

There are simply too many galactic oddities to mention here, but we will cite M64, a.k.a. the Black Eye Galaxy. It exhibits a well-defined inner ring from which spiral arms spring in a counterclockwise direction. But it also possesses an outer pseudoring from which two low-contrast spiral arms unwind in a *clockwise* direction. Add to this M85, a peculiar a luminous lenticular outlier of the Virgo cluster. It has apparently interacted with its barred-spiral neighbor, NGC 4394, the result being an unusual swirly spiral structure in the outer regions of M85. And, of course, we have to include NGC 4676 AB (Arp 242), known as the Mice for their double-tailed structure, the result of a close interaction that will lead to their eventual merger and reincarnation as an elliptical galaxy hundreds of millions of years hence. Other galaxies, such as NGC 4565 (the Needle Galaxy), M95 (with its prominent bar), the grand design spiral M100, and the two supergiant central elliptical galaxies in the Coma Cluster, NGC 4889 and NGC 4874, are just beautiful systems to study observationally or image.

And let's not forget little Corona Australis, the Southern Crown, which despite its southerly location can be seen in the southerly latitudes of the Northern Hemisphere. This little jewel hosts a very old globular cluster (NGC 6541) and a binary galaxy (NGC 6768), with overlapping halos. Also interspersed among the stars of Corona Australis is the Corona Australis Molecular Cloud. Good things do come in small packages!

The Navajo people traditionally greet each day with a morning prayer that evokes their spiritual attachment with everyone and with Mother Earth. There are many variations of this prayer, but the one I like best encapsulates the simplicity, and continual pursuit, of beauty in the universe.

> With beauty may I walk.
>
> With beauty before me, may I walk.
>
> With beauty behind me, may I walk.
>
> With beauty below me, may I walk.
>
> With beauty above me, may I walk.
>
> With beauty all around me, may I walk.

Enough said. We hope readers enjoy this volume of *Annals*. Perhaps it will provide new inspiration when looking up at the stars.

Chamaeleon

Chamaeleon, the German Chamäleon, the French Caméléon, and the Italian Camaleonte, is a small and unimportant constellation below Carina, Octans separating it from the south pole.

— Richard Hinckley Allen

It is not *Annals* policy to deem any constellation "unimportant," but judging by the popular literature — old and new — Chamaeleon comes close. Robert Burnham Jr. devoted a single page of tabulated data to the constellation in his *Celestial Handbook*, and E. J. Hartung admitted in *Astronomical Objects for Southern Telescopes*, "There is little telescopic interest in this constellation." It would seem so. Its brightest star, Alpha (α) Chamaeleontis, glimmers squarely at magnitude 4, and the other stars comprising the main astronomical figure are somewhat fainter. The constellation lies off the Milky Way in a very dim region of sky, overshadowed by Carina to the north. Its deep-sky fare amounts to one planetary nebula and several faint galaxies. On the other hand, it does possess what stellar astronomers refer to as the Chamaeleon molecular cloud complex, one of the nearer star-forming sites and of intense interest.

Chamaeleon was one of 12 constellations, most of them representing exotic creatures, introduced in the late 16th century by Dutch navigators Pieter Dirkszoon Keyser and Fred-

Chamaeleon, the Chameleon	
Abbreviation: **Cha**	Pronunciation: **cuh-MEAL-yun, cuh-MEAL-ee-yun**
Genitive: **Chamaeleontis**	Pronunciation: **cuh-MEAL-ee-on-tiss**
Midnight culmination: **March 1**	
Size on the sky: **131.6 square degrees**	
Bright stars: **None**	
Bright nonstellar objects: **None**	
Popular asterisms: **None**	
Note: One of 12 constellations introduced by Dutch navigators Pieter Dirkszoon Keyser and Frederick de Houtman, circa 1596–1603.	

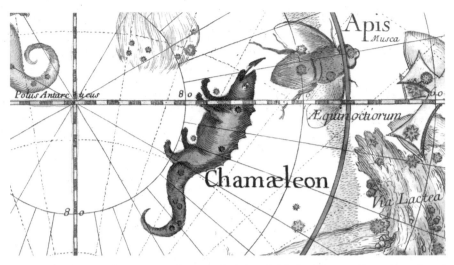

Figure 1: Chamaeleon, near the South Celestial Pole. The small reptile, related to iguanas, treads the far southern declinations near the *Via Lactea* (Milky Way), depicted here in Ignace-Gaston Pardies's *Globi Coelestis*, 1693 edition. Atlases of this time illustrated star maps with depictions of the figure referenced in the constellation's name, here the small reptile. Pardies's engravers made some remarkable art, but this rendering only roughly reflects the Mediterranean creature.

erick de Houtman at the request of cartographer Petrus Plancius. Little is known about Keyser and de Houtman, and not much more about Plancius, but their contributions, at least, have endured. Plancius was a Calvinist theologian and scholar whose interest in missionary work provided the inspiration for his cartographic pursuits. His 1589 celestial globe, published with Michael van Langren, featured stars in the Southern Hemisphere that had not been previously depicted: *Crux, Triangulum Antarcticus* (later renamed Triangulum Australis) and the *Nubeculae Magellani*. Plancius persuaded Keyser, who served on one of the first trade voyages to Asia, and de Houtman to provide further observations of the southern skies during their voyage aboard the *Hollandia* to the East Indies in 1595–1597. The expedition spent several months anchored at Madagascar, where Keyser made most of his observations. It was said that Keyser, assisted by Houtman, worked perched on the ship's crow's nest using either a cross-staff or astrolabe given to him by Plancius. Keyser died during the voyage in September 1596, but his observations were

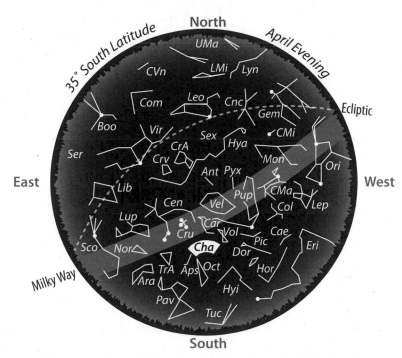

Figure 2: Chamaeleon located on the celestial sphere.

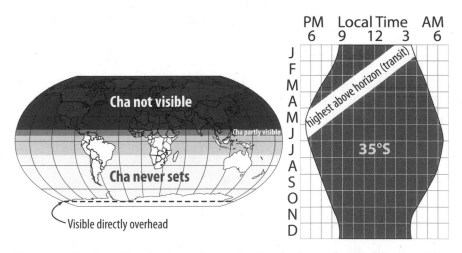

Figure 3: Seeing Chamaeleon from the Earth throughout the year. This small constellation is near the South Celestial Pole. The hourglass figure on the right shows the time at which Chamaeleon appears highest in the sky across the months of the year and the duration of night at 35° S latitude. Transit times may be used at any latitude.

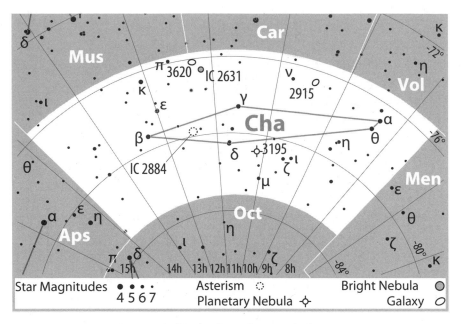

Figure 4: Chamaeleon featured objects.

delivered to Plancius when the fleet returned to Holland the following year. Because Keyser's original manuscript has been lost, it is not known if he sorted the stars into the new constellations or whether Plancius or someone else did that. In any case, the new constellations were incorporated into Plancius' new globe, published by Jodocus Hondius the Elder in 1598, and were subsequently adopted by Johann Bayer and included in his *Uranometria* of 1603. On a globe published in 1612 with Pieter van den Keere, Plancius added another eight constellations, a number of which had biblical references. These did not survive, but others such as Monoceros, Camelopardalis, and Columba remain.

THE CHAMAELEON MOLECULAR CLOUD

Nearby star-forming region

We begin, not with stars, but with clouds, namely the Chamaeleon molecular cloud complex, which occupies most of the eastern and central regions of the constellation. Deep,

> ## Chamaeleon Featured Objects, North to South
> **NGC 3620:** nearly edge-on system with possible active nucleus (**page 28**).
>
> **IC 2631:** reflection nebula illuminated by Herbig Ae/Be star (**page 20**).
>
> **NGC 2915:** dwarf spiral immersed in a voluminous disk of neutral hydrogen (**page 24**).
>
> **Alpha (α) Chamaeleontis:** a dwarf that appears to be a giant (**page 8**).
>
> **IC 2884:** chain of five stars (**page 19**).
>
> **Epsilon (ε) Chamaeleontis:** member of the Epsilon Chamaeleontis stellar association (**page 11**).
>
> **Delta (δ) 1 and 2 Chamaeleontis:** wide optical double (**page 10**).
>
> **NGC 3195:** smaller version of the Dumbbell Nebula (**page 22**).

widefield image surveys show the entire region swathed in smeary palls of interstellar dust (see images in WikiSky or Google Sky, for example). It is one of the nearest star-forming sites at a distance of 150 to 180 parsecs (500 to 600 light-years). Many of the stars we see in this part of the constellation either lie in the cloud's foreground or are slightly embedded within. The complex comprises three molecular subgroups, Chamaeleon I, II, and III.

Table 1: Chamaeleon I, II, III

Molecular Clouds	RA 2000.0 Dec	
	h m	° ′
Cha I	11 06	−77 18
Cha II	12 53	−77 10
Cha III	12 37	−80 15

Interestingly, as infrared observations have revealed (de Oliveira et al., 2014), each cloud has a different star formation history and structure, and yet all three may be physically related. Cha I has established stars and appears to have arrived at the end of its main star-formation phase. It is dominated by a central ridge of emission surrounded by striations that run parallel with the Galactic magnetic field. Cha II is actively forming stars and has a more fragmented appearance with extended emission regions and some faint striations. Cha III appears quiescent and shows no clear signs of star formation. It is organized into a complex network of filaments and exhibits fewer structures that resemble striations.

Given that the three subgroups are part of a coherent formation, the question arises as to why each should have evolved differently. The most likely explanation is that their formation has been governed by large-scale turbulence from stellar winds or expanding shock fronts from supernova explosions. As we shall see, the Chamaeleon region is exposed to the Scorpius-Centaurus OB association, an active and robust star-forming region that has been the site of a number of supernovae. The stellar wind gusts from these outbursts might have affected their evolutionary history. Different initial distributions of neutral hydrogen and dynamics (like colliding H I flows) also could have sculpted the clouds at different times, acting to merge and build up larger structures or dissolve them. This could also explain the ridge-like formation seen in Cha I, where these processes have already ended. In addition, the magnetic field might also have played a significant role in shaping both cloud structure and star-formation activity.

Only Cha I exhibits some visual features that are best appreciated in deep images. The most prominent telescopic feature is IC 2631, a reflection nebula produced by the embedded Herbig Ae/Be B9 dwarf, HD 97300. We profile IC 2631 later in this constellation. Some 47 arcminutes SSW of this object, the 11th-magnitude T Tauri star TYC 9414-787-1 seems to peer from a corner of some rather heavy extinction lying west and SW. About 16 arcminutes to the SSE is a pair of stars 2.3 arcminutes apart. The more northern of the two, DI Cha (magnitude 11), is another T Tauri star; the other to the ESE, HD 97048 (magnitude 9), is a Herbig Ae/Be star. Both are seen through a screen of Pleiades-like dust. Finally, a little over 5 arcminutes SSE of HD 97048 we find another curiosity, HH909A, a Herbig-Haro star that is still in the process of forming, but doing it fitfully, ejecting streamers of gas from its poles. *Hubble Space Telescope* images reveal two V-shaped cones forming a bipolar nebula, with the star itself partially shrouded by dense equatorial dust.

Although not always visually appealing (in fact, they are sometimes not visible at all), molecular clouds in the Galaxy exhibit complex spatial structures that need to be understood

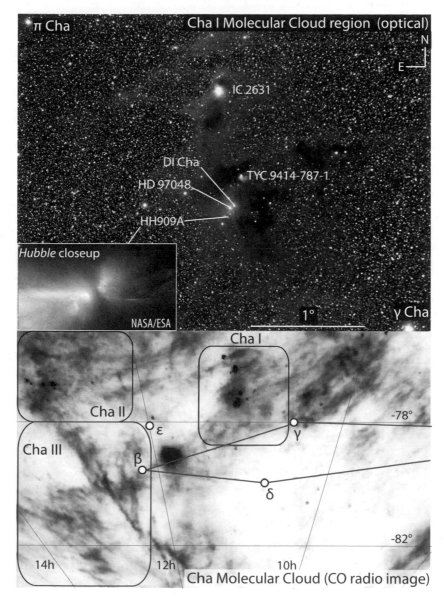

Figure 5: Chamaeleon Molecular Cloud, annotated. Cha I, top photograph, is the most visually interesting of the three, courtesy Bernhard Hubl, Christoph Kaltseis, Wolfgang Leitner, and Herbert Walter of ccdguide.com. Inset at left is a *Hubble* close-up of Herbig-Haro star HH909A. All three clouds are depicted in the radio map of carbon monoxide below, courtesy Boulanger et al., 1998. **Contemplative observing:** Locate the triangle of stars Beta, Gamma, and Delta in the constellation Chamaeleon. Visualize the vast, intricately textured clouds of gas, a product of billions of years of supernovae, condensing to become stars once again.

in order to study their large-scale evolution. The Chamaeleon clouds make a perfect laboratory for this. Plus, they leave hordes of stars in their place.

NOTABLE STARS IN CHAMAELEON

Alpha (α) Chamaeleontis

A dwarf that appears to be a giant

The brightest star in Chamaeleon has been included in numerous surveys such as age, metallicity, and kinematic studies (of 14,000 F and G dwarfs); rotation and lithium abundances (for 309 stars); and X-ray emission from A0-F6 stars (56 samples). It was even included in an investigation as to whether life could develop in habitable zones of subgiant and giant stars (Lopez at al., 2005). The answer is yes; it is possible, depending on where the potential life forms are with respect to the star as it evolves toward the asymptotic giant branch. For a single solar-mass star at the first stages of its post-main-sequence evolution, the habitable zone is estimated to last several billion years at 2 AU and around 100 million years at 9 AU. Life could even occupy a habitable zone between 7 and 22 AU after the helium flash phase for an additional billion years. Thus, any life in the environs of Alpha Chamaeleontis could form at — or (if technologically capable) remove itself to — these distances during its final evolutionary stages. The study is an intellectual exercise in how intelligent life among the stars could "make do" with what it is given.

The star is sometimes typified as a white F giant or subgiant, but it is not what it appears. Its parameters are straightforward enough. At a distance of about 72 light-years, it is a solar neighbor. Its luminosity is nearly eight times that of the Sun and it has an effective surface temperature of 6,700 K. Its rotation velocity is 36 kilometers per second, so it makes a full rotation in about 2.3 days. However, stellar theory based on luminosity and temperature tells us that Alpha Cha is not a true giant but an advanced hydrogen-fusing dwarf with a

Alpha (α) Chamaeleontis Star	HD 71243 SAO 256496	RA 08ʰ 18ᵐ 31.5ˢ Dec −76° 55′ 10.9″ Mag 4.0 SpType F5V

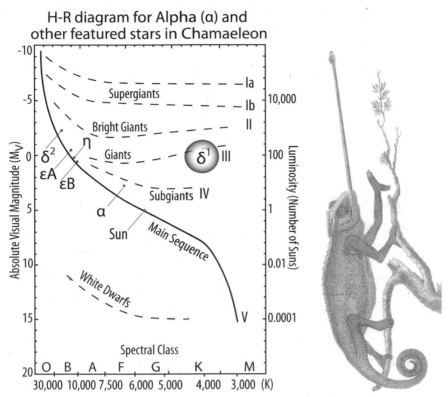

Figure 6: Alpha (α) Chamaeleontis and other featured stars on the Hertz-sprung-Russell diagram.

mass 1.6 times that of the Sun. Like the Sun, it has an outer corona heated via magnetic activity to a temperature of nearly 4 million K that also radiates in X-rays. Stellar specialist James Kaler notes that true giant stars dredge up newly formed nitrogen, leading to a high ratio of nitrogen to carbon. Lithium, meanwhile, is drawn downward by convective currents and easily destroyed by nuclear processes. Therefore, such stars should have both high nitrogen and low lithium abundances. But for some unknown reason, the abundances of both elements in Alpha Cha are high, making the star look

Delta (δ) 1 and 2 Chamaeleontis Star pair	HD 93779 (δ¹) HD 93845 (δ²)	RA 10h 45m 16.3s Mag 5.5 (δ¹), 4.4 (δ²)	Dec –80° 28' 10.5" SpType K0III (δ¹), B3V (δ²)

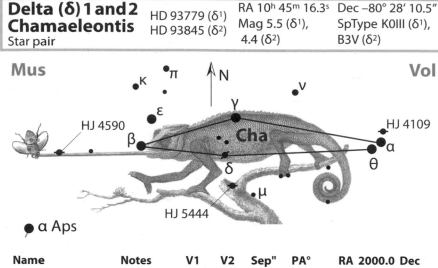

Name	Notes	V1	V2	Sep"	PA°	RA 2000.0 Dec	
Delta (δ) Cha	yellow-white	5.5	4.4	258.0	164	10 45 16	–80 28 10
HJ 4109	AB	7.2	8.2	26.0	130	08 22 48	–76 25 51
HJ 4590	AB	6.6	9.2	21.6	133	13 33 14	–77 34 10
HJ 5444	AB	7.0	9.1	41.3	236	10 31 52	–81 55 16

Figure 7: Delta (δ) Chamaeleontis and other double stars for beginners. The figure at the top is a basic star chart of the easier double stars in Chamaeleon, in the style of the Northern Hemisphere book *In Starland With a Three-inch Telescope* (1909) by William Tyler Olcott.

simultaneously old and young. "Consistently," writes Kaler, "its spectrum shows it to be an older giant with a dead helium core, yet its luminosity and temperature show it to be a younger dwarf." That's one sneaky star.

Delta (δ) 1 and 2 Chamaeleontis

Wide optical double

Delta Cha consists of two components, Delta¹ and Delta², with visual magnitudes of 5.5 and 4.4, respectively. They form a wide pair with a separation of 4.3 arcminutes in PA 163.8°. According to double star observer Sissy Haas, both are yellow in color, with δ¹ having a deeper yellow hue. (Note that some observers report that δ^2 is bluish-white.) They also each have different proper motions; hence, this is an optical pair. δ^2 is a B3 dwarf for which there are several discordant distance estimates. The *Extended Hipparcos Compilation* (2012) cites 107 parsecs (350 light-years); the *Hipparcos* estimate for δ^1 is 106 parsecs (345 light-years), so, if we trust these distance values, the stars are at least near each other in space. δ^1's luminosity is some 86 times that of the Sun, while δ^2 comes in at 600 $L_\odot$. From a hypothetical planet orbiting either star, both must appear dazzling in their sky.

δ^1 forms a close pair with a magnitude 6.5 companion at 0.8 arcsecond in PA 85° (epoch 1996). In 1898 Robert Innes measured the separation and PA as being 0.6 arcsecond and 60°, respectively, so both the angle and separation have increased. Their common proper motion indicates that this is a probable binary. Hartung claims to separate the pair with a 20-centimeter (7.8-inch) telescope. We recommend high magnification and steady seeing.

Epsilon (ε) Chamaeleontis

Member of the Epsilon Chamaeleontis stellar association

For those who assume that nothing much is going on anywhere within the bounds of Chamaeleon, read on. Some time spent with Epsilon Chamaeleontis will dispel this illusion. To begin with, it is a challenging binary star. Discovered and measured by John Herschel in 1835, the position angle at the time was 179° and the separation 1.6 arcseconds. For epoch 2017, these are now 247° and 0.2 arcsecond. In *Double Stars for Small Telescopes* (2006), Sissy Haas reports the pair could be separated in a 12-inch, while smaller apertures would probably show an elongated star. Given its most recently measured separation, though, that latter description may now apply to larger apertures. Epsilon A is a B9 dwarf with an effective temperature of 10,000 K, while its companion is an undetermined A-class star with an estimated temperature of about 9,600 K. Their projected physical separation falls somewhere

Epsilon (ε) Chamaeleontis	HD 104174 SAO 256894	RA 11ʰ 59ᵐ 37.5ˢ Dec −78° 13′ 18.6″ Mag 4.9+6.0 SpType B9V(n)+A PA (AB) 247 Sep (AB) 0.2″ Epoch 2017

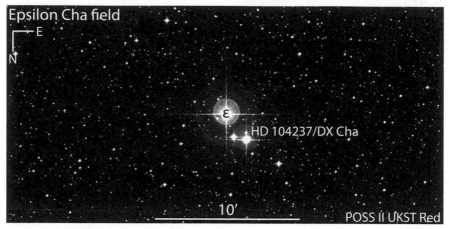

Epsilon Cha field

HD 104237/DX Cha

10′

POSS II UKST Red

Figure 8: Epsilon (ε) Chamaeleontis. The small group only hints at the larger story, seen here in a UKST Red plate.

between 50 and 200 AU, which implies an orbital period of many centuries. The *Washington Double Star Catalog* also notes a component closer in, with a separation of 0.1 arcsecond at PA 29° (epoch 2017). Its spectral type is unknown.

In the same field with Epsilon is a star positioned 2.3 arc-minutes to the NNE (PA 38°). One could argue that it may actually be the more interesting study. Cataloged as HD 104237, it is an irregular variable with a magnitude range between 6.6 and 6.7; its alias is DX Cha. What attracts astron-omers is that it is the visually brightest known young Herbig Ae/Be star and one of the nearest as well (about 104 parsecs). Such stellar specimens are pre-main-sequence stars, still con-tracting and surrounded by gas and dust from their natal cloud. (Their lower-mass brethren are T Tauri stars.) Many possess circumstellar disks that are considered sites of ongo-ing planet formation. The spectra of Ae/Be stars are picketed with emission lines of hydrogen and calcium arising from associated nebular material.

Now here is where things get a little complicated. It turns out that the Epsilon Cha AB system is a comoving neighbor of HD 104237. Moreover, HD 104237 is not an isolated star but a

Table 2: Epsilon Cha group's brighter members

Name	RA 2000.0 Dec h m s ° ′ ″	Mag V	Spec	Star type
CPD-68 1388	10 57 49 −69 13 60	10.3	K1V(e)	Pre-Main Seq
TYC 9414-191-1	11 16 29 −78 25 21	11.0	K5	
DZ Cha	11 49 32 −78 51 01	12.8	M0Ve	Orion Variable
T Cha	11 57 14 −79 21 32	11.9	K0e	Orion Variable
DW Cha	11 58 28 −77 54 30	10.5	K4Ve	BY Dra Var
EE Cha	11 58 35 −77 49 31	6.7	A7V	Delta Sct Var
Eps Cha	11 59 38 −78 13 19	4.9	B9V	
HIP 58490	11 59 42 −76 01 26	11.1	K4Ve	T Tauri
HD 104237/DX Cha	12 00 05 −78 11 35	6.6	A4V	
HD 104467	12 01 39 −78 59 17	8.5	G3V(e)	T Tauri
GSC 09420-00948	12 02 04 −78 53 01	12.5	M0e	T Tauri
EF Cha	12 07 06 −78 44 28	7.5	A9III/IV	Delta Sct Var
HD 105515	12 09 08 −78 46 53	6.9	A6III/IV	Pulsating var
HD 105923	12 11 38 −71 10 36	9.1	G8V	Pre-Main Seq
RX J1220.4-7407	12 20 22 −74 07 39	12.8	M1V	T Tauri
GSC 09235-01702	12 21 05 −71 16 49	11.7	K7V	Suspected Var
CD-74 712	12 39 21 −75 02 39	10.3	K3Ve	T Tauri
CD-69 1055	12 58 26 −70 28 49	10.0	K0Ve	Pre-Main Seq
CPD-68 1894	13 22 08 −69 38 12	10.4	K1Ve	T Tauri

member of a small stellar community that shares the same motion through space as HD 104237 and Epsilon. Both the cluster and Epsilon are referred to as the Epsilon Chamaeleontis association (**Table 2**) in the tradition of naming these stellar collectives after the most massive member. It lies in the foreground of the Chamaeleon molecular cloud complex (**Figure 5**), with Cha I to the NW and Cha II and Cha III to the west and SW, respectively. The existence of the association has been noted in the literature since 1998, when several young *ROSAT* sources were detected between the Cha I and II dark clouds with proper motions that placed them much closer to the Sun (Frink et al.). Subsequent observations turned up additional proper-motion members, and the group of scattered stars began to take on the appearance of a kinematic association. Just how many stars are true members is still unfolding, but here's what is known so far.

A *Chandra* study using the telescope's imaging spectrometer (Feigelson et al., 2003) discovered that the HD 104237 system is at least a quintet ranging in spectral types from B9 to M5. Four of its components are low-mass pre-main-sequence stars in "nonhierarchical orbits" within a projected separation of 1,500 AU from the Herbig Ae/Be primary. Two of those low-mass members are actively accreting T Tauri stars.

A multiwavelength campaign employing optical coronagraphic, near- and mid-infrared, optical, and ultraviolet observations using the *Hubble Space Telescope* and the Very Large Telescope in Chile revealed even more about HD 104237 and its cluster (Grady et al., 2004). A new spectral type was derived (A7.5-8Ve) along with a revised luminosity estimate some 1.4 times that of the Sun. The temperature is around 8,250 K, with the caveat that the uncertainty is ± 200 K. HD 104237's age, and hence the age of the cluster, is between 3 and 5 million years. The star is still accreting mass, and as such, it exhibits conspicuous ultraviolet and far-ultraviolet excess (hence the "e" in the spectral classification) as well as a bipolar "microjet" (**Figure 9**). Like all Herbig Ae/Be stars, HD 104237 also exhibits considerable infrared excess, first discovered in *Infrared Astronomical Satellite* data in 1988 (Walker and Wolstencroft; Hu et al., 1989). The star is embedded in a hot, optically thick circumstellar disk, which is viewed nearly face-on (about 20° from pole-on). Its radial extent is at most 0.6 arcseconds, which from a distance of 115 parsecs amounts to 70 AU. Six additional components were observed in the system during the 2004 study, and these and other components were confirmed in subsequent observations. In all, the Epsilon Cha association contains at least 12 components, including one (HD 104237C) that has a mass between 13 and 15 Jupiters, putting it at the boundary between brown dwarfs and free-floating planets (Fang et al., 2013).

There's more. The Epsilon Cha association is not the only sparse cluster in Chamaeleon. Another young stellar aggregate, the Eta Cha association (**Table 3**), was discovered in 1999 (Mamajek et al.). Eta is a magnitude 5.4, B8 dwarf located 9.5°

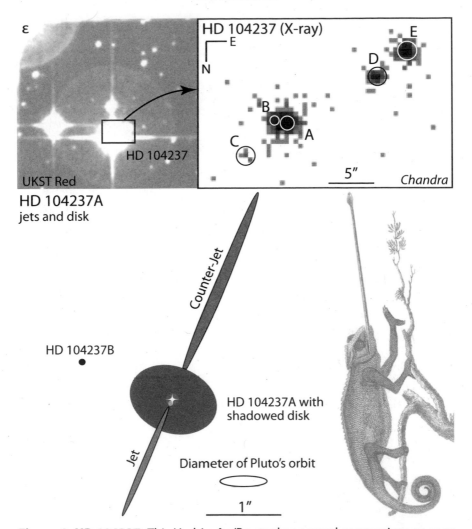

Figure 9: HD 104237. This Herbig Ae/Be star has several companions as seen in an X-ray detail of the UKST image at upper right (from Feigelson et al., 2003), as well as a jet and disk system (lower panel, Grady et al., 2004). **Contemplative observing:** Find this star NE of Epsilon Chamaeleontis with a telescope, try to resolve its companions at high power, and consider that the brighter star has a disk and jets that seed the interstellar medium with molecules.

WSW of Epsilon. In addition to Eta, the system consists of an A7+A8 binary, RS Cha (HD 75747) 8.4 arcminutes in PA 141°; this pair also has a likely lower mass companion. The other member is HD 75505, 5.3 arcminutes in PA 166°. They have a projected separation of less than a quarter parsec. To date, at

Table 3: Eta Cha group's brighter members

Name	RA 2000.0 Dec h m s ° ′ ″		Mag V	Spec	Star type
EG Cha	08 36 56	−78 56 46	10.5	K4Ve	Orion Variable
Eta Cha	08 41 20	−78 57 48	5.5	B8V	
HD 75505	08 41 45	−79 02 53	7.4	A1V	
EI Cha	08 42 24	−79 04 03	12.7	K7	Orion Variable
EM Cha	08 43 07	−79 04 52	10.8	K3	Orion Variable
RS Cha	08 43 12	−79 04 12	6.1	A7V	Algol Variable
EO Cha	08 44 32	−78 46 31	12.5	M0	Orion Variable
EP Cha	08 47 02	−78 59 34	11.1	K5	Orion Variable
EQ Cha	08 47 57	−78 54 53	13.3	M3	Orion Variable

least 18 cluster members with spectral types ranging from B8 to M5.5 have been accounted for. Several are binaries, and some still possess detectable amounts of gas in their protoplanetary disks, which is unusual given the association's age of ~ 7 million years; disks are believed to dissipate in timescales less than 10 million years (Riviere-Marichalar et al., 2015).

At any rate, if distance estimates are correct, the Eta Cha association, at a mean distance of 97 parsecs, is slightly nearer than the Epsilon Cha association; hence, both are foreground associations to the Ophiuchus-Scorpius-Centaurus association (OSCA, 115 to 215 parsecs). Intriguingly, initial studies found that Epsilon Cha appeared to be moving in the same general direction across the sky, in tandem, in fact, with the OSCA and its subgroups (Upper Scorpius, Upper Centaurus-Lupus, and Lower Centaurus-Crux). According to one study (Feigelson 2003), the extrapolated motions of both HD 104237 and Epsilon Cha put them within 10 parsecs of the center of the OSCA subgroups in the past 10 million years. Hence, it appeared there was a kinematic link between the OSCA and the Epsilon Cha association, indicating that they may have originated in the same giant molecular cloud (GMC).

But, like human aspirations, stellar contrivances are rarely so linear. One nagging concern with this scenario was the discrepancy in ages between the Epsilon Cha group (3-5

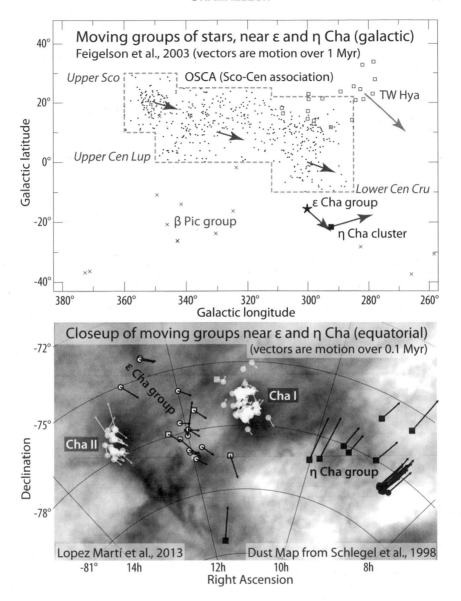

Figure 10: Eta and Epsilon Cha proper motions with nearby groups. A wide field at top relates these moving groups to the northerly Scorpius-Centaurus Association, discussed in Centaurus in Volume 5. Below is a close-up of the region showing spatial locations of some member stars, including those from Cha I & II groups. Note that the two maps are in different coordinate systems. **Contemplative observing:** Locate Epsilon and Eta Cha visually. Consider these stars represent groups of stars born together and moving through the Galaxy, among other such groups.

million years) and the OSCA subgroups nearest to Epsilon — Upper Centaurus-Lupus and Lower Centaurus-Crux — which are about 17 and 16 million years old, respectively. Moreover, a kinematic and comparative age analysis (Murphy et al., 2013) showed that the Eta Cha association formed 4 to 8 million years ago in the outskirts of Scorpius-Centaurus, 1 to 3 million years *before* the majority of Epsilon Cha members. Evidently, the two groups were separated by about 30 parsecs when Eta Cha subsequently formed in the outskirts of the Scorpius-Centaurus Group. Based on proper motion studies, the Chamaeleon I and II moving groups constitute two physical entities that exhibit slightly different spatial motion, further suggesting different origins for the populations in both clouds, but just how different remains unclear. The kinematic data also indicates that Cha I and II are unrelated to the foreground clusters, Epsilon and Eta, which constitute two different proper motion groups.

As it is sometimes said of incredulous situations, it's complicated. With some arm waving, age discrepancies may be explained by how the cloud complex, in which stars form, disperses over time based on proper motion velocity vectors established by internal turbulence processes (Feigelson 1996). In this scenario, some portions of the GMC may collapse quickly to form rich clusters and dissipate their molecular material, while other portions remain gaseous as they disperse, forming stars with a range of ages over wide areas. Different regions of the complex "fly apart" without collisions; hence, relatively young, sparse groups, such as those around Epsilon and Eta Cha, may be found near older clusters like the OSCA subgroups, but on different space motions. The older

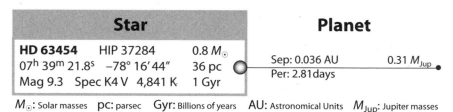

Star			Planet	
HD 63454 HIP 37284	0.8 $M_\odot$		Sep: 0.036 AU	0.31 M_{Jup}
07^h 39^m 21.8^s −78° 16′ 44″	36 pc		Per: 2.81 days	
Mag 9.3 Spec K4 V 4,841 K	1 Gyr			

$M_\odot$: Solar masses pc: parsec Gyr: Billions of years AU: Astronomical Units M_{Jup}: Jupiter masses

Figure 11: One star with an exoplanet in Chamaeleon.

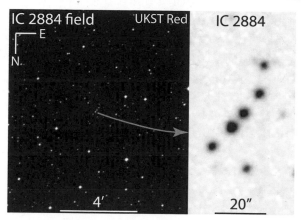

Figure 12: IC 2884. This tiny arc of stars was mistaken for a nebula, earning its IC designation. Its discoverer, DeLisle Stewart (1870–1941), was an early scientific astrophotographer at Harvard's Southern Hemisphere observatory in Peru.

ages of the OSCA subgroups implies that a wave of star formation proceeded north to south across the Galactic plane 15 to 20 million years ago, and that it is now ending with the birth of these last two sparse clusters.

As starless as the constellation Chamaeleon appears to the eye now, one has to admit that it has been the scene of past robust star activity and migration, and may still hold surprises in the future. Sometimes, to really appreciate our universe one has to see it not how it is, but how it was and will be.

GALACTIC OBJECTS IN CHAMAELEON

IC 2884

Chain of five stars

Observers with telescopes of at least 18 inches will have to reach for this one. The SIMBAD and Aladin Sky Atlas databases do not recognize it, and it is not listed in Archinal and Hynes *Star Clusters*, though it is plotted in WikiSky, Starry

Night, and MegaStar, and various data are available from VizieR. It is located about 2.3° WSW of Beta (β) Chamaeleontis. Archinal and Hynes don't list it because this really isn't a star cluster at all but a tight little chain of five stars of similar brightness (around magnitude 16) extending in a north-south curve over about 40 arcseconds. If you're determined to observe it, you will need the necessary aperture and high magnifications. The proper motions of this stellar aggregate indicate that it is not a true cluster, but it is an interesting alignment nonetheless. If you can locate 6th-magnitude HD 98617 (11^h 18^m 34.4^s; −79° 40' 07") and 8th-magnitude HD 99016 just 8 arcminutes east, IC 2884 is 17 arcminutes to the ESE of that latter star.

American astronomer DeLisle Stewart discovered IC 2884 in May 1900. Stewart was a staff member at Harvard College Observatory's Arequipa, Peru, station at the time of the discovery. According to NGC/IC scholar Wolfgang Steinicke, Stewart found 672 IC objects, most of which were new. One can speculate that, since a large fraction of IC objects were discovered photographically, this object perhaps looked nebulous on the plate. Stewart, it turns out, was an early proponent of astrophotography. He later founded the Cincinnati Astronomical Society in 1911 and was its president until his death, February 2, 1941.

There are actually countless star trains, chains, gyres, and loops apparent in the sky, some rather impressive, other not so much. This one, we think, falls into the latter group; still we know many observers who love to seek out these curious star patterns, be they physically associated or not.

IC 2631

Reflection nebula illuminated by Herbig Ae/Be star

This modest reflection nebula may be found near the Carina-Musca border with Chamaeleon, nearly three degrees NE of Gamma (γ) Cha. Observers using 12- to 14-inch telescopes describe it in volume 3 (the southern sky) of *The Night Sky*

IC 2631 Reflection Nebula	Ced 112	RA 11h 09m 52.4s Dec −76° 36′ 57″ Mag − Size 8′

IC 2631   5′   ESO
E
N

Figure 13: IC 2631. Deep ESO image of the region from the La Silla Observatory in Chile shows the reflection nebula and subtle glowing as well as dark areas nearby.

Observer's Guide as a "bright bluish-white, irregularly round haze surrounding a white 9th-magnitude star." That star, HD 97300, is a newborn Herbig Ae/Be B9 dwarf, and is the cause of the nebula's luminance. Images show a delicate drapery of dust in streamers, part of the Chamaeleon I molecular cloud. Impenetrable pockets of absorption material span the main nebular form to the north, with a considerably larger extent falling away to the south. A stunning image captured by the MPG/ESO 2.2-meter telescope at La Silla, Chile, faithfully rendered the intense localized blaze of reflected light from HD 97300, as well as dark nebulae and globules. Although there is scant research on this intriguing object, we encourage our friends in the Southern Hemisphere to both observe and image it.

NGC 3195 Planetary Nebula	Hen 2-44 PK 296-20.1	RA 10ʰ 09ᵐ 20.9ˢ Dec −80° 51′ 31″ Mag 11.6 Size 42″ Central *Vm 15.3

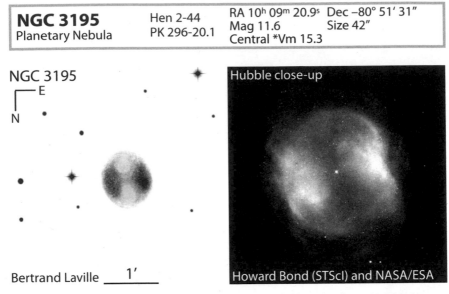

Figure 14: NGC 3195. An eyepiece impression, left, and a deep *Hubble* image, right, show the rich structure of this planetary nebula.

A nearly edge-on spiral galaxy, NGC 3620 (ESO 38-10), lies 32.5 arcminutes to the NE along the edge of the tenuous IC 2631 nebular field. We profile this object later in this constellation.

NGC 3195

Smaller version of the Dumbbell Nebula

Lying a mere 9° from the South Celestial Pole, NGC 3195 is the southernmost of the bright planetary nebulae, which means that it is, unfortunately, unavailable to observers in the Northern Hemisphere. It may be found near the right rear leg of the Chameleon, some 1.3° WSW of δ² Chamaeleontis. John Herschel discovered this small-disk planetary in 1835. Southern observers report that, at minimum, it is just detectable in a 4-inch, while an 8-inch shows it as little more than faint oval nub. Observers with larger telescopes remark that it resembles a smaller version of the Dumbbell Nebula, M27, in Vulpecula (not to be confused with M76, known as the Little Dumbbell, in Perseus). An irregular outer ring may be glimpsed in telescopes of between 12 and 15 inches, particularly when an O III filter is employed. The western edge is typically described as being better defined than its eastern counterpart. The magnitude 15.3 central star, however, is notoriously difficult to discern. One observer who has glimpsed it — Stephen O'Meara — advises using a telescope of at least 10 inches in aperture combined with very high magnifications (350x or greater). At the same time, we would not discourage observers with smaller instruments from trying their hand at it using high magnifications as well.

NGC 3195 has appeared in a number of surveys, including an *HST* study of the morphologies of planetary nebulae with sun-like progenitors, as well as abundance and dust content studies. Images render an elongated pall with an opaque outer rim mottled with patchy dark regions, a roughly kidney-bean-shaped inner glory suffused with a tenuous glow, and a broad S-shaped swirl centered on the central star, suggesting a bipolar morphology. The overall impression is looking down into an outer cylinder filled with equal parts light and shadow stirred gently about a central luminary. The structural details of such planetary nebulae have compelled astronomers to consider what factors, such as companion stars, planets, brown dwarfs, and outflows from the progenitor itself, might play a role in shaping these luminescent sculptures. For example, the spiral structure in the central halo of NGC 3195 appears to have formed via some symmetrical type of ejection, such that the ejecta pattern is mirrored on opposite sides of the star.

Spectroscopic observations show that the nebular envelope is expanding at about 40 kilometers per second. The radial velocity is 16 kilometers per second in approach. The distance, always a question with planetary nebulae, has been estimated at around 2 kiloparsecs (6,500 light-years), based on its 5-gigahertz brightness temperature and its intrinsic radio luminosity (Phillips 2004).

Nearly 30 arcminutes NNW of this object is the small galaxy NGC 3149. It is both faint (magnitude 12.6) and small (2.0' x 1.9'), and images render a very bright nucleus with patchy outer arms. Its morphology suggests an Sa-type spiral with both an inner and outer ring. The galaxy is described in *The Night Sky Observer's Guide* as exhibiting (in 16- to 18-inch telescopes) a faint, round 45-arcsecond-diameter halo that brightens gradually toward the center to a faint stellar nucleus.

EXTRAGALACTIC OBJECTS IN CHAMAELEON

We wish to point out that there are quite a number of galaxies in Chamaeleon, though many of them are 13th-magnitude and fainter, and thus avail themselves only to observers using telescopes with minimum apertures of 16 to 18 inches. Even then, most are mere shadows of low visual presence. **Table 4** features the brighter ESO-cataloged galaxies, though with one magnitude 14 exception (ESO 19-6) that we think has an especially striking appearance. More complete visual descriptions of these objects may be found in *The Night Sky Observer's Guide*, by Ian Cooper, Jenni Kay, and George Robert Kepple. The observing notes are abridged versions, but note that the operative descriptor is "faint."

NGC 2915
Dwarf spiral immersed in a voluminous disk of neutral hydrogen

In northwestern Chamaeleon, the isolated, enigmatic galaxy NGC 2915 floats alone in a sea of dim stars. It lies about 4° east of Alpha Cha, and despite its unusual morphology, it is little observed or imaged by amateurs, though professional astronomers have pursued this object since the 1970s. It was included in a number of surveys of the redshifts and distributions of southern galaxies, and was part of the roster of peculiar galaxies in Halton Arp and Barry Madore's *Catalogue of Southern Peculiar Galaxies and Associations*, 1987. John Herschel discovered this unassuming system in 1837, describing it as faint, large, and round with a gradually brightening center. Hartung either did not observe it or failed to mention it in his record of southern objects. Contemporary reports can hardly be deemed scintillating: faint elongated halo with a brighter center; a slightly longer SE extension (*The Night Sky Observer's Guide*).

Table 4: Additional Galaxies in Chamaeleon
with observing notes for 16"/18" apertures

Galaxy	Mag	Size (')	SB	Type	PA	RA (2000.0) h m s	Dec ° ′ ″
ESO 18-2	12.7	2.4 x 1.2	13.6	SA(rs)bc	150	08 19 14.2	−78 41 46
		Faint, hazy oval of uniform brightness					
ESO 18-13	12.7	2.1 x 0.7	12.8	SB(s)c	121	08 43 48.7	−78 56 58
		Faint, featureless streak					
ESO 19-3	13.0	1.6 x 0.8	13.0	SB(rs)c:	137	10 38 01.0	−81 05 51
		Faint elongated oval					
ESO 19-6	14.7	2.0 x 0.3	13.9	Sc: sp	75	11 16 11.0	−79 23 51
		Faint, thin streak					
ESO 21-3	13.4	1.7 x 1.1	13.9	SB(rs)bc	54	13 32 25.2	−80 25 56
		Faint, ghostly elongated oval					
ESO 21-4	12.5	2.4 x 1.4	13.6	SA?0/a	100	13 32 40.6	−77 50 41
		Small, obvious oval haze with a central bulge and strong core					
ESO 35-18	13.0	2.8 x 0.7	13.5	SB?(s)bc	135	07 55 04.2	−76 24 45
		Nice, moderately bright streak with broad central area					
ESO 36-19	12.9	1.9 x 0.6	12.8	(R')SBbc pec:	153	09 06 35.7	−75 49 32
		Faint, elongated ellipse					
ESO 40-12	13.3	2.3 x 0.5	13.2	Sb: sp	113	13 35 16.2	−77 38 29
		Faint, elongated ellipse					

Deep images render a smooth halo, but a center that is marked with coarse star streams leading to the nucleus. Sérsic et al. (1977) thought the streams resembled ejecta and hence described it as an Irr II galaxy of the explosive class (similar to M82). Their 21-centimeter observations detected astonishingly high neutral hydrogen (H I) content: it was as if the galaxy were immersed in a huge pool of H I with a radius well over a dozen times that of the visible disk. The profile resembled that of an early type S0 galaxy with an oversized nuclear complex. At the time, the only explanation was that NGC 2915 represented a post-eruptive galaxy triggered by gas falling into a deep potential well inside of an old system. What remained unclear, however, was how such a relatively large amount of gas could arise from evolved stars.

Today, NGC 2915 is classified as a non-Magellanic irregular galaxy, which has the optical properties of a blue compact dwarf. Photometry (Meurer et al., 1994) turned up two distinct stellar populations: a blue stellar core, in which most

NGC 2915 Galaxy	ESO 37-3 LEDA 26761	RA 09h 26m 11.8s Dec −76° 37′ 38″ Mag 12.7 Size 1.9′ x 1.0′ Type I0 PA 129

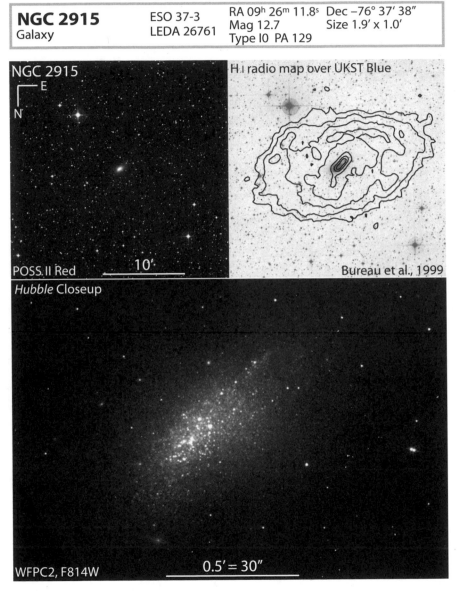

Figure 15: NGC 2915. This inconspicuous galaxy is much larger in radio emissions of unseen gas, upper right, courtesy Bureau et al., 1999.

of the current star formation is occurring, and an outer diffuse older population. The blue core is confined within a very small region with a radius of only 70 arcseconds, which, at a distance of 4 megaparsecs, is about 1.8 kiloparsecs. However, this stellar nugget is embedded within a vast, nearly starless disk of neutral hydrogen with a galactocentric radius of more than 500 arcseconds, or more than five times its Holmberg radius, which is 2.3 kiloparsecs.[*] The H I disk has a well-defined spiral structure as well as a bar-like feature corresponding to the optical component, endowing the system with the characteristics of a late-type spiral galaxy. Deep H-alpha (Hα) images (Meurer et al., 1999) turned up a few faint H II regions, but more recent *HST* photometry (Bruzzese et al., 2015) revealed an elliptical distribution of red giant stars, as well as a clumpy distribution of young main-sequence stars in the outer H I disk that are probably less than 160 million years old. Five of the brightest main-sequence stars may actually either be binaries or compact clusters of lower-mass stars.

Together, these features make NGC 2915 a useful subject for examining the effects of star formation in the H I, stellar, and dark matter mass components, as well as the kinematics of the gaseous and stellar disks. Spectroscopic observations (Werk et al., 2010) determined that its outer disk is considerably more metal-rich and that the central region is underabundant. There are three possible scenarios to explain this unexpected finding: the transport of metals generated in the core out to large radii; the dispersal of metals to the outer regions via supernova-driven winds; or a past interaction with another galaxy leading to the accretion of enriched gas. Mass modeling of the galaxy's observed rotation curve (Meurer et al., 1996) showed the galaxy to be dark-matter-dominated at nearly all radii. Based on the last measured point on the rotation curve, the galaxy has a mass-to-luminosity ratio of 140 $M_\odot/L_\odot$. For comparison, the rich Coma galaxy cluster has a mass-luminosity ratio of about 200, indicating the presence of a considerable amount of dark matter. NGC 2915's mass-luminosity ratio, then, makes it one of the most dark-matter-dominated galaxies known.

---

[*] The Holmberg radius is a measure of the dimensions of a galaxy based on its surface brightness. Specifically, it is the radius at which the surface brightness in blue light falls to 26.6 magnitudes per square arcsecond. It is 100 times fainter than the natural sky glow.

NGC 3620 Galaxy	ESO 38-10 LEDA 34366	RA 11ʰ 16ᵐ 05ˢ Mag 12.2 SB 13.1 Size 2.8' x 1.1' PA 78	Dec −76° 13' 01" Type (R')SB(s)ab pec

Figure 16: NGC 3620.

NGC 3620

Nearly edge-on system with possible active nucleus

This is another system that has cropped up in a number of *en masse* surveys and morphological studies but that has not received that much specific attention. It was discovered in 1837 by John Herschel, who described it as faint, pretty small, pretty much elongated, with a gradually brighter middle. Morphologically, it is a barred spiral with an outer pseudoring and peculiar inner structure, including dark patchy absorption nebulosity crossing its northern disk. In their *Southern Galaxy Catalogue*, Harold Corwin and Gérard and Antoinette de Vaucouleurs characterized it as having a small bright nucleus, and a possible bar with dust and embryonic arms. They also noted that it was partly obscured by Galactic diffuse nebulosity. Indeed, just 32.4 arcminutes to the SW is the reflection nebula IC 2631, the nebulosity of which extends to the shores of NGC 3620. As its magnitude 14.4 surface brightness indicates, this is a faint galaxy with just a hint of a stellar nucleus even in a 16-inch. It is best seen using averted vision. Images show some internal dust absorp-

LOOKING TOWARD CHAMAELEON THROUGH THE MILKY WAY

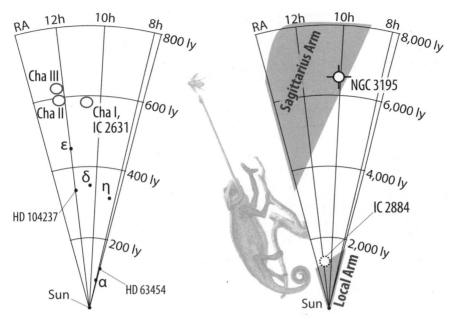

Figure 17: Chamaeleon's featured stars and nonstellar objects located by distance from the Sun. The nearby stars and the three Chamaeleon molecular clouds (left panel) all reside in the Local Arm, our small neighborhood in the Milky Way. At right, the asterism of faint stars, IC 2884, suggests the edge of the Local Arm, with planetary NGC 3195 marking the close side of the Sagittarius Arm.

tion around the nucleus and a decidedly warped, but tenuous, spiral arm winding north of the disk.

Attention was first drawn to the galaxy when, in the course of an objective-prism survey for Hα emission stars and Herbig-Haro objects in the southern sky (Schwartz 1977 a,b), it was discovered that it exhibited prominent emission lines that indicated a strong differential velocity across the nucleus. The velocity measurements were attributed to a rotating ring of nuclear gas. More recently, 22 GHz water maser emission was detected issuing from the galactic center (Tarchi et al., 2009). These observations hint at a possible low-luminosity active galactic nucleus. The distance estimates for this system vary widely, from 18.5 to 27 megaparsecs. Those published more recently appear to favor median values of between 23 and 24 megaparsecs.

LOOKING THROUGH CHAMAELEON: THE EXTRAGALACTIC VIEW

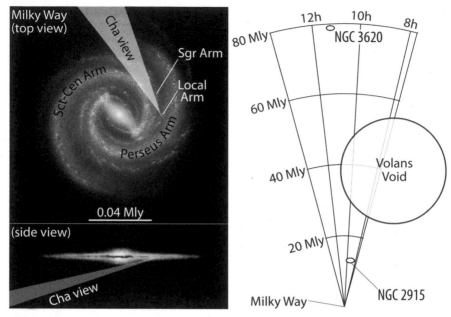

Figure 18: Chamaeleon's view out of the Milky Way. This constellation occupies a small part of the sky, with no recognized large-scale extragalactic structures beyond an intrusion of Fairall's 1998 Volans Void between the two featured galaxies. Beyond these maps are the ESO galaxies in **Table 3** (83–259 Mly), not prominent in notable large-scale structures. Beyond this, there are only two Abell Galaxy Clusters, one with an uncertain distance and the other, Abell 3454, at 1,700 Mly and not a part of any known large-scale structure. The large-scale structure in Chamaeleon's window is further hidden by the low angle across the Milky Way.

Circinus

Circinus, the pair of compasses formed by La Caille, lies close to the front feet of the Centaur, south from Lupus and Norma, its inventor appropriately associating it with the latter.

— Richard Hinckley Allen

This constellation is another invention of Abbé Nicolas-Louis de Lacaille to represent important technological innovations of the 17th and 18th centuries. Others include Pyxis the Mariner's Compass, Antlia the Air Pump, Fornax the Chemical Furnace, and Reticulum the Reticle. The compass, in this case, refers to the drafting tool used for tracing out circles. The constellation's alpha star represents the hinge of the compass, while Beta (β) and Gamma (γ) Circini traditionally represent the legs (the needle and inscriber). Circinus occupies a dim region of sky despite being well into the edge of the Milky Way. Part of the reason is that its brightest star, Alpha (α) Circini, is a magnitude 3.2 A7 dwarf. The other reason is that the constellation is draped in dark nebulae stretching ENE and SE of Rigil Kentaurus (α Centauri). For imagers, this is a splendid area of the Milky Way, full of star clouds contrasted by dark nebulosity. The constellation itself offers a few open clusters; the diminutive but fascinating planetary nebula NGC 5315; and a Seyfert 2 galaxy, ESO 97-13, also known as the Circinus Galaxy.

Circinus, the Drafting Compass	
Abbreviation: **Cir**	Pronunciation: **SER-sin-us**
Genitive: **Circini**	Pronunciation: **SER-sin-eye**
Midnight culmination: **April 30**	
Size on the sky: **93.3 square degrees**	
Bright stars: **None**	
Bright nonstellar objects: **None**	
Popular asterisms: **None**	
Note: One of 14 constellations introduced by Abbé Nicolas-Louis de Lacaille during his sojourn at the Cape of Good Hope, 1750–1754.	

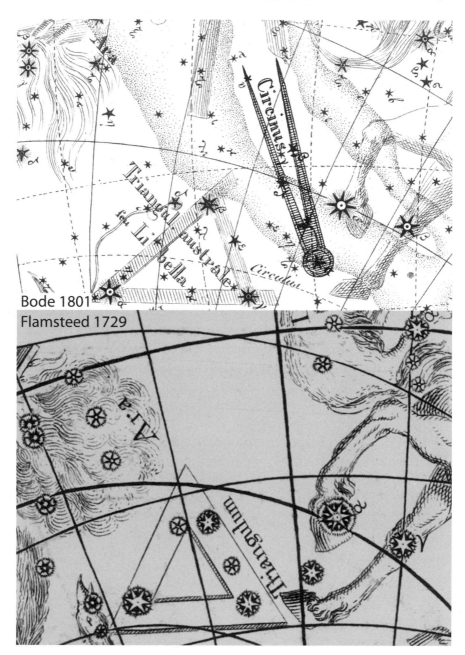

Bode 1801

Flamsteed 1729

Figure 1: Circinus. Nicolas-Louis de Lacaille proposed additional southern constellations in 1763, including Circinus. Thirteen such constellations were incorporated into later atlases, including Bode's 1801 *Uranographia*, excerpted at top, courtesy History of Science Collections, University of Oklahoma Libraries. Compare to Flamsteed's 1729 *Atlas Coelestis*, without Circinus, courtesy the University of Michigan's Map Library.

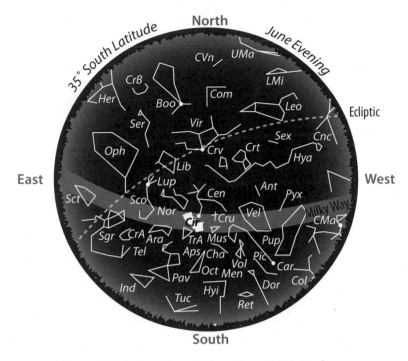

Figure 2: Circinus located on the celestial sphere.

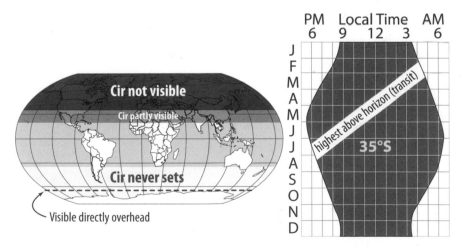

Figure 3: Seeing Circinus from the Earth throughout the year. This small constellation is near the South Celestial Pole. The hourglass figure on the right shows the time at which Circinus appears highest in the sky across the months of the year and the duration of night at 35° S latitude. Transit times may be used at any latitude.

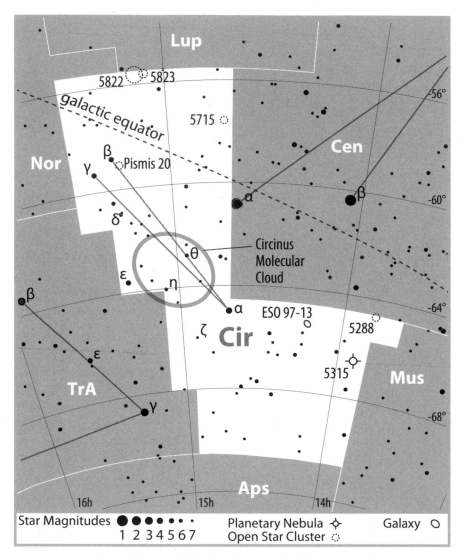

Figure 4: Circinus featured objects.

Those with binoculars or widefield refractors might want to take a look 11.7 arcminutes NNW of Gamma Circini. There you'll find a tight little triangular asterism (magnitudes 7.5–8) set amid a scattering of three or four fainter stars. The western-most member of the triangle is of some interest to stellar astron-omers because it is a pulsating B2 supergiant, designated CZ Circini. The period is unknown, and its fluctuations amount to

Circinus Featured Objects, North to South

NGC 5823: open cluster bordering larger open cluster (NGC 5822) **(page 47)**.

NGC 5715: open cluster in crowded stellar field **(page 45)**.

Beta (β) Circini: star with infrared excess; brown dwarf companion **(page 38)**.

Pismis 20: small stellar aggregate; may be two separate clusters **(page 51)**.

Gamma (γ) Circini: challenging binary system **(page 40)**.

Circinus Molecular Cloud: dark complex **(page 42)**.

NGC 5288: open cluster with extended low-density corona **(page 48)**.

Alpha (α) Circini: chemically peculiar; rapid oscillations **(page 36)**.

ESO 97-13: (Circinus Galaxy) nearby Seyfert 2 galaxy **(page 57)**.

NGC 5315: planetary nebula with luminous X-ray source **(page 49)**.

only 0.1 magnitude, too slight for the human eye to appreciate. The star marking the southernmost apex (magnitude 7.6) is a fine little optical double, HD 136285. A 10.6-magnitude companion lies 7.2 arcseconds away at position angle (PA) 56°. The easternmost star, HD 136303, is a B7 giant. Note that if you do a VizieR search, the data for HD 136285 will pop up again, because VizieR defaults to finding everything within 2 arcminutes of the search coordinates. Since HD 136285 and 136303 are about 1.7′ apart, checking either of them in VizieR against the WDS catalog will bring up HD 136285 as a match.

Circinus is also known for hosting a supernova witnessed in 185 CE by Chinese astronomers (SN 185 or SNR G315.0-02.3). The SIMBAD coordinates are 14^h 43′ and −62° 30′, which is very near the Centaurus border, or 1.7° south of Alpha Centauri. It is considered the first supernova documented in history. Nothing can be seen of the supernova remnant itself at those coordinates, but *Chandra* and the *XMM-Newton* X-ray observatories have imaged the vestiges of a 45-arcminute-diameter expanding debris ring (RCW 86) straddling the Circinus/Centaurus border. See more in the Alpha Centauri (Rigil Kentaurus) profile in Centaurus.

NOTABLE STARS IN CIRCINUS

Alpha (α) Circini
Chemically peculiar; rapid oscillations

Located 4.1° south of Rigil Kentaurus (α Centauri), Alpha Circini is an unassuming sun, but one that has a special place in the hearts and minds of stellar spectroscopists everywhere. You can tell just by looking at its spectral type: A7VpSrCrEu. Unpacking the classification string tells us we're dealing with an A7 main-sequence dwarf (effective surface temperature of 8,000 K) with a peculiar spectrum that exhibits strong enhancements of strontium, chromium, and europium. These elements are not distributed evenly throughout the atmosphere but are confined to magnetic patches on the star's surface, rather like sunspots. Rotation brings these different chemical "pools" in and out of view, Doppler shifting the different chemically enhanced and depleted regions.

Ap stars encompass a range of chemically anomalous objects, including Alpha Cir, and span spectral classes from roughly B8 to F2. The prototype is Alpha^2 Canum Venaticorum, which we profile in volume 3. Ap stars typically have strong magnetic fields and low rotation rates. Alpha Cir's magnetic field is about 500 times that of the Sun, which is considerable but not overly so; atypically, it completes one rotation in 4.47 days. The origin of the magnetic field is a mystery, as astronomers don't know if magnetic fields are inborn or subsequently created in the stars themselves. Another interesting trait is that the star oscillates creating a slight variation in visual magnitude (about 0.02 magnitude) over a period of just 6.826 minutes. These last two characteristics put it in yet another class, that of a "roAp," or rapidly oscillating class A peculiar star. Alpha Cir was the fifth such star discovered (Kurtz and Cropper, 1981) and is the brightest in this class.

Observations made using the BRITE*-Constellation (Weiss et al., 2016), a coordinated mission of five nanosatellites that

---

* BRITE stands for BRight Target Explorer.

Alpha (α) Circini	HD 128898	RA 14ʰ 42ᵐ 30.4ˢ Dec −64° 58′ 30.5″
Double Star	HIP 71908	Mag 3.17 + 8.47 SpType A7VpSrCrE
		Sep 15.4 PA 226 Epoch 2013

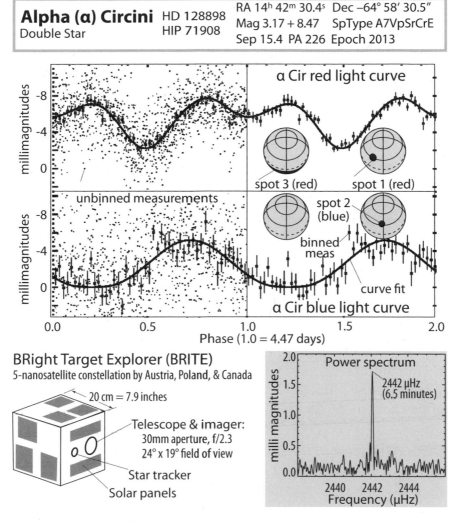

Figure 5: Alpha (α) Circini. Light curves, top, suggest three surface spots of different colors, rotating through our view during the star's 4.47-day rotation. The photometric signal is very faint ("millimagnitudes") and noisy (left side of curve, statistically cleaned on the right). Analyzing the light curves in the frequency domain, lower right, highlights a faint pulsation with a period of 6.5 minutes, or 2442 microhertz. Weiss et al., 2016, collected these measurements over 146 days, using four of the five satellites of the *BRIght Target Explorer* (BRITE) nanosatellite constellation, lower left. These small satellites were built on the lessons learned from the earlier *Microvariability and Oscillations of STars* (MOST), discussed in *Annals* Volume 4, Beta CMi.

collects continuous millimagnitude-precision photometry of bright stars for up to 180 days at a time in two colors, delivered a surprising result. The light curve seen in the red band had a considerably different shape than the blue-band light curve, something not seen before. Models addressing the question suggest that two large-scale photometrically bright spots on the star might lead to different light curve shapes in the red and blue bands.

Alpha Cir is also a fine double star, with a magnitude 8.4 class K5 dwarf common-motion companion floating a little over 15 arcseconds to the SW. Noted southern observer E. J. Hartung described it as consisting of a "very bright yellow star" with a "fainter red companion." The pair is easily resolved in any small telescope of decent optical quality. James Dunlop discovered and measured the components in 1826. Since that time the separation has been gradually increasing, while the PA has been decreasing. At the star's distance of 54 light-years, as cited in the Extended *Hipparcos* Compilation, the true separation amounts to 260 AU with a period of about 2,600 years.

We mention two other components for the record. Alpha-C (magnitude 12) lies a little over an arcminute to the west while Alpha-D (magnitude 19) may be found a mere 6.4 arcseconds away in PA 28°. Good luck with finding that one!

Beta (β) Circini

Star with infrared excess; brown dwarf companion

The two other stars comprising the main figure of Circinus lie 7.5° NE of Alpha, or a little over 5° ENE of Rigil Kentaurus. Beta has one known substellar companion (**Figure 6**), 56 times the mass of Jupiter and located at the unusually remote distance of 6,656 AU from the host star. The object, which may be more properly described as a brown dwarf or L-type dwarf companion, probably has an effective surface temperature around 2,000 K. Infrared surveys have also revealed an infrared excess, indicating the presence of circumstellar dust. Such stars are considered "Vega-like," since that star is known to possess a debris disk (although Beta Pictoris is the more

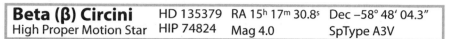

Beta (β) Circini	HD 135379	RA 15h 17m 30.8s	Dec −58° 48′ 04.3″
High Proper Motion Star	HIP 74824	Mag 4.0	SpType A3V

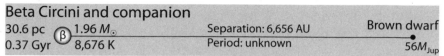

Beta Circini and companion

| 30.6 pc | β 1.96 $M_\odot$ | Separation: 6,656 AU | Brown dwarf |
| 0.37 Gyr | 8,676 K | Period: unknown | 56M_{Jup} |

H-R diagram for Beta (β) and other featured stars in Circinus

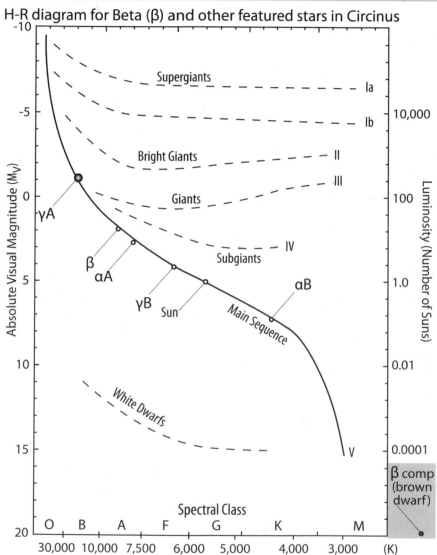

Figure 6: Beta (β) Circini and other featured stars on a Hertzsprung-Russell diagram. Beta's companion is shown at top.

famous example). A photometric analysis (Song et al., 2001), which derived ages for a number of A-type Vega stars, found a median age of 166 million years for Beta Cir; the main-sequence lifetime for a typical A3 dwarf is 1.25 billion years, so it is still fairly young. The distance is about 100 light-years.

Beta Cir is noted for its high proper motion, which amounts to −97.7 and −135.4 milliarcseconds per year in right ascension and declination, respectively. (We'd like to point out, however, that Alpha Cir's motion of 193 and 234 milliarcseconds per year is about twice that of Beta Cir.) It also has the distinction of being on the list of least-variable stars, which makes it an excellent standard for calibrating photometric systems.

Gamma (γ) Circini
Challenging binary system

Gamma Cir is a well-known binary system first measured by John Herschel in 1837. The PA at the time was 107° and today (epoch 2014) it has made a slow counterclockwise change to 359°. The separation of the pair has decreased very slightly, from 1 arcsecond to 0.8 arcsecond. A plot of the orbit shows that, from our perspective and distance (about 440 light-years), the companion never strays too far from the primary during its 270-year (preliminary) orbital period, even around apastron. Precision astrometry is difficult for so close a pair, and an analysis of the astrometric data of this star shows that the observations could apply to either elliptical or linear motion. These findings prompted some astronomers to question whether Gamma Cir was a true binary or an optical double (Buscombe and Barkstrom, 1969). However, we think it is safe to conclude that two naked-eye stars observed for nearly two centuries moving across the sky within an arcsecond of each other is clear evidence they must be related. The problem with making the physical link is that the primary, which specs out to be a class B3 or 4 star, has an absolute magnitude around −1.5, while the companion, which has been observed many times to be either an F8 or G0 dwarf, has an absolute magnitude of 4.0. The magnitude difference should therefore

Gamma (γ) Circini Double Star	HD 136415J HIP 75323	RA 15ʰ 23ᵐ 22.6ˢ Mag 4.94 + 5.73 Sep 0.80″ PA 359	Dec −59° 19′ 14.8″ SpType B3/4V + F8V Epoch 2014

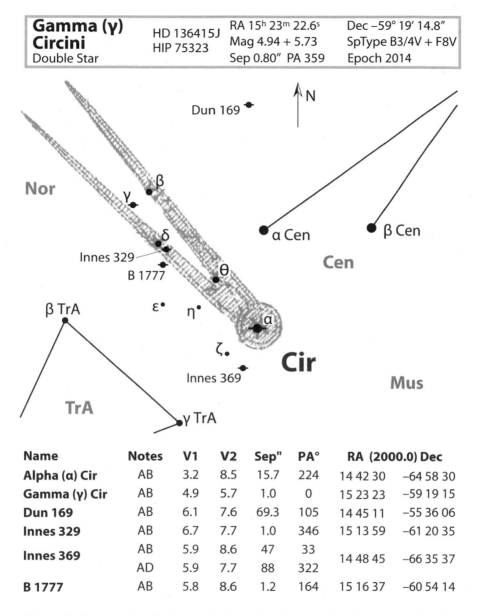

Name	Notes	V1	V2	Sep"	PA°	RA (2000.0) Dec
Alpha (α) Cir	AB	3.2	8.5	15.7	224	14 42 30 −64 58 30
Gamma (γ) Cir	AB	4.9	5.7	1.0	0	15 23 23 −59 19 15
Dun 169	AB	6.1	7.6	69.3	105	14 45 11 −55 36 06
Innes 329	AB	6.7	7.7	1.0	346	15 13 59 −61 20 35
Innes 369	AB	5.9	8.6	47	33	14 48 45 −66 35 37
	AD	5.9	7.7	88	322	
B 1777	AB	5.8	8.6	1.2	164	15 16 37 −60 54 14

Figure 7: Gamma (γ) Circini and other double stars for beginners. The figure at top is a basic star chart of the easier double stars in Circinus, in the style of the Northern Hemisphere book *In Starland With a Three-inch Telescope* (1909) by William Tyler Olcott.

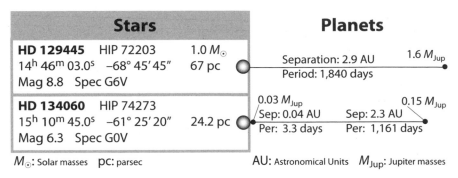

Figure 8: Two stars with planets in Circinus.

amount to about five magnitudes or more. Instead, the difference is only about 0.8 magnitude. So we see that the orbital elements, which are essentially unknown, have nothing to do with the pair being physically associated; it is the conflicting inferred luminosities of the stars that is the problem.

Splitting the two may prove to be challenging, especially since both stars are so close in brightness. A 6-inch should show some elongation at magnifications of between 130x and 150x; higher magnifications, coupled with excellent seeing, might even resolve the pair, though ever so slightly.

GALACTIC OBJECTS IN CIRCINUS

Circinus Molecular Cloud
Dark complex

Located roughly between Epsilon (ε) and Theta (θ) Circinus (or about 4 degrees SE of Alpha Centauri), this dark molecular cloud complex makes for a fine, widefield deep-imaging opportunity silhouetted by the starry backdrop of the Milky Way. It is listed as DC 319.3-3.5 in the *Catalogue of Southern Dark Clouds* (Hartley et al., 1986), which is meant to serve as a southern complement to the Lynds *Catalog of Dark Nebulae* (1962). The NE extent is an elongated patch that devolves into spidery filaments along its outer edges, while the SW region forms a partial arc encompassing Eta (η) Cir. Visually the

Circinus Molecular Cloud Dark Nebula	SDC 319. 3-3.5 TGU 1978	RA 15ʰ 02ᵐ Size 3.5° x 2°	Dec −63° 00′

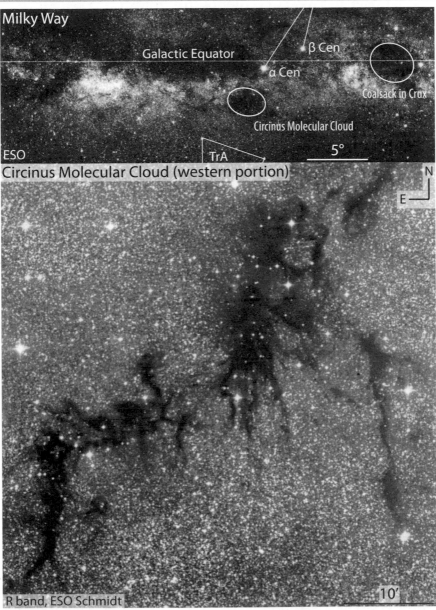

Figure 9: Circinus Molecular Cloud. The dark clouds near the Galactic equator, the densest part of the Milky Way, show complex structure and texture at all image scales. The widefield image at the top is courtesy ESO, and the detail below is courtesy Bally et al., 1999.

cloud is not apparent, although in 10x50 or 8x56 binoculars, one may notice a dearth of stars in a ~10-arcminute diameter patch about half a degree SE of Theta. HD 132022 (9.5-magnitude) floats just west of center of this void.

The Circinus cloud is located close to the Galactic plane (**Figure 9**, longitude 318°, latitude −4°), but the distance is poorly established with estimates ranging between 700 and 1,260 parsecs. The total molecular mass is estimated to be 25,000 $M_\odot$, based on the nearer distance estimate. The cloud contains several carbon monoxide (CO) clumps, though two (Circinus-E and Circinus-W) predominate, each with a mass of about 5,000 $M_\odot$. They are associated with a number of embedded infrared sources, young stellar objects (YSOs), and Herbig-Haro objects, and thus comprise the most active low-mass star-forming sites in the Circinus cloud. CO data sets (Shimoikura and Dobashi, 2011) show that Circinus-E consists of two distinct velocity components, one in the range of about 10 kilometers per second (Circinus-Ea) and the other 6 kilometers per second (Circinus-Eb). Both manifest in elongated ridges of CO emission extending from SE to NW in the case of Circinus-Ea, and from SW to NE in the case of Circinus-Eb. Infrared images (Liu et al., 2011) reveal that a range of YSOs and H-alpha (Hα) emission-line objects (mostly T Tauri stars) are located along these ridges, which are coincident with dark filamentary structures. Clearly, these objects formed *in situ*. The locations of several of these objects correspond to known dense cores and CO outflows. The CO intensity peak of Circinus-Ea corresponds to a "dent" in Circinus-Eb, while the peak of Circinus-Eb corresponds to a dent in Circinus-Ea. This suggests that the two components might be colliding, thus inducing star formation.

Millimeter-wave observations (Bally et al., 1999) demonstrate that the morphology of the Circinus cloud has been significantly modified over the past few million years. Chaotic motions produced in the wake of active star formation has both shredded and "churned" the cloud, producing dozens of fossil outflow cavities surrounded by dense filaments of compressed gas that may be responsible for its ragged appearance. Dark as the region appears now, in the next few million years one can

NGC 5715 Open Cluster	CI VDBH 163	RA 14ʰ 43ᵐ 39.0ˢ Mag 9.8 30 stars Bt*Vm 11.0	Dec –57° 34' 13" Size 7.0' Type III 2m

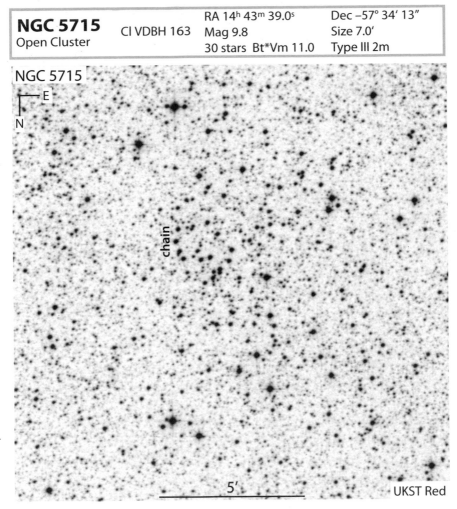

Figure 10: NGC 5715, an open cluster in a busy starfield.

expect dozens of new stars to emerge in the form of a brilliant young cluster.

NGC 5715

Open cluster in crowded stellar field

NGC 5715 is a sparse but compact little aggregate occupying the NNW region of the constellation. One needs to sneak up on this object beginning with low magnifications, as too much can uncluster the cluster, even though it only spans some 7 arcminutes. Its location in a crowded field doesn't help. Once found, zoom in with increasingly higher magnifications until your field is about 12 or 15 arcminutes across. Look for a looping chain of stars just SW of the cluster's center consisting of about a dozen magnitude 12 and 13 stars. Other loops and chains may be seen throughout. A 10.7-magnitude foreground star (TYC 8688-1051-1) lies in the NE quadrant.

The dense star field, mostly made up of Galactic bulge stars based on color-magnitude diagrams, has made it difficult to separate members from nonmembers. Up until recently, no photometric or structural parameters were available for this object. In the mid-1970s, astronomers determined NGC 5715 had an angular diameter of about 10 arcminutes, and estimated a medium richness for the cluster, with the Trumpler classification shifting from II 2m to III 2m. Open clusters near the Galactic plane usually have strongly reddened field stars, but this is especially true for open clusters seen projected on the central region of the Galaxy (of which there are few within the solar circle, the region confined within the Sun's orbit around the center of the Galaxy). Determining the membership of such clusters is essential in establishing the fraction of true star clusters as opposed to dense stellar fields in those directions. Such studies can be used to investigate whether the scarcity of open clusters in the solar circle is due to observational limitations because of dense stellar fields, or tidal disruptions from molecular clouds in the proximity of the bulge — important considerations in galactic dynamics and evolution.

Color-magnitude decontamination algorithms have been developed to address these questions and to better determine the number of true cluster members, ages, and masses (Bonatto and Bica, 2007). The algorithm works on a statistical basis and reckons the relative number-densities of stars in a cluster region as well as a comparison field. For NGC 5715, the cluster harbors over 800 stars within a 5-arcminute radius with an average age of a billion years and mass of at least 1,400 $M_\odot$. The distance is about 1.5 kiloparsecs.

NGC 5823

Open cluster bordering a larger open cluster (NGC 5822)

NGC 5823 is larger and richer than NGC 5715, with a membership of about 100 apparent stars. Steve Gottlieb, using an 18-inch at 76x, found the cluster to be rich and impressive with about 80 stars confined to an area of 9 x 7 arcminutes, many with magnitudes between 11 and 13: "The periphery is well defined by curving sprays of stars roughly forming a heart-shape." Higher magnification resolves many more stars.

The cluster is located nearly on the border with Lupus, a little over 20 arcminutes south of NGC 5822, an even larger (about 35 arcminutes) open cluster in that same constellation (and a worthy binocular object). For a number of years beginning in the 1960s, a running theme was whether they constituted a double system. A photometric study conducted in the late 1960s (Brück et al., 1968) deduced that the two clusters were associated, because, in addition to their proximity, they had similar distances and ages. Conversely, a search for red giants in the region (Dawson 1978) found a significant range in their photo-

NGC 5823 Open Cluster	Melotte 131	RA 15ʰ 05ᵐ 30.5ˢ	Dec −55° 36′ 13″
		Mag 7.9	Size 12.0′
		103 stars Bt*Vm 13.0	Type II 2r

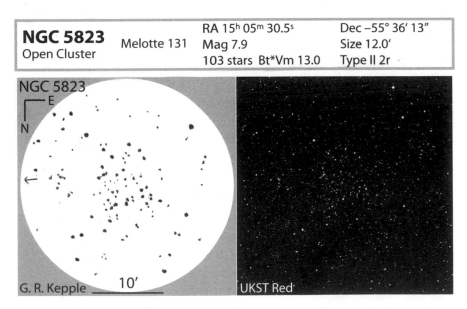

Figure 11: NGC 5823. An eyepiece impression is compared to an observatory survey photograph of this open cluster.

metric properties, indicating the two clusters were not associated. Both studies questioned the reality of NGC 5823 due to considerable scatter in its color-magnitude diagram, but each investigation also surveyed stars that were assumed members in an area somewhat larger than its obvious concentration; hence, nonmembers were inadvertently included. Photographic and photoelectric *BV* photometry (Janes 1981) concluded that NGC 5823 was a normal disk cluster and was unlikely to be associated with NGC 5822. The WEBDA database cites ages for NGC 5823 and NGC 5822 as 794 million and 662 million years, respectively; distances are 1,192 and 917 parsecs.

NGC 5288

Open cluster with extended low-density corona

We find NGC 5288 in the SW corner of the constellation, very near the border with Centaurus and adjacent to the open cluster/star cloud NGC 5155. Images show a Christmas-tree-like grouping, pointing north and consisting of about a dozen stars around magnitude 12 and fainter. A magnitude 8 star (HD 119941) lies 2.8 arcminutes off to the west. A halo of fainter stars surrounds the angular arrangement, and these extend well to the edge of the field and beyond.

Photometric observations coupled with star counts (Piatti et al., 2006) show that the cluster may actually be the central nucleus of a low-density corona of stars extending out to a radius of 6.3 arcminutes, which at the distance of NGC 5288 (2.1 kiloparsecs) translates into a diameter of nearly 8 parsecs (26 light-years). A median age for the cluster is 130 million years, though it could be as much as 170 million or as little as 100 million years (the WEBDA age is 126 million years). Its location 7.4 kiloparsecs from the Galactic center and 0.9 kiloparsecs below the Galactic plane indicates it belongs to and formed in the thin disk. That also places it beyond the Carina spiral feature (not to be confused with the Carina spiral arm), a segment of a spiral arm in the Carina-Centaurus region that can be seen from our position in the Galaxy extending to great distances. A comparison with over 60 other open clusters of nearly the same age

NGC 5288 Open Cluster	CR 278 Lund 648	RA 13^h 48^m 45.6^s Mag 11.8 25 stars Bt*Vm –	Dec –64° 41′ 11″ Size 3.0′ Type II 1p

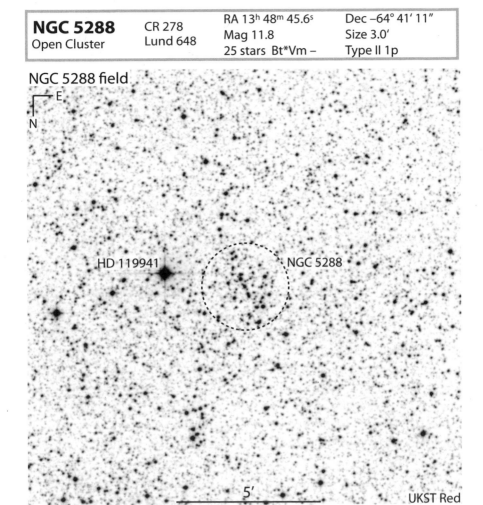

Figure 12: NGC 5288. Some observers see a Christmas-tree pattern of stars pointing north.

points to NGC 5288 as being one of the most distant inner disk clusters of this age.

NGC 5315

Planetary nebula with luminous X-ray source

NGC 5315 lies nearly 2 degrees south of NGC 5288 near the Musca border. This was one of 35 NGC objects discovered by

English astronomer Ralph Copeland (1837–1905) using a visual spectroscope during an expedition to South America. It is the only nonstellar object in Circinus that Hartung describes in his book *Astronomical Objects for Southern Telescopes*: "The nebula is fairly well defined, about 5 arcseconds across and 10.5 cm shows it clearly as a bluish star." It can be coaxed out of the background by "blinking" with an O III filter, as Steve Gottlieb did using an 18-inch at 128x. Observers agree that the best views are at higher magnifications (approaching 300x), where it exhibits its bluish tinge and slightly squarish form. The central star, however, is overwhelmed by the nebula's high surface brightness. For the record, we note that the apparent size and visual magnitude of this object are approximate at best.

Deep images, of course, reveal quite a bit more detail. Undoubtedly one of the most famous is that taken by the *Hubble Space Telescope* (**Figure 13**), which revealed elongated extensions perpendicular to one another and a ragged 8,000-AU radius cavity surrounding the central star (assuming a distance of 2.5 kiloparsecs). The extensions indicate that the central star ejected two diametrically opposed outbursts of material.

In the early 1990s it was determined that the nebula's central star was a Wolf-Rayet type WC4 star, based on its strong carbon-oxygen emission lines. It is also hydrogen deficient, although the nebula itself is not, indicating that the mass-loss process from the star is likely responsible for the enrichment. Estimates of the central star's temperature range from 56,000 K and 82,000 K, with a median falling around 60,000 K. A spectroscopic study (Peimbert et al., 2004) found that the chemical composition of the nebula is similar to both the Orion Nebula and the Sun, but with an excess of nitrogen and helium, which implies that the progenitor had a mass greater than 2.1 $M_\odot$ while on the main sequence. Such a star typically remains on the main sequence less than a billion years. The nebula's age, based on theoretical post-asymptotic giant branch evolutionary tracks, is probably less than 3,000 years.

Observations with the *Chandra X-ray Observatory* (Kastner et al., 2008) found the nebula to be among the most luminous

NGC 5315 ESO 97-PN9	RA 13ʰ 53ᵐ 57.1ˢ Dec −66° 30′ 51″
Planetary Nebula PK 309-4.2	Mag 10 Central *Vm 14.3 Size 14.3″?

NGC 5315 field

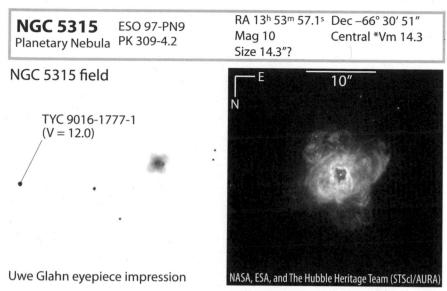

TYC 9016-1777-1
(V = 12.0)

E
N
10″

Uwe Glahn eyepiece impression

NASA, ESA, and The Hubble Heritage Team (STScI/AURA)

Figure 13: NGC 5315. An eyepiece impression of this planetary nebula is compared to a high-resolution image from the *Hubble Space Telescope*.

"hot-bubble" X-ray sources detected within a planetary nebula. The X-rays emanate from plasma with a temperature of 2.5 million K generated by the same winds that cleared the nebula's central cavity.

Pismis 20

Small stellar aggregate; may be two separate clusters

Armenian-Mexican astronomer Paris Pişmiş (see sidebar **page 54**) first recognized this object as a star cluster in the late 1950s. It is compact (2 arcminutes), distant (somewhere between 2.1 and 4.4 kiloparsecs), and young (with an estimated age of 5 million years). Pişmiş estimated the visual magnitude as 12 and the number of stars as 64. She remarked on its compactness, noting that the five brightest stars were within 0.6 arcminutes of each other. According to Brian Skiff, this is one of several similar clusters in the southern Milky Way that have no comparison in the north in terms of visual appearance. About the only comparable northern objects, he says, are NGC 6823 in Vulpecula, IC 4996 in Cygnus, and

Pismis 20 Open Cluster	BH 170 Lund 672	RA 15h 15m 23.1s Mag 7.8 12 stars Bt*Vm 8.2	Dec −59° 04′ 24″ Size 4.5′ Type I 3p

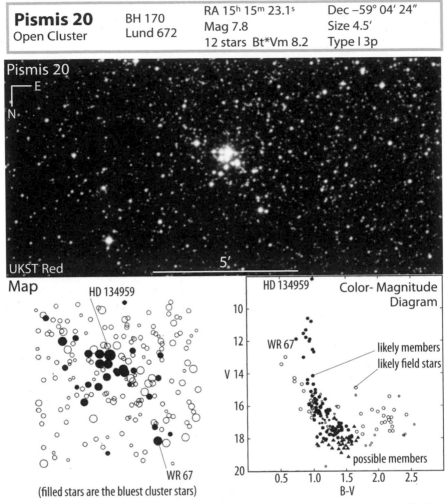

Figure 14: Pismis 20. A magnitude 8 star, HD 134959, dominates the field of this small, sparse cluster (top). Below, courtesy Vazquez et al., 1995, is a map of the field stars, left, and a color-magnitude diagram, at right. A Wolf-Rayet star, WR 67, is likely a cluster member.

Trumpler 1 in Cassiopeia, though they are all trapezia involving three or four codominant stars rather than just one. Images render a central clot of stars accompanied by a scattering of a dozen or more in the field. Long exposures tend to blend the central stars into a single blobby mass. The cluster lies in the Norma Arm of the Galaxy, in the heart of the Circinus OB 1 association; hence, it suffers from considerable reddening. Widefield images show that the cluster is poised near the edge of a star cloud, with lanes of dark nebulae in a corridor extending NE to SW.

Pismis 20 harbors one luminous supergiant (HD 134959) near the cluster's center; with a visual magnitude of 8.2, it is easily the brightest star in the aggregate. It is also a pulsating variable designated CX Circini. The period is irregular and brightness fluctuations amount to less than 0.2-magnitude. Apart from this evolved star, most members are just arriving on the main sequence. Some 2 arcminutes NNE of the cluster's central core is WR 67, a WN6 Wolf-Rayet star of magnitude 11.8. Its membership in Pismis 20 has been in doubt for years, although a number of investigations suggest it is bona fide (but see below).

Polarimetric analysis of the light from 15 suspected cluster members determined that they fall into two groups — A and B — with significantly different polarimetric properties, something not typically observed in open clusters (Orsatti et al., 2003). Two possibilities may explain this conundrum: either polarizing dust particles with a chemical composition different from that of the foreground dust exist between certain members of the cluster, or Pismis 20 actually consists of two separate clusters superposed along our line of sight. Astronomers know of three dust clouds lying between the Sun and Pismis 20. The first lies in the Local Arm about 1 kiloparsec from the Sun, but is only partly responsible for the measured polarizations. Another is situated at a distance of about 1.2 kiloparsecs in front of group A; the third lies behind group A, but in front of group B. If Pismis 20 is in fact not one but two separate clusters, group B, which includes WR 67, would comprise a loose group lying behind group A, and the polarization would arise from dust between those locations. Radial velocity measurements might settle the matter, though they would not be as decisive if both are truly subgroups of Pismis 20.

Figure 15: Paris Marie Pişmiş. Pişmiş, often pronounced and spelled "Pish-mish," had a long career observing, researching, and teaching at the Universidad Nacional Autónoma de México (UNAM) in the Instituto de Astronomía. In 1998, she published her autobiography, *Reminiscences in the Life of Paris Pişmiş: a Woman Astronomer*. Portrait courtesy J. C. Yustis and Silvia Torres Peimbert of the Instituto de Astronomia, Universidad Nacional Autónoma de México.

Paris Marie Pişmiş: Research Astronomer and Role Model

Most professional and amateur astronomers have heard of the Pismis star clusters, but few are aware of the personage behind the name. The career of Paris Marie Pişmiş (1911–1999) spanned galactic research, stellar winds, teaching, and advancing the publication of Mexican astronomical journals, in particular the *Revista Mexicana de Astronomía y Astrofísica* (*Mexican Journal of Astronomy and Astrophysics*), which she edited from its founding in 1974. She published more than 120 research papers on various topics of astrophysics, though her primary area of interest was galactic structure.

Pişmiş was born into an Armenian family living in Turkey. Against her parents' wishes, not to mention Turkish tradition, she was one of the first women to attend Istanbul University, earning her PhD in mathematics in 1937. During this time, she

Paris Marie Pişmiş (c. 1947) 64-cm Schmidt Telescope

Figure 16: Paris Marie Pişmiş. After earning her PhD in mathematics in Istanbul, Pişmiş studied astronomy at Harvard and earned a PhD in astronomy in Mexico in 1955. She is shown here as a graduate student in Mexico around 1947, courtesy her daughter Elsa Recillas Pişmiş, who is also an astrophysicist. In 1959, Paris Pişmiş published her list of new southern open clusters, using the Schmidt telescope at Observatorio Astrofísico de Tonantzintla, near Puebla, Mexico, at right, photograph courtesy Bill Keel. Guillermo Haro also used this telescope, installed in 1942, to identify the first Herbig-Haro objects, with George Herbig, an American working in Hawaii.

worked as a research assistant at the Istanbul University Observatory. Prior to World War II, she traveled to the United States to pursue postdoctoral studies and between 1938 and 1942 worked as an assistant astronomer at the Harvard College Observatory for 30 hours a week at 50 cents per hour. There she met astronomers Bart Bok, Harlow Shapley, Sergei and Cecilia Payne Gaposchkin, and Donald Menzel. Pişmiş also met Félix Recillas, a Mexican mathematician and astronomy student who became her husband in 1942. That year, she and Recillas moved to Mexico and joined the staff of the newly founded Tonantzintla Observatory, which is still in operation today in the municipality of San Andrés Cholula in the state of Puebla (**Figure 16**). During this period, she collaborated with Guillermo Haro who became the observatory's director. (Haro, along with George Herbig, was the first to study the small nebulous jets associated with newly born stars, Herbig-Haro objects.) Pişmiş and Recillas had two children, Elsa and Sevín Recillas, who became scientists in their own right.

She moved to Mexico City in 1948 and joined the National Astronomical Observatory of Tacubaya, part of the National Autonomous University of Mexico (UNAM), now named the Institute of Astronomy. At UNAM she conducted research and taught courses in astronomy and astrophysics. For her entire teaching career, she was a major inspiration to generations of new astronomers, many of them women. As her reputation spread, she was invited to lecture at many universities and institutions around the world.

Pişmiş carried out the first photometric observations of young stellar clusters in Mexico. Among other areas of research, she studied emission nebulae, interstellar absorption, and planetary nebulae, and worked to theoretically explain spiral structure and kinematics in galaxies. She was also the first to introduce Fabry-Perot interferometry to Mexico to study the velocity field of Galactic emission nebulae.

In 1959, she compiled and published her now-famous list of 24 open clusters in the Southern Hemisphere that she had noted on photographic plates taken at Tonantzintla Observatory. She also discovered a globular cluster, Tonantzintla 2 (Ton 2), which is identified as Pismis 26. Pismis 25's story is a bit more complicated. It was actually an independent discovery by Pişmiş of the faint globular NGC 6380, discovered by James Dunlop in 1826. It had long been thought that this object was an open cluster, but research by Andrew David Thackeray in the 1950s disclosed its true nature. Pişmiş cataloged it as Tonantzintla 1 ("No. 1" in her 1959 paper), though it came to be referred to as Pismis 25.

She had a wide variety of interests outside of astronomy. She was fluent in several languages, loved literature and travel, painted, and played the piano and flute. According to her entry in the *Biographical Encyclopedia of Astronomers*, she was also a good singer and dancer. Perhaps her most important contribution was serving as a role model for women in science throughout Mexico and the world. In collaboration with her grandson, Gabriel Cruz-González, Pişmiş published her memoirs in 1998 under the title *Reminiscences in the Life of Paris Pişmiş: A Woman Astronomer*.

EXTRAGALACTIC OBJECTS IN CIRCINUS

ESO 97-13
Nearest Seyfert 2 galaxy

The only named galaxy in Circinus may also be considered the constellation's wonder of wonders. You will find it in the Milky Way, 3.1° west of Alpha Circini in a field sown with stars. The fact that it can be seen only 4° below the Galactic plane testifies that we are looking through a "window" where interstellar absorption happens to be thinner than in other locales. Nevertheless, it was only discovered on a photographic plate published in the atlas of *Nebulae of the Southern Milky Way* (Lyngå and Hansson, 1972) and subsequently detected as a radio source in a Parkes radio survey in 1975. It was paired with an optical counterpart the following year (Savage 1976). The note referring to the optical source describes it as "probably the nucleus of a heavily obscured spiral." The galaxy was subsequently rephotographed during which its photometric properties, distance, and other parameters were investigated in detail (Freeman et al., 1977). One of the major conclusions was that the Circinus Galaxy was not a normal galaxy, and we certainly concur.

Despite its visual magnitude and size, this ghostly spiral is best imaged or observed with large telescopes, although theoretically the nucleus should just be visible in a 4-inch. What stands out visually in 12- to 15-inch telescopes is its ~30-arcsec-

ESO 97-13	Circinus Galaxy	RA 14h 13m 09.9s	Dec −65° 20′ 20.4″
Seyfert Galaxy	LEDA 50779	Mag 10.6 SB 13.8	Type SA(s)b?
		Size 6.9′ x 3.0′	PA 38

ESO 97-13, The Circinus Galaxy

Steve Crouch   5′

Figure 17: ESO 97-13, the Circinus Galaxy. This faint galaxy, near the Milky Way, shines dimly through foreground stars. Amateur astronomer Steve Crouch of Canberra, Australia, made this image using his 0.32-meter telescope.

ond nucleus, which rises just enough above the sky background to be recognizable. Surrounding this is a highly inclined disk (65°) that can just be perceived (via averted vision) in larger telescopes. HD 123975, a magnitude 10 A7 giant, delineates the SSE edge of the disk, 1.7 arcminutes from the nucleus along the minor axis (**Figure 17**).

The Circinus Galaxy (Circinus, hereafter) has seen much robust research since 1975. It has some 42 identifiers and over

830 references and counting. Interest is spurred by the fact that it has an active galactic nucleus, a very dusty disk, and is relatively nearby (about 4 megaparsecs or 13 million light-years). These qualities make it a prime candidate for detailed studies of its nuclear distribution of gas and dust and its central engine. Over the years, a variety of multiwavelength observations have gradually revealed a fascinating galaxy lurking in our backyard.

The proximity of Circinus has offered astronomers the chance to grapple with a longstanding question about Seyfert galaxies: whether or not type 1 and type 2 Seyferts are actually the same kind of object seen from different viewing angles, a hypothesis called the "unification scheme." The spectra of type 1 Seyferts exhibit both broad and narrow emission lines of hydrogen, helium, nitrogen, and oxygen. The broad lines are a product of the Doppler effect as the gas moves hundreds of kilometers per second within the innermost accretion disk surrounding a supermassive black hole. The narrow lines originate from the outer region of the active nuclei, where the velocity of the gas is slower. Type 2 Seyferts exhibit only narrow emission lines. According to the unification scheme, however, they may be oriented to our line of sight such that the broad line region of the nucleus is obscured by a thick dusty torus surrounding the accretion disk. Evidence supporting the unification theme has come from the detection of broad line regions reflected in polarized light above the galaxy's disk, and ionization cones that indicate a collimation of the radiation and outflows from the nuclear region by the torus. Additional evidence is based on observations of circumnuclear starburst rings, which may be either associated with the active galactic nucleus or the remnants of a precursor starburst fueling or forming a central black hole.

It turns out that Circinus exhibits all of these features and more. Early radio observations (Moorwood and Glass, 1984) supported the galaxy's classification as a Seyfert 2 based on the detection of narrow emission lines only. The nonstellar emission was found to originate within a region less than 100 parsecs in diameter. Moreover, its ratio of infrared to nonthermal radio luminosity was similar to the starburst galaxy M82. Although the nucleus is obscured from direct view, spectropolarimetry (Oliva et al., 1998) revealed that the region responsible for broad line emission (i.e., the inner accretion disk) is visible in reflection through polarized light. This may be why NED classifies this galaxy as a Seyfert 1.

A big sign of a cloaked AGN is a phenomenon called Compton reflection, whereby cold, thick matter (i.e., the torus) intercepts and reprocesses some fraction of the primary X-ray continuum, thus imprinting atomic features in the observed spectrum. X-ray reflection gives rise to a broad reflection Compton "hump" around 30 kiloelectron volts (keV) and strong iron emission lines peaking typically at 6.4 keV, on the upper end of soft X-ray flux. Circinus was identified in 1994 as an X-ray source based on data from the *ROSAT* All Sky Survey (Brinkmann et al.). Strong Compton reflection was attributed to high-energy photons from the AGN reflecting from heavily obscured cold, circumnuclear matter, consistent with a type 2 Seyfert. The presence of X-ray emission at higher energies was interpreted as Compton-scattered AGN continuum passing through the molecular torus (Guainazzi et al., 1999). The Compton-scattered component in the Circinus galaxy appears in all directions, not only towards the ionization cone, which should be in view of the nucleus. The lack of "shadow" features in the reflection of the diffuse gas indicates the torus may be clumpy or leaky, which allows the AGN continuum to illuminate material in all directions (Arévalo et al., 2014).

Images of Circinus made using various filters (Marconi et al., 1994) revealed a number of intriguing features that also support the unification scheme. A prominent ionization cone was detected originating in the nucleus, with hot coronal gas near its apex and cooler gas (lower excitation emission) further out; the cone measures more than 400 parsecs long. Radio observations (Elmouttie et al., 1995) also revealed two polarized radio lobes at right angles to the galaxy's plane, with the northern plume coincident with the ionization cone. In addition, a partial starburst ring was detected some 10 arcseconds from the nucleus (220 parsecs) and almost encircling it. Visible and infrared images showed that the nucleus suffers from

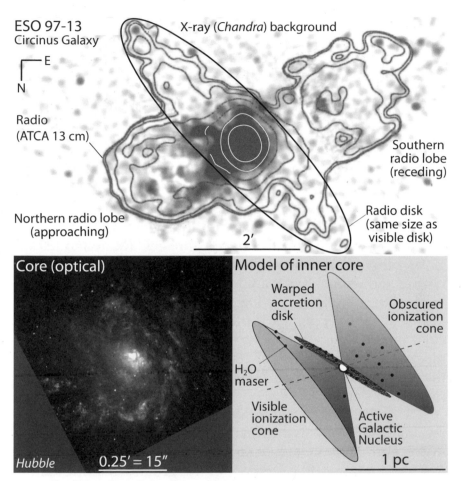

Figure 18: A Seyfert galaxy explodes. The Circinus Galaxy reveals its energetic, chaotic engine at the core across wavelengths. The radio map over an X-ray image, top, (courtesy Mingo et al., 2012) shows results of the hot outflow from the core, most intense to the NW, the side facing us. The high-resolution *Hubble* optical image, below left, shows the chaotic region around the asymmetric core. Greenhill et al., 2003, used the Very Long Baseline Interferometer to map water masers within a parsec of the core, suggesting a thin, warped accretion disk; earlier research had suggested a thick "torus." The warp may contribute to the unusual structure of the outflows.

about 20 magnitudes of extinction, indicating the presence of an obscuring dusty torus.

With respect to the radio lobes, *Chandra* observations (Mingo et al., 2012) revealed that the X-ray emission associated with those structures is shocked gas expanding into the halo regions of the galaxy at Mach speeds of between 2.7 and 3.6 for the west shell and 2.8 and 5.3 for the east shell (**Figure 18**). These velocities, along with the total energy (2×10^{55} ergs), indicate that the X-ray shells are not a result of AGN photoionization but rather the interaction of a radio jet with the surrounding gas. Their estimated age is about a million years. Moreover, the presence of what appears to be two jet termination points or "hotspots" with slightly different X-ray spectra suggests the jet may still be active, even though it is not visible. Such "invisible" jets may be a more common trait among Seyfert and late-type galaxies than previously thought.

High-resolution near-infrared images (Maiolino et al., 1998) pinpointed a nonstellar nuclear source at 2.2 microns with a radius smaller than 1.5 parsecs (about 5 light-years, **Figure 18**). Very long baseline maps of the water maser emission (Greenhill et al., 2003) traced a warped, edge-on disk as close in as 0.1 parsec (about a third of a light-year). The innermost disk rotation speed of 260 kilometers per second implies the presence of a central black hole of at least a million solar masses.

A study made with a combination of high-resolution infrared images, neutral hydrogen (H I) observations, and submillimeter carbon monoxide maps succeeded in removing the foreground stars and a segment of foreground Galactic neutral hydrogen, giving the first unobstructed look at the galaxy's "sprung" two-armed spiral form, which extends well beyond the visible disk (**Figure 19**). The infrared images revealed 12 individual star-forming regions tracing out the spiral arms, which are rich in H I (For et al., 2012). Based on the images and the H I velocity field, it was determined that the galaxy rotates counterclockwise. Stellar mass-to-light ratios were utilized to infer a total mass of $9.5 \times 10^{10}\ M_\odot$.

Infrared interferometric observations (Tristram et al., 2014) paint a complex picture of the dust emission in the Circinus nucleus. These revealed that the nuclear emission consists of two distinct components: a disk-like emission consistent with a

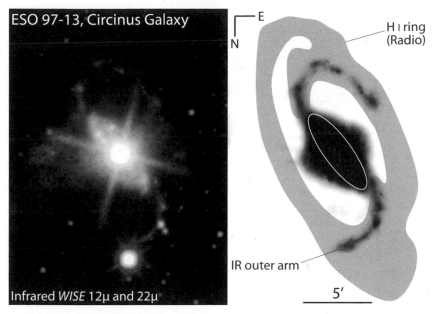

Figure 19: Star formation beyond the visible disk. The Circinus Galaxy is making new stars well beyond the familiar visible disk (white ellipse at left). The infrared image, courtesy NASA/JPL-Caltech/UCLA, shows two external arms of hot dust, a marker of star formation. Enveloping these arms is a still larger ring structure of H I emission, detected with a radio telescope, also suggestive of star formation. **Contemplative observing:** Observe the field with any telescope. Whether you can see the bright part of the galaxy or not, consider that the explosive galaxy hidden behind the dense field of Milky Way stars is a monster, whose energetic nucleus animates and illuminates complex structures, visible across the electromagnetic spectrum.

size of 0.2 x 1.1 parsec and an extended region with a size of 0.8 x 1.9 parsec. The disk-like component is elongated and oriented perpendicular to the ionization cone and outflow, while the extended disk is also elongated but oriented roughly perpendicular to the disk component in a polar direction. This part of the torus, which is responsible for most of the mid-infrared emission, is interpreted as emission from the inner funnel of a more extended distribution of dust. The dense inner disk alone is probably insufficient to obscure the nucleus and collimate the ionization cone, the function normally attributed to dusty tori in

LOOKING TOWARD CIRCINUS THROUGH THE MILKY WAY

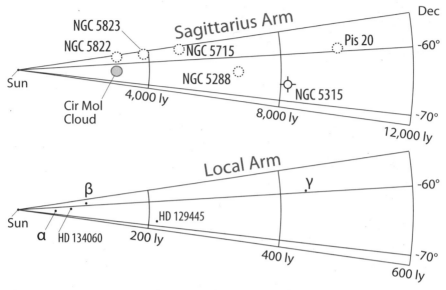

Figure 20: Circinus featured stars and Galactic objects, located according to distance from the Sun, in the nearby Milky Way.

Table 1: Brighter Galaxies in Circinus

ESO	RA h m s	Dec ° ' "	V mag	SB	Size (')	Type	Mly
67-2	14 37 03.3	−70 28 49	15.5	13.9	1.0 x 0.3	Sc? sp	145
67-3	14 43 45.3	−70 07 48	15.3	13.7	1.0 x 0.3	Sb? sp	255
67-4	14 56 22.6	−69 30 19	14.1	13.5	1.1 x 0.7	SAB(s)c	390
97-12	14 10 36.2	−65 34 58	14.2	12.4	0.8 x 0.3	Sa?	130
97-13	14 13 09.8	−65 20 19	10.6	13.8	6.9 x 3.0	SA(s)b?	14
99-2	15 14 52.6	−63 48 20	14.1	12.8	1.0 x 0.4	Sb?	130

unified schemes of AGN. Rather, these must be caused by additional material on scales of 1 parsec above and below the disk. It is this material, therefore, that constitutes the obscuring torus.

It might be said that the Circinus Galaxy is the one that got away from John Herschel when he was conducting his southern survey in the 1830s. Fortunately, we know of its existence now, and, as is apparent, we still have a lot to learn from it.

LOOKING THROUGH CIRCINUS: THE EXTRAGALACTIC VIEW

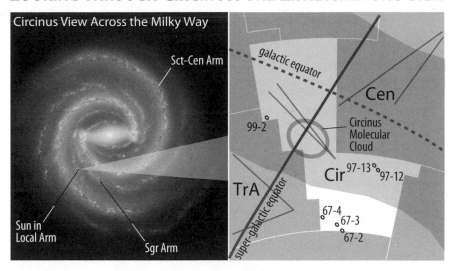

Circinus View Across the Milky Way

Sct-Cen Arm

galactic equator

Cen

99-2°

Circinus
Molecular
Cloud

Cir 97-13° 97-12

TrA

super-galactic equator

67-4
67-3
67-2

Sun in
Local Arm

Sgr Arm

Figure 21: Circinus' view out of the Milky Way. The Circinus view of the extra-galactic realm is heavily obscured as it looks through a thick part of the Milky Way. To see beyond our galaxy, we look through our own local arm, the Sagittarius Arm, a long thick segment of the Scutum-Centaurus Arm, and a farther segment of the Sagittarius Arm. All of the Galactic objects we discuss are in the Local Arm and the nearer part of the Sagittarius Arm, left panel. Within Circinus is the inter-section of the Galactic equator (centerline of the densest part of the Milky Way) and the super-galactic equator (the centerline of a dense structure of galaxies and galaxy clusters). By all rights, Circinus should be teeming with galaxies, but the Milky Way, the undulating gray overlay in the right panel, mostly hides them. A few brighter galaxies, including ESO 97-13, the Circinus Galaxy, peek through to the south, though they reveal little about the large-scale structure of the universe. **Contemplative observing:** Locate Circinus with the naked eye, between Centaurus and Triangulum Australis, and note the Milky Way. Consider that the stars you see are in the Local Arm, and that the glow of the Milky Way is mostly from the nearby Sagittarius Arm and the Scutum-Centaurus Arm. Also consider that there are amazing wonders inside our galaxy and beyond, hidden by the nearby interstellar dust we discuss in this chapter.

Detail

Figure 22: Circinus, the mariner's compass. Among the tools of nautical navigation is the compass or dividers, used to measure distance on a map. In the detail shown here, at left a navigator measures on a map in a book and at right another measures on a globe. The full engraving (top) is the allegorical frontispiece from *Het Licht der Zeevaert* ("The Light of Navigation"), by Willem Blaeu, 1608, a Dutch celestial navagation handbook.

Columba

And the dove came in to him in the evening, and, lo, in her mouth was an olive leaf plucked off: so Noah knew that the waters were abated from off the earth.

— Genesis 8:11

Columba is another small, dim constellation, all of which lies well south of the celestial equator but most of which can be seen from the more southerly latitudes of the Northern Hemisphere. From latitude 30° north, 4th-magnitude Eta (η) Columbae, one of the constellation's brightest southernmost stars, reaches an altitude of nearly 17.5° as it crosses the meridian. From 30° south, Columba may be found very near the zenith during mid-December evenings.

Although Columba is a little thin on celestial fare, we can point the way toward a few objects worth checking out if you find yourself in a favorable geographic vicinity.

Like many constellations, Columba has a convoluted lineage that is as difficult to understand as it is to trace. Modern scholars (Ridpath, Bakich, and Kanas) hold that Columba was formed by Dutchman Petrus Plancius in 1592 from stars Ptolemy cataloged in his *Almagest* as outliers of Canis Major near the ship Argo Navis, which Plancius renamed *Arca Noachi*, or Noah's Ark. He, in turn, christened Columba as Noah's

Columba, the Dove	
Abbreviation: **Col**	Pronunciation: **cuh-LUM-bah**
Genitive: **Columbae**	Pronunciation: **cuh-LUM-bee**
Midnight culmination: **December 18**	
Size on the sky: **270 square degrees**	
Bright stars: **Phact, Wazn**	
Bright nonstellar objects: **None**	
Popular asterisms: **None**	
Note: One of the only surviving constellations representing a Biblical figure, the dove released by Noah after the flood that returned with an olive leaf, proving the waters were receding.	

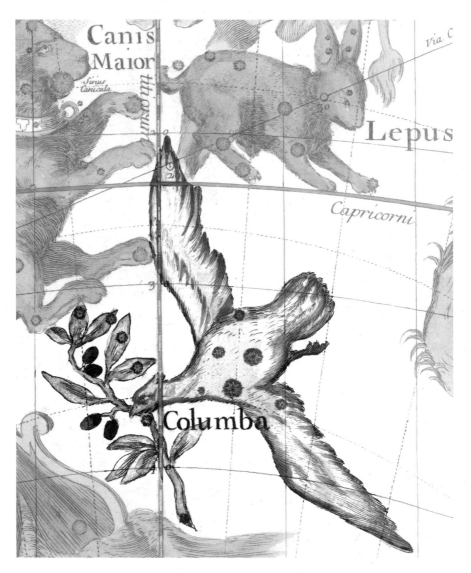

Figure 1: Columba. Ignace-Gaston Pardies' *Globi coelestis in tabulas planas redacti descriptio* was first published after his death in 1674, with later editions in 1693 and 1700. The compact atlas used six plates to show the whole sky (Columba the dove is from Plate 3) and could be assembled into a cube. While small, the engraved figures have a vitality comparable to other atlases of the time.

Dove (*Columba Noachi*). The constellation later appeared in Johann Bayer's *Uranometria* of 1603. Its provenance, however, is not that straightforward.

Readers may recall that in our chapter on Carina, we noted that Argo Navis, the mythical vessel that bore Jason and the Argonauts on their quest for the Golden Fleece, was described in Aratus' epic poem about the constellations, *Phaenomena* (ca 270 BCE). The events of Argo Navis and the Argonauts occur a generation before the Trojan War, which in literature is said to have occurred sometime in the 13th or 12th century BCE. The myth was retold in Homer's poems the *Iliad* and *Odyssey*, written sometime between the 9th and 6th centuries BCE.

All of this transpired centuries before Aratus' reference in *Phaenomena*, but it poses a question: did the Greeks contrive a celestial ship called the Argo Navis, or did it spring from a still earlier source? British mythographer Jacob Bryant (1715–1804) proposed that the fable of the Argonauts predates the Greeks and was instead based on Egyptian traditions, which originally referred to the group of stars as representing Noah's Ark and the Deluge. According to John C. Barentine, author of *The Lost Constellations*, Bryant was renowned for ferreting out the historical facts behind various pagan myths through Judeo-Christian tradition. Bryant argued that the ancient Greek and Egyptian myths were drawn from narratives in the Book of Genesis and that, more specifically, the Greeks misinterpreted the Biblical account of the flood and Noah's ark. In this, we may be seeing how early Christians interpreted what would later become the classical Greek constellations. Such a viewpoint, observes Barentine, anticipates by nearly 1,500 years the remaking of the heavens in biblical imagery by Julius Schiller in *Coelum Stellatum Christianum*. Schiller's Atlas (1627) replaced the pagan constellations with Biblical and early Christian counterparts. For example, the 12 apostles were substituted for the 12 zodiacal constellations, while Eridanus represented the parting of the Red Sea. Corona became the Crown of Thorns, Lyra the Manger of Christ, and Orion Saint Joseph, husband of Mary. Columba was Noah's Dove and Argo Navis, Noah's ark (**Figure 2**).

Over the centuries, all of the Biblical constellations passed into history except Columba. We are still left to speculate as to whether Columba was Plancius' invention alone, but Richard

Figure 2: Noah's Dove. In 1627 Julian Schiller published his *Coelum Stellatum Christianum*, an excellent technical star atlas of its time, detail here courtesy of Adler Planetarium, Chicago, Illinois. Schiller replaced the ancient mythological figures with occasionally equivalent imagery from the Christian Bible, here substituting Noah on his ark for Jason on the *Argo Navis*. Schiller repurposed Columba, the dove at lower left, as a sign to Noah of a nearby shore. Schiller's Christianization of the celestial firmament was not widely embraced, but the atlas features lively engravings by Lucas Killian.

Hinckley Allen, in *Star Names: Their Lore and Meaning*, suggested that the roots of the constellation lead back to antiquity. In a translation by Caesius (the German poet and writer Philipp von Zesen) of the *Paedagogus of Saint Clement of Alexandria*, he writes:

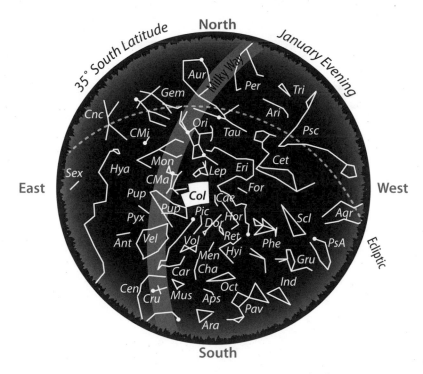

Figure 3: Columba located on the celestial sphere.

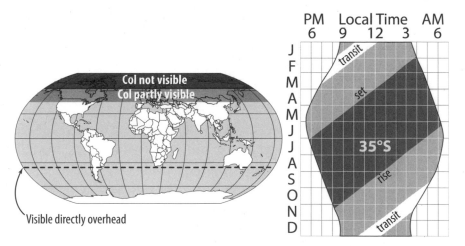

Figure 4: Seeing Columba from the Earth throughout the year. This small constellation is near the South Celestial Pole. The hourglass figure on the right shows the time at which Columba appears highest in the sky across the months of the year and the duration of night at 35° S latitude. Transit times may be used at any latitude.

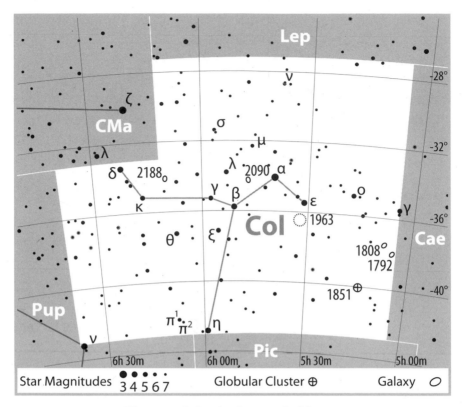

Figure 5: Columba featured objects.

> The signs or symbols of you are the Dove, or the
> course of the Heavenly Ship stretching across the
> sky or the musical Lyre, in remembrance of the
> Fisherman Apostle [Peter].

Clement of Alexandria (150–215 CE) was a Christian theologian educated in classical Greek philosophy and literature. In
one of his works, he asserts that Greek philosophy had its origin in non-Greek sources, arguing that Egyptian scholars
taught both Pythagoras and Plato. Such are the insubstantial
clues of constellation mythography and derivation that we
must grasp the few words of ancient, long-dead scholars to link
our modern appreciation of the night sky with its origins, or
possible origins.

Insofar as content is concerned, Columba hosts two relatively bright stars —Phact and Wazn (magnitudes 2.6 and 3.1,
respectively) — each with interesting traits, a handful of color-

> ## Columba Featured Objects, North to South
>
> **Mu (μ) Columbae:** runaway star; "weak winds" **(page 77).**
>
> **Phact, Alpha (α) Columbae:** Be star; rapid rotator **(page 73).**
>
> **NGC 2188:** disturbed, bar-shaped galaxy **(page 88).**
>
> **NGC 2090:** spiral with bright prominent center **(page 102).**
>
> **Wazn, Beta (β) Columbae:** fast-moving giant **(page 75).**
>
> **NGC 1963:** asterism with nearby galaxies **(page 75).**
>
> **NGC 1808 and NGC 1792:** starburst activity triggered by previous interaction **(page 94).**
>
> **NGC 1851:** compact, bright globular cluster; possible remnant of a dwarf galaxy **(page 80).**

ful double stars, a bright, condensed globular cluster with a secret (NGC 1851), and a number of spiral galaxies worthy of appreciation.

NOTABLE STARS IN COLUMBA

Phact, Alpha (α) Columbae
Be star; rapid rotator

This star's name derives from an Arabic word, *al-fakhita*, meaning "the ring dove." It is a moderately hot subgiant (between 12,500 and 14,000 K) of class B9 (some put it closer to B7), with a luminosity some 1,000 times that of the Sun. As the letter "e" in its spectral type indicates, it produces emission lines arising most likely from circumstellar material ejected by the star's rapid rotation. (For more on these fascinating objects, see Gamma (γ) Cassiopeiae in volume 4.) And Phact's rotational speed is, indeed, fleet, amounting to at least 180 kilometers per second at its equator, though it could be as high as 210 km/s. The average rotational velocity for a Be star is about 130 kilometers per second, which is some one-quarter the "breakup speed."

Phact is about three times the diameter of the Sun, and over 4.5 times as massive. The age is on the order of 100 million years, meaning it is on the verge of ceasing fusing hydrogen to

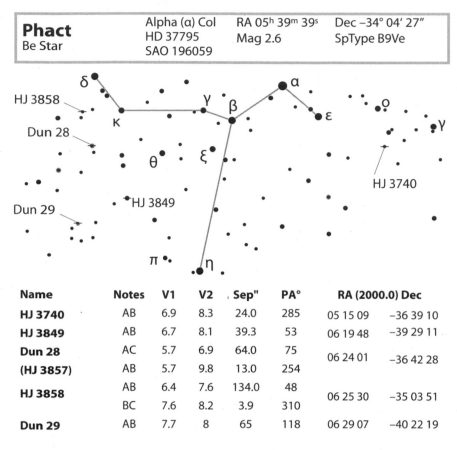

Phact Be Star	Alpha (α) Col HD 37795 SAO 196059	RA 05ʰ 39ᵐ 39ˢ Mag 2.6	Dec −34° 04′ 27″ SpType B9Ve

Name	Notes	V1	V2	Sep"	PA°	RA (2000.0) Dec	
HJ 3740	AB	6.9	8.3	24.0	285	05 15 09	−36 39 10
HJ 3849	AB	6.7	8.1	39.3	53	06 19 48	−39 29 11
Dun 28	AC	5.7	6.9	64.0	75	06 24 01	−36 42 28
(HJ 3857)	AB	5.7	9.8	13.0	254		
HJ 3858	AB	6.4	7.6	134.0	48	06 25 30	−35 03 51
	BC	7.6	8.2	3.9	310		
Dun 29	AB	7.7	8	65	118	06 29 07	−40 22 19

Figure 6: Alpha Columbae and other double stars for beginners. The figure at top is a basic star chart of the easier double stars in Columba in the style of the Northern Hemisphere book *In Starland With a Three-inch Telescope* (1909) by William Tyler Olcott.

helium in its core. Over the next few million years it will transit rapidly into a bright orange giant. The distance is fairly well established at 80 parsecs or 260 light-years. The annual proper motion is about 0.024 arcseconds, and the radial velocity is 35 kilometers per second in recession.

A magnitude 12.5 companion floats 14 arcseconds off to the north, in epoch 2008 measurements. When first measured in 1896, its separation was 6 arcseconds. In that same 112-year interval, the PA has changed slightly, so this is likely an optical double.

Wazn, Beta (ß) Columbae

Fast-moving giant

Wazn is another name whose significance is not known with respect to both star and constellation. As a common noun in Arabic, *al-wazn* means "the weight," but what weight it refers to is a mystery. In *A Dictionary of Modern Star Names*, Paul Kunitzsch and Tim Smart note that some Arabic scholars have proposed that the term "Wezen" applies to one of a pair of stars, either Alpha and Beta Centauri or Alpha and Beta Columbae, but which two stars were intended and the significance of their names is a mystery.

Columba's Wazn is an ordinary yellow-orange K1 giant with a surface temperature of 4,500 K and a luminosity of over 50 suns, yielding an absolute magnitude of about 1.0. Based on these values, the radius calculates out to about 11 or 12 suns and the mass 1.7 solar. The age is estimated to be at least 2 billion years.

One of the star's two unusual characteristics is its space motion, clocked at a little over 100 kilometers per second. This is almost as fast as Mu (μ) Columbae, one of the most famous runaway stars known (and our next stop). The high speed is indicative of its being an interloper passing through the Galactic disk from the halo. As James Kaler points out, most high-speed stars possess the halo's low metal abundance; however — and this is the star's other atypical characteristic — Wazn's metal-to-hydrogen ratio is about 30 times greater than the Sun's. Why this is the case is not understood, though the star could have obtained it via a stellar interaction with a passing star in our galaxy, or some other mechanism. In any case, although it entered the main sequence as a class A dwarf, it is now on its way to expelling its hydrogen envelope and forming a planetary nebula before dwindling away as an ordinary white dwarf.

The *Washington Visual Double Star Catalog* indicates a 10th-magnitude companion with a separation of over 2 arcminutes (126 arcseconds) at PA 161° (epoch 1999). Proper-motion measurements indicate this is an optical double.

Wazn	Beta (β) Col	RA 05ʰ 50ᵐ 57.6ˢ	Dec −35° 46′ 00.5″
High Proper Motion	HD 39425	Mag 3.1	SpType K1III
Star	SAO 196240		

H-R diagram for Beta (β) and other featured stars in Columba

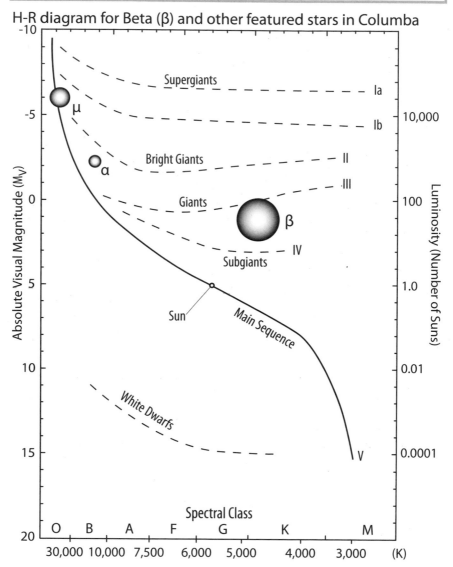

Figure 7: Beta (β) Columbae and other featured stars on a Hertzsprung-Russell diagram.

Mu (μ) Columbae

Runaway star; "weak winds"

We first encountered Mu Columbae in the constellation Auriga during our discussion of the runaway star AE Aurigae. As we noted there, Mu lies over 65° south of AE Aurigae, corresponding to an actual separation of over 1,600 light-years. Intriguingly, the two stars share the same space velocity of over 100 kilometers per second with respect to the Sun, but in opposite directions. Moreover, both stars are about the same age and stellar type. So, what is the connection? If you run their space motions backward for 2.5 million years, you find they intersect on the sky near the location of another star, the massive spectroscopic binary and multiple system Iota (ι) Orionis, a mere 30 arcminutes south of the Orion Nebula, the bottom star of Orion's "sword." When astronomers first came across these runaway stars in the 1950s, they speculated that their motions resulted from the kick of a supernova explosion in a close binary system with a high orbital velocity (the binary-supernova scenario). Since then, observational evidence points to runaway stars as being ejected from the crowded environs of a very young star cluster via gravitational interaction with other stars. Called the dynamical ejection scenario, the interaction essentially involves a collision between two binary star systems, resulting in the simultaneous splitting and ejection of one pair so that they fly apart in opposite directions. In the case of AE Aur and Mu Col, Iota Orionis and its spectroscopic companion would represent the surviving binary of a binary-binary collision (Gualandris et al., 2004). Confirming this idea is the fact that the stars in the Iota system have orbital velocities similar to the space velocities of AE and Mu, and a high orbital eccentricity (0.76), symptomatic of a previous interaction.

Mu itself is a hot O-class dwarf with a temperature of over 31,000 K. Factoring in its distance (about 400 parsecs), some interstellar extinction (0.1 magnitude), and its ultraviolet emission, the star must be at least 15,000 times as luminous as the Sun. That translates into a radius over nearly five times solar

Mu (μ) Columbae	HIP 27204	RA 05ʰ 45ᵐ 59.8ˢ	Dec −32° 18′ 23″
Runaway O Star	SAO 196149	Mag 5.2	SpType O9.5V

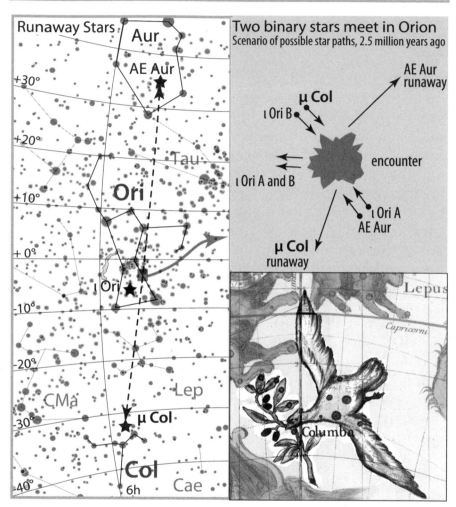

Figure 8: Mu (μ) Columbae, a runaway star. A stellar encounter in Orion appears to have sent two stars flying away, one now racing through Columba and the other in Auriga, discussed in *Annals* Volume 2. A simulation (upper right) after Gualandris et al., 2004, proposes that two double stars met, hurling two stars away in opposite directions and leaving a different double star in Orion.

and a mass around 11 $M_\odot$. The absolute magnitude is slightly brighter than −4.2.

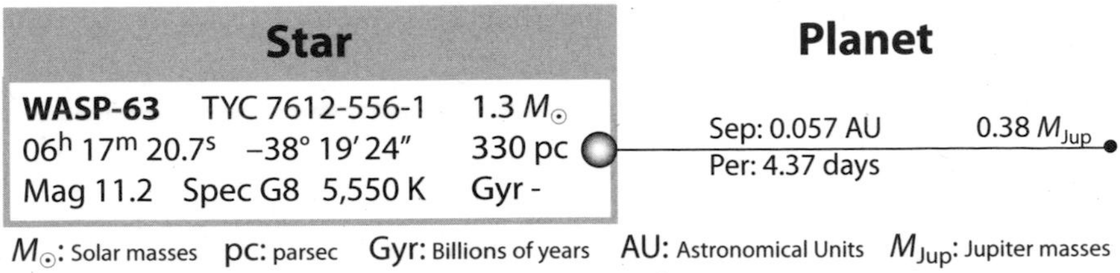

Star				Planet	
WASP-63	TYC 7612-556-1	1.3 $M_\odot$		Sep: 0.057 AU	0.38 M_{Jup}
$06^h\,17^m\,20.7^s$	$-38°\,19'\,24''$	330 pc		Per: 4.37 days	
Mag 11.2	Spec G8	5,550 K	Gyr -		

$M_\odot$: Solar masses pc: parsec Gyr: Billions of years AU: Astronomical Units M_{Jup}: Jupiter masses

Figure 9: A Columba star with a planet.

Mu figures prominently in research into the so-called "weak winds" issuing from hot O-type stars. All stars exhibit some wind-driven radiation that carries away mass, but hot O and B stars produce the highest velocity outflows. The winds produce absorption and emission features in the star's ultraviolet spectrum called P Cygni profiles, which appear as strong emission lines (at long wavelengths) flanked by sharp, blueshifted absorption lines (at short wavelengths), indicating an outflow of material either in the form of a stellar wind or an expanding gas shell in the direction of the observer.[*] The width of the P Cygni lines is indicative of the star's terminal wind velocity. For the hottest O stars velocities can range as high as 4,000 kilometers per second. Typically, these luminous stars have mass-loss rates as high as 10^{-5} $M_\odot$ or 10^{-6} $M_\odot$ per year. Compare that with the Sun, which loses only 10^{-14} $M_\odot$ per year. Such a negligible mass loss would be undetectable even from the Sun's nearest neighbors.

Not all O-type stars exhibit robust wind velocities, however, and their mass-loss rates are consequently more of a slight breeze. The outflow velocities are still high by the Sun's standard, but not as high as stellar wind models would predict. Some of these weak-wind stars have been found in the Small Magellanic Cloud, with mass-loss rates on the order of 10^{-8} $M_\odot$ per year (Martins et al., 2002, 2004). Such values are on par with cool luminous stars but certainly not hot O stars like Mu Col. And yet, Mu's estimated terminal wind velocity — 1,200 kilometers per second — does not reflect its mass-loss rate of only $10^{-9.5}$ $M_\odot$ a year. As is usually the case, stellar wind velocities

---

[*] P Cygni is a variable blue supergiant (B1-2Ia) in Cygnus removed to a distance of over 2 kiloparsecs. Nevertheless, it is still visible as a 5th-magnitude star.

are determined using both H-alpha (Hα) and ultraviolet spectral lines. However, an analysis of the star's X-ray emission (Huenemoerder et al., 2012) revealed the presence of a massive hot wind an order of magnitude greater than that derived by Hα and UV lines alone, which corresponds with the nominal wind-velocity relationships for O stars. Accounting for the hot wind in X-rays, therefore, would appear to resolve the "weak-wind" problem for O stars: the wind is not weak but rather hot, with most of its emission detectable only in X-rays.

GALACTIC OBJECTS IN COLUMBA

NGC 1851

Compact globular cluster; possible remnant of a dwarf galaxy

Tucked in the SW corner of Columba, NGC 1851 is often overlooked by avocational astronomers, not just due to its southerly locale but also because it is somewhat overshadowed by other brighter and more spectacular globulars located in more interesting regions of the southern sky. Globulars like Omega Centauri, M22, and NGC 2808 are showcase objects to be sure, but we think NGC 1851 should be added to this list. It may be a tad compact (12 arcminutes), but it is bright and has one of the densest cores known. Plus, it may not be a globular cluster at all, as we'll soon explain.

James Dunlop first laid eyes on this object in 1826 using his 9-inch reflector. He described it as:

> An exceedingly bright, round, well-defined nebula, about 1½′ diameter, exceedingly condensed, almost to the very margin. This is the brightest small nebula I have seen. I tried several magnifying powers on this beautiful globe; a considerable portion round the margin is resolvable, but the compression to the centre is so great, that I cannot reasonably expect to separate the stars.

Down through the years, most observers have echoed Dunlop's effusive description, consistently using two words to

NGC 1851 Globular Cluster	GCl 9 ESO 305-SC 16	RA 05h 14m 06.8s Mag 7.1 Bt*Vm 13.2	Dec –40° 02' 50" Size 12' Conc Class II

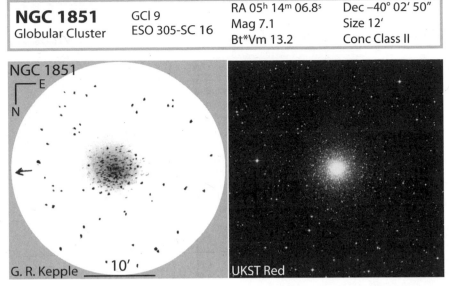

Figure 10: NGC 1851. An eyepiece impression is compared to an observatory survey photograph of this open cluster.

describe it: "bright" and "beautiful." E. J. Hartung writes, "This beautiful globular cluster rises sharply to a very bright centre; including outliers it is about 4' across and well resolved into gleaming points." Steve Gottlieb notes that in his 13.1-inch, the core is "very lively." I would use the word "seething" if not "effervescent" to describe it as it appears in a 15-inch at 132x. These aren't very scientific descriptions, but they do reflect our appreciation for this starry swarm. Observers also describe a considerable halo in the outer region, and, as we will see, this feature is not an artifact but a real structure inherent to the cluster. Closer in, stars appear to be evaporating in strings from the nucleus, again conveying an uncanny sense of movement to something that appears frozen in time. Deep images resolve these strings into "bristling" filaments extending in every direction.

It turns out that, for a globular cluster, NGC 1851 has some unusual traits. A number of photometric studies (e.g. Walker, 1992) found that its core, though unresolved, appeared to be blue and the horizontal branch (HB) bimodal, showing a clump

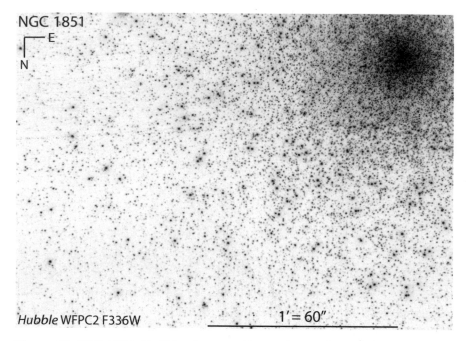

NGC 1851

E

N

Hubble WFPC2 F336W   1' = 60"

Figure 11: NGC 1851, *Hubble* close-up. Our understanding of the appearance of globular clusters is a product of the limitations of ground-based instruments. The *Hubble Space Telescope* makes images of much higher resolution, without the effects of atmospheric seeing, producing the image above. This looks like a familiar globular, but, comparing the scale with that of Figure 10, the steady gradient of star density all the way to the center is apparent. In this way, *Hubble* reveals that globular clusters are "fractal," a structure that exhibits similar patterns at increasingly small scales.

of red stars and a blue "tail" of younger stars. This indicates that at least two subpopulations of stars formed during separate epochs. The color bimodality is probably due to metallicity differences between the two old subpopulations. These kinds of clusters also exhibit spreads in their iron and s-process element abundances. (The s-process is "slow neutron capture," whereby nucleosynthesis takes place in the intershell regions during the red-giant phase of evolution.) Astronomers refer to such globulars as "anomalous." Other well-known anomalous globular clusters include Omega Centauri, M2, M22, and M54, the latter of which lies at the center of the Sagittarius dwarf galaxy that is being tidally disrupted by the Milky Way (Ibata et al., 1994; Sarajedini and Layden, 1995).

Photometric observations using *HST*'s Advanced Camera for Surveys revealed that the subgiant branch (SGB) of NGC 1851 is also split into two well-defined branches (Milone et al., 2008). Assuming the width of the split is due strictly to age (**Figure 12**), the two SGBs would indicate two episodes of star formation about a billion years apart. There's just one drawback with this conclusion, however. According to the study, the relative frequency of red-to-blue HB stars and the population of the two SGBs imply that the progeny of the brighter SGB stars (55 percent) occupy the red part of the HB, while those of the fainter SGB stars (45 percent) occupy the blue HB (i.e., the blue side of the instability strip). While this distribution is in accordance with stellar evolution models, an age difference of only a billion years is not enough time for stars to transit from the red to the blue side of the HB. Such a move would require between 2 and 3 billion years. Hence some additional parameter, such as a difference in the stars' carbon-oxygen-nitrogen abundances[*] or a combination of parameters, must be at work in order to explain the bifurcated horizontal branch of NGC 1851. A spectroscopic analysis of the two subgiant branches (Gratton et al., 2012) found that the brighter SGB stars were slightly more metal-poor than their fainter counterparts, suggesting that the fainter ones are only slightly older, by about 0.6 billion years. Hence, the 1-billion-year difference ultimately may not be that problematic. Nevertheless, as of this writing, the formation of these two subgiant branches is still under debate.

Now about that halo. A study using archival photometric data (Marino et al., 2016) strengthened the notion that what we're seeing in NGC 1851 is not a globular cluster in the conventional sense, but the stellar nugget of a former dwarf satellite galaxy. Such a scenario would go a long way in explaining the bimodality and abundance differences, as well as support the hypothesis that anomalous globular clusters were once as massive as small galaxies and thus able to retain supernova ejecta, which enriched subsequent stellar generations with metals.

---

[*] In stars about 1.3 times more massive than the Sun, the carbon-nitrogen-oxygen cycle is a fusion reaction in which carbon, nitrogen, and oxygen are used as catalysts to convert hydrogen into helium. The CNO cycle is used to estimate the ages of not only globular clusters, but also the universe itself.

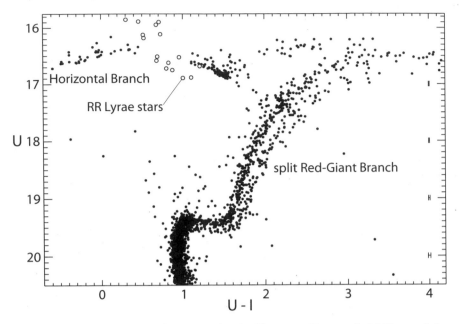

Figure 12: NGC 1851's color-magnitude diagram. Han et al., 2009, used the CTIO 4-meter Blanco Telescope to analyze the globular cluster's stars, producing this CMD. Their selection of ultraviolet and infrared bands showed the split red-giant branch. RR Lyrae variable stars are marked on the horizontal branch.

Recent evidence puts a slight spin on this storyline. A massive, elongated structure called the "Gaia Sausage" emerged in a 2018 kinematic analysis of metal-rich halo stars in the SDSS-*Gaia* astrometric catalog (Belokurov et al.). A subsequent search for globular clusters associated with the Gaia Sausage found that NGC 1851 is one of eight and possibly ten globulars (**Table 1**) that were once part of this system. The clusters are "clumped in azimuthal and vertical action, yet strung out like beads on a chain" (Myeong et al., 2018). They move on orbits that are all highly eccentric, a telltale sign of their extragalactic origin, and also show age-metallicity trends that are more compatible with dwarf spheroidal galaxies than the bulk of Milky Way globulars.

The presence of the Gaia Sausage's globular clusters indicates that they were deposited in the Milky Way during a single event, which is estimated to have occurred between 8 and 10 billion years ago (between redshifts of 3 and 1). This, in

Table 1: Members of the Gaia Sausage

NGC 1851	Columba
NGC 1904	(M79): Lepus
NGC 2298	Puppis
NGC 2808	Carina
NGC 5286	Centaurus
NGC 6864	(M75): Sagittarius
NGC 6779	(M56): Lyra
NGC 7089	(M2): Aquarius
Two other possible candidates:	
NGC 362	Tucana (in the Small Magellanic Cloud)
NGC 1261	Horologium

turn, allows astronomers to estimate the mass of the progenitor. Judging from the number of globular clusters involved, it (the Sausage) must have been more massive than the Fornax Dwarf but comparable to the Sagittarius Dwarf Spheroidal Galaxy, which is estimated as $5 \times 10^{10}\ M_\odot$ (Gibbons et al., 2017). This is in good agreement with the mass estimate from simulations, and suggests that as much as two-thirds of the local stellar halo may consist of precipitate from this massive star system (Belokurov et al., 2018b).

So we now have two scenarios to consider: that NGC 1851 is either one of several large globular clusters deposited in the Milky Way by a massive dwarf galaxy, or that it is the kernel of a former dwarf satellite galaxy. In either case, it appears to be of extragalactic origin and as such may be able to shed light on another mystery, that of the "missing satellites" (also known as the dwarf galaxy problem). Cosmological simulations predict an overabundance of cold dark matter subhaloes compared to the number of satellite galaxies known to exist, but observations show that the number of dwarf galaxies is orders of magnitude lower than expected from these simulations (Moore et al., 1999; Klypin et al., 1999). The Milky Way should have thousands of dwarf satellites orbiting around it; to date, however, only a few dozen have been detected. With the surfeit of cold dark matter assumed, why are we not seeing more dwarf

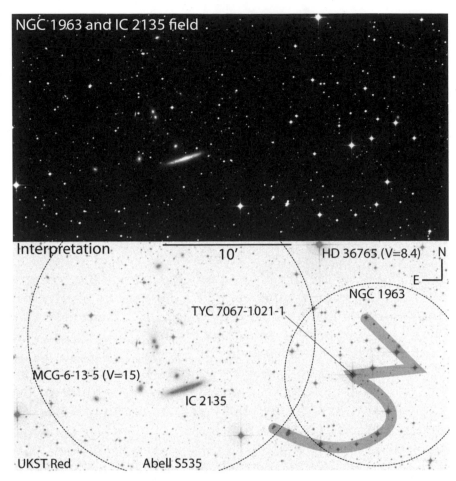

Figure 13: Supplementary objects NGC 1963 and IC 2135, an asterism and a galaxy. The distinctive looping chain of stars at the right comprise the open cluster NGC 1963. Roughly 14 arcminutes across, it forms an unusual pattern that John Herschel interpreted as the numeral 3. Herschel likely referenced the then-common "old style" version of "3" with the angled top and extended descender, depicted above right. The star near the center, TYC 7067-1021-1, is the brightest member, in which "member" is used loosely as this is not a physical group but an asterism of stars arrayed at different distances along our line of sight. The edge-on galaxy to the left is IC 2135, though some catalogs erroneously identify this object as NGC 1963. The galaxy's magnitude of 13.5 makes this a challenging object in small telescopes, but try it anyway. Its distance is about 15 megaparsecs, though some sources suggest 20 Mpc. Note several background galaxies, members of galaxy cluster Abell S535, far behind at 193 Mpc.

galaxies? Although this subject is well beyond the scope of this profile, we'll mention at least three possible solutions. One posits that these objects do exist but that the smallest halos are inefficient at attracting enough baryonic matter to form stars. Another is that some globular clusters have been transformed from their former dwarf galaxy identities by tidal stripping of their less-bound external stars during successive passes through the Milky Way. Omega Centauri was one of the first anomalous globulars proposed to be such an object; NGC 1851 is another, as are the others mentioned earlier (M2, M22, and M54). Still another hypothesis, recently proposed (Wetzel et al., 2016), is that the missing dwarfs aren't missing at all, because they may have never existed. According to this solution, the problem may not lie in the observations but, rather, in simulations that put too much stock in dark matter alone without incorporating the dynamic effects of gas and dust as well, which could destroy dark matter clumps before a dwarf satellite could coalesce.

NGC 1851's halo is huge, with a radius of 67 arcminutes, or 250 parsecs at the distance to the cluster (about 12 kiloparsecs). In actual size, this is well beyond the so-called King radius, the distance from the cluster's center where cluster stars are expected to be lost to tidal interactions. Although the halo's origin is unknown, the dwarf galaxy scenario, again, is a plausible explanation. The fact that it has retained such a tenuous halo is surprising, as its passage should have drawn stars out in a tidal stream over the age of the universe. While there is no apparent photometric evidence for such a structure associated with NGC 1851, other researchers (Sollima et al., 2012) have reported the presence of a possible star stream with a radial velocity of 150 kilometers per second. (For more on tidal streams from globular clusters, see NGC 5466 in Auriga.) It is possible that we are seeing this object at a particular phase in its evolution, with halo stars in the process of escaping the cluster but still bound to it. The halo may have formed during the last passage through the disk some 200 million years ago and may be tidally disrupted during the next disk crossing. The halo, then, would represent that last vestige of its former self as a dwarf galaxy.

The emission line galaxy ESO 305-14 (PGC 16920) floats 21 arcminutes to the NW. With a magnitude of 14.1 and only 1.7 arcminutes across its major axis, observers will need at least a 15-inch to coax it out of the background sky. Images show that this highly inclined spiral (61°) has two prominent arms as well as several narrower offshoots and a broad, bar-shaped nuclear region. The distance is at least 65 megaparsecs.

EXTRAGALACTIC OBJECTS IN COLUMBA

NGC 2188
Disturbed, bar-shaped galaxy

This is an odd galaxy to be sure. Located 1.7° NW of Kappa (κ) Columbae, it presents as a grayish streak running NNW to SSE in telescopes with 4- to 8-inch apertures. In 12- to 15-inch class instruments at magnifications approaching 300x, it is much brighter and ribbon-like; it even exhibits some concentrated mottling within the disk toward its southern extent

NGC 2188 H II Galaxy	ESO 364-37 LEDA 18536	RA 06h 10m 09.7s Mag 11.7 SB 13.2 Size 4.2' x 1.1'	Dec –34° 06' 18" Type SBm(s)m PA 175

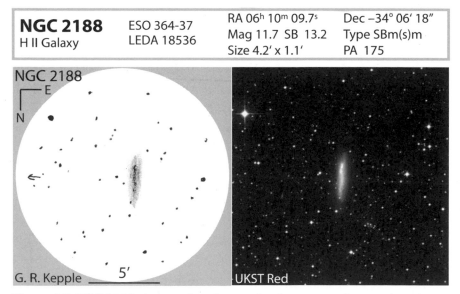

Figure 14: NGC 2188. An eyepiece impression is compared to an observatory survey photograph of this galaxy.

where the streak tapers slightly. With just the right exposure times, images resolve the knots and reveal a kind of diffuse ridge running along the major axis, kinked slightly to the east on the southern end, as well as a tenuous, laminar halo. If one integrates for too long, the ridge burns out, but the exposure reveals more extent to the halo (not to mention much galactic fluff in the background). Two bright field stars, TYC 7080-228-1 (magnitude 9.1) and HD 42519 (magnitude 8.5), lie about 8 arcminutes to the west and WSW, respectively. The former is an A-class main-sequence dwarf, and the latter a class F5. The *Washington Visual Double Star Catalog* lists HD 42519 as a close double with a 10th-magnitude companion 0.3 arcsecond away at PA 311° (epoch 1991).

NGC 2188 is a member of a small group of just three galaxies. The other two are NGC 2090 (which we profile below) and ESO 364-29 (which has a visual magnitude of 13.3, a size of 2.6′ x 1.6′, and a surface brightness of 14.7). ESO 364-29 lies 1.4° NW of NGC 2188, and NGC 2090 is nearly 5° almost due west. Both NGC 2188 and ESO 364-29 share similar redshifts; NGC 2090, however, has a slightly higher redshift, so it likely lies at a greater distance.

In recent years, NGC 2188 has been included in a large number of surveys concerning various aspects of star formation in galaxies in the Local Volume (comprising 824 objects), ultraviolet imaging of galaxies (465 objects), the Carnegie-Irvine Galaxy Survey (617 objects), and galactic morphology (811 objects), to name a few. Other than these sweeping investigations, the galaxy has not been that well studied. Vera Rubin and Geoffrey and Margaret Burbidge made one of the first dedicated studies in the early 1960s (Rubin, Burbidge, and Burbidge, 1964). They photographed the galaxy using McDonald Observatory's 82-inch reflector and took three spectra. The plate showed the galaxy consisting of a string of giant, high-excitation H II knots with little apparent structure. They determined a luminosity of a billion suns, which indicated that NGC 2188 was a dwarf galaxy. Based on these considerations and the flatness of the velocity curve they obtained, Rubin and the Burbidges concluded that the galaxy was not an edge-on spiral, although they speculated it could be an edge-on barred spiral with the line of sight at some oblique angle to the bar. They also discussed the morphology, writing in their paper that it presented a real puzzle:

> It is obviously flattened in one coordinate and possibly in two so that it might be approximated either by a thick disk or a rod. However, the very small amount of rotation in it cannot be increased significantly by supposing that it is not practically edge-on. This suggests that its figure was determined by forces other than centrifugal force. It has all of the characteristics which we associate with a galaxy in an early evolutionary state; its figure may have been determined by forces acting in the condensation process which are no longer present.

If the galaxy indeed had the configurations and dynamics of a spinning rod, they predicted that large velocity gradients would show up in spectra taken with the slit aligned perpendicular to the major axis of the galaxy. To our knowledge, this hypothesis has never been tested, probably because we know more about galaxies as rotating disk systems, not spinning rods.

They estimated a distance of 7.1 megaparsecs based on the Hubble constant in vogue at the time (75 kilometers per second per megaparsec). The actual distance is usually considered to be to be closer to 10 megaparsecs.

A short burst of investigations was conducted in the 1990s. 21-centimeter observations made using the Very Large Array (Domgörgen et al., 1995, 1996) found, among other things: an asymmetric distribution of neutral hydrogen (H I) perpendicular to the galaxy's disk; a low surface brightness component extending nearly two kiloparsecs into the halo SW of the disk; and superbubbles and filaments of H I expanding into the halo from the disk (**Figure 15**). A superposition of the neutral hydrogen map on an Hα image of the star-forming disk showed a good correspondence between the disk and H I distribution, but also revealed that the disk's position angle was not the same over the whole disk. Rather, both ends were very slightly bent toward the east, calling to mind the shape of a banana. The distribution of stars and gas were also substantially different. While there is plenty of neutral gas in places where there is no optical emission (i.e., stars), optical emission is found in the disk plane at the northern end of the disk, which is strongly gas deficient.

An image taken in Hα + [N II] captured details in a number of filamentary structures coincident with the H II regions located in the southern part of the disk (Domgörgen et al., 1997). These were interpreted as ionized gas emerging from the star-forming complex in NGC 2188, similar to the extraplanar gas seen in the edge-on spiral NGC 891, in Andromeda (see its entry in volume 1).

Taken together, all of these features suggest that the galaxy has undergone some large-scale disturbance. One possibility is an interaction with ESO 364-29 (Domgörgen et al., 1996). Its velocity is only about 40 kilometers per second higher than NGC 2188 and the projected separation distance of the two systems is only 180 kiloparsecs. It is also smaller than NGC 2188. Assuming a relative velocity of 200 kilometers per second for the two systems, they would have had their most recent interaction 2 billion years ago. Unfortunately, the interaction scenario does not work out because 200 kilometers per second is higher than 129 ± 22 kilometers per second, the square root of the average squared root-mean-square radial velocity of the galaxies in a group with respect to its average system velocity. To put it another way, their mutual velocities do not indicate a past interaction.

The other possibility proposed is that NGC 2188 has interacted or is interacting with an intergalactic H I cloud. This would explain the peculiar gas dynamics observed in this system and the absence of an external disturber. Supporting this scenario is the morphology of the neutral gas distribution in NGC 2188: it strongly resembles similar features in the starburst galaxy IC 10 in Cassiopeia, which has been interpreted as an interaction with an H I plume.

After observing NGC 2188, observers with telescopes larger than about 12 inches will want to slew 31 arcminutes to the north into the heart of the galaxy cluster Abell 3381 (**Figure 16**), which occupies almost a half-degree of sky. This is a collection of over 30 galaxies, many of them with magni-

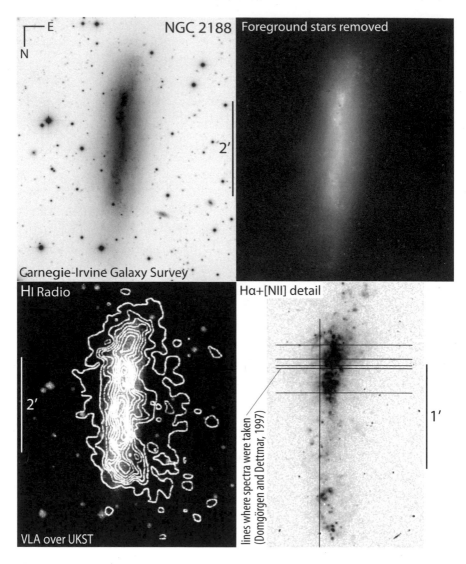

Figure 15: NGC 2188 deconstructed. Optical images of the galaxy, courtesy the Carnegie-Irvine Galaxy Survey, appear at top, with the right panel showing how the galaxy might appear without the intervening Milky Way stars. A radio image, lower left, courtesy Domgörgen et al., 1996, shows emission to the east; the narrowband image at lower right, courtesy Domgörgen and Dettmar, 1997, shows the inner region structure.

tudes 14 and fainter. At the cluster's center resides MCG –06-14-5, a magnitude 15 dwarf S0 galaxy. Two of the other brighter members are ESO 364-35 and ESO 364-36 (both mag-

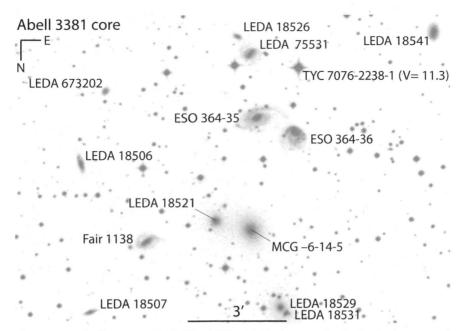

Figure 16: Abell 3381, 27′ NNW of NGC 2188. A map of galaxies in the core of Abell Galaxy Cluster 3381, courtesy UKST red plate.

Table 2: Galaxies near the core of Abell 3381

Galaxy	RA h m s	Dec ° ′ ″	V Mag	SB	Size (′)	Type	Mly
ESO 364-35	06 09 56	−33 38 56	13.9	13.8	1.5 x 0.9	SB(rs)b	395
ESO 364-36	06 10 01	−33 38 28	13.8	13.3	1.1 x 0.7	SAB(s)bc p	380
MCG −6-14-5	06 09 54	−33 35 33	14.3	14.0	1.0: x 1.0:	S0⁻	510
LEDA 18506	06 09 30	−33 37 41	15.5	13.1	0.7 x 0.2	Sab	490
LEDA 18507	06 09 31	−33 33 07	16.0	13.2	0.5 x 0.2	Sb:	455
LEDA 18521	06 09 49	−33 35 51	15.1	13.7	0.7 x 0.5	S0	495
LEDA 18526	06 09 53	−33 41 29	16.2	13.2	0.4 x 0.2	SB?0⁺: p	490
LEDA 18529	06 09 58	−33 33 10	15.4	13.4	0.5 x 0.4	S0°:	500
LEDA 18531	06 09 59	−33 32 59	15.9:	12.9:	0.4: x 0.2:	E/S0:	495
LEDA 18541	06 10 22	−33 41 28	14.9	13.2	0.7 x 0.4	SB:(s?)ab	400
LEDA 75531	06 09 54	−33 40 56	14.6	13.4	0.7 x 0.6	SB(r)b	490
LEDA 673202	06 09 33	−33 39 53	15.8	13.0	0.4 x 0.3	SA:a	1,075
Fairall 1138	06 09 39	-33 35 16	15.0	14.0	1.0 x 0.5	SB(r)ab p	490

Note: LEDA galaxies appear in some databases as PGC, except LEDA 673202, beyond Abell 3381. Colons (:) denote uncertainty.

NGC 1808 Seyfert II Galaxy	ESO 305-8 LEDA 16779	RA 05ʰ 07ᵐ 42.3ˢ Mag 9.9 SB 13.3 Size 6.5' x 3.9'	Dec –37° 30' 47" Type (R)SAB(s)a PA 133
NGC 1792 Emission-line Galaxy	ESO 305-6 LEDA 16709	RA 05ʰ 05ᵐ 14.4ˢ Mag 10.2 SB 12.9 Size 5.2' x 2.6'	Dec –37° 58' 47" Type SA(rs)bc II-III PA 137

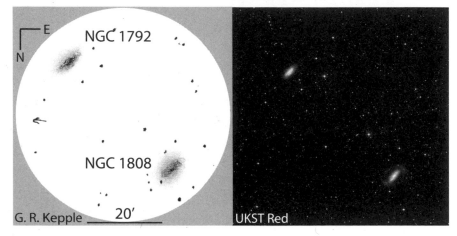

Figure 17: NGC 1808 and NGC 1792. An eyepiece impression is compared to an observatory survey photograph of these galaxies.

nitude 14), two disturbed spirals. The distance to MCG –06-14-5 is between 166 and 170 megaparsecs; hence, this is (very) roughly the distance to Abell 3381.

NGC 1808 and NGC 1792

Starburst activity triggered by previous interaction

One cannot discuss NGC 1808 without also discussing NGC 1792, because observations indicate their morphology is a result of a former interaction. Hence, we profile them together. Both are James Dunlop discoveries (1826), although his cursory descriptions — NGC 1808's faintness and NGC 1792's elliptical and well defined appearance — belie their more intriguing characteristics. Their separation on the sky is only some 41 arcminutes and their distances are roughly similar, about 10 to 11 megaparsecs (although the uncertainty is such that some studies place them as much as three to five megaparsecs beyond those values). If we go by the 11-mega-parsec value, their true separation in space is 130 kiloparsecs or 426,500 light-years. Their inclinations are also similar and their position angles nearly mirror each other. If you go by their radial velocities, NGC 1808 is slightly closer, so for this ostensible reason, we will discuss that galaxy first.

Hartung casts NGC 1808 as a long, bright elliptical nebula, 4.5' x 1.5' in PA 145°. "It has a small bright lengthened nucleus about 20" across." On dark nights of good seeing, they can be detected in the same wide field in telescopes of 5 and 6 inches, but little in the way of detail emerges, other than their elongated appearance. Telescopes of 11 to 15 inches render the elongation quite clearly and flesh out a bit more of the visual presence of the halo. The nucleus is faint but stellar and set within a coarse or mottled surround. Christian B. Luginbuhl and Brian Skiff in their *Observing Handbook and Catalogue of Deep-Sky Objects* report that in a 25-centimeter, NGC 1808 is elongated in nearly the same position angle as NGC 1792 but is narrower and longer: "The faint outer halo extends to 3.5' x 1', encompassing a small core with a moderately bright nucleus." A 30-centimeter resolves slightly more detail, in particular a faint stellar nucleus visible within the unevenly bright core. Steve Gottlieb, using a 17.5-inch, describes it as "bright, fairly large, small elongated core."

Deep images render a compact nucleus surrounded by a nonconcentric multiarmed spiral pattern (Wray 1988). The main disk appears to be a highly inclined Sb-type spiral with significant nearside extinction produced by fibrils of dark dust. On the far side, several peculiar linear dust filaments appear to radiate from the compact nucleus, which consists of several bright knots. Perhaps one of the most stunning features, seen best in negative images, is a faint outer ring formed by a prominent spiral arm springing from the NW major axis of the galaxy and sweeping around the entire disk. Clearly, this galaxy has been disturbed.

The lion's share of previous research goes to NGC 1808; it has appeared as the subject or part of a survey in nearly 600 papers since 1965 (compared with over 170 for NGC 1792).

Interest in NGC 1808, however, goes back considerably further than 1965. Edwin Hubble's attention was drawn to it in 1938 when he considered it a member of a small class of galaxies with multiple nuclei. W. W. Morgan first mentioned the galaxy in the literature in 1958, calling the compact nuclear condensations "hot spots." J. L. Sérsic and M. Pastoriza listed NGC 1808 as a galaxy with a peculiar nucleus (1965), and Geoffrey and Margaret Burbidge obtained spectra in an attempt to derive the galaxy's rotation curve and mass (1968). The Burbidges assumed that the nuclear components were H II regions, rotating about the center at more or less fixed distances. Halton Arp and Francesco Bertola (1970) obtained redshifts of five individual condensations and deduced that rather than merely rotating about the center, they were expanding and probably moving outward from the nucleus. They noted narrow dark lanes that curve slightly as they emerge NE of the nucleus, along the minor axis, which they interpreted as the passage of compact bodies outwards from the nucleus. (Those familiar with Arp's research will appreciate that these were the "formative years" of his theories on the ejections of material from the nuclei of galaxies.) In another study, M.-P. Véron-Cetty and P. Véron (1985) found that the dust filaments were emerging from the galactic plane (saying nothing about ejection) and obscuring part of the far side of the galaxy (**Figure 18**). They also found evidence for Seyfert activity in the central region. Bolstering the active nucleus scenario, high-resolution radio maps (Saikia et al., 1990) revealed a population of compact sources within the central starburst region reminiscent of those found in the starburst center of M82 (in Ursa Major) and NGC 253 (in Sculptor).

Observations of radio continuum emission at 6 and 20 centimeters, as well as neutral hydrogen (Dahlem et al., 1990), showed that the radio continuum is confined to the inner 13 kiloparsecs — essentially the central disk, with the bulk emitted by the central source. No emission was detected in the outer spiral arms. The gas in the inner region is optically thin, hot, and surrounded by a rotating molecular ring 1.4 kiloparsecs in diameter. The central region is punctuated with infrared and radio sources, signatures of young star clusters and supernova

Figure 18: NGC 1808 and its core. A color index image, lower left, courtesy Véron-Cetty and Véron, 1985, highlights the dusty filaments emerging from the near side of the core; this image was made with an early CCD camera on a 1.5-m telescope at La Silla. At lower right is a *Hubble* close-up of the inner core by Jim Flood (Amateur Astronomers Inc., Sperry Observatory) and Max Mutchler (STScI). Amateurs were invited to propose observations using *Hubble,* and this was the last of that program in 1997.

remnants (Saikia et al., 1990; Kotilainen et al., 1996), while the galactic center harbors what may be a low-luminosity active galactic nucleus. Hydrogen-alpha (Hα) observations also reveal a string of linearly aligned ionized gas clumps located *above* the disk, interpreted as either hot gas escaping from the central starburst region or the ionization of (originally) cold gas by a jet produced in the active central region. Observations of neutral hydrogen using the Very Large Array (Koribalski et al., 1993) confirmed not only the outflow but also a warped outer disk, both consistent with a past interaction.

An optical polarization map of NGC 1808 (Scarrott et al., 1993) showed that on kiloparsec scales the polarization orientations follow that of the spiral arms, indicative of a coherent magnetic field on a galactic scale. The inner 750 parsecs surrounding the central starburst region resemble a reflection nebula illuminated mainly by the galactic nucleus, but with minor contributions from some of the hotspots.

The features found in the central region of NGC 1808 are strikingly similar to the starburst galaxy M82. In that galaxy, it is known that a tidal interaction with M81 induced starburst activity in its central region. It seems reasonable to assume that that is the case here. The best possible interaction candidate is NGC 1792, so let's now turn our attention to that system.

Visually, Hartung describes NGC 1792 as a bright elliptical nebula 3.5′ x 1.5′ that "rises in brightness broadly to the central axis." Luginbuhl and Skiff describe it as large and bright in a 25-centimeter, with "a smooth outline and glittering spots along the major axis." In a 13.1-inch at 105x, Gottlieb notes "a large bright core . . . sharply concentrated with a bright, 15″ nucleus. The surface brightness is irregular with a mottled texture." Some observers report that the overall disk appears as a stretched-out letter S, owing to the embedded spiral pattern. Deep images reveal a highly chaotic disk due to the patchy distribution of dust and numerous emission knots tracing the locations of H II regions.

The structure of NGC 1792 depicted in images is that of a well-defined multiarmed spiral embedded within a bright background disk. Like NGC 1808, it has a small core, but its central disk presents a more chaotic, patchy appearance due to the irregular dust distribution and a large number of emission knots tracing the locations of H II regions that roughly follow the spiral-arm pattern. Observations of the distribution of H II regions in Hα images and in the radio continuum (Dahlem et al., 1994) found a strong asymmetry of star-forming regions along the major axis; the asymmetry appeared even stronger in the radio continuum. Clearly, NGC 1792 is undergoing a spate of robust star formation, though it is not happening simultaneously throughout the galaxy but rather spreading across it in two stages. The spatial distribution of these features indicates that supernova activity began earlier in the NE half of the disk than SW of the nucleus. The NE region exhibits both Hα and nonthermal radio continuum emission, the latter being a semaphore for past and present supernova activity. The SW half of the disk, meanwhile, exhibits Hα but no nonthermal radio continuum; hence, it appears that star formation is propagating in a southwesterly direction across the disk. The onset of star formation SW of the nucleus, where supernovae are apparently absent, probably began less than 10 million years ago. In the NE quadrant, where the nonthermal continuum is greatest, the age of star formation is greater than 10 million years. The most prodigious regions of star-formation activity appear in the north and SE sectors of the galaxy. Interestingly, both present different morphologies. Two very bright, point-like H II regions dominate the northern complex, while the SE region consists of several bright, but more extended, H II knots (**Figure 19**).

The strong asymmetry of the emission with respect to the major axis in Hα and nonthermal radio is inconsistent with an internal triggering system that works symmetrically, such as a density wave. Rather, researchers think it more likely that an external factor, such as an interaction with NGC 1808 some 100 million years ago, triggered the lopsided star-forming episodes. An interaction accounts for all the apparent features: the starburst activity in NGC 1808 and its warped outer ring, and the asymmetric distributions of star-forming regions in the spiral arms of NGC 1792.

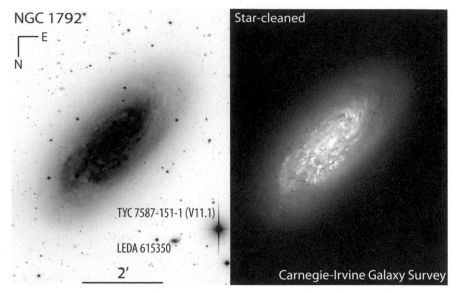

NGC 1792°

E

N

TYC 7587-151-1 (V11.1)

LEDA 615350

2'

Star-cleaned

Carnegie-Irvine Galaxy Survey

Figure 19: NGC 1792. A deep ground-based image, courtesy the Carnegie-Irvine Galaxy Survey, shows the well-defined spiral arms, chaotic inner disk, extended outer disk, and subtle dust features. The image at right is this same image with foreground stars and background galaxies removed. Note the hints of a halo of globular clusters.

Getting back to NGC 1808, ^{12}CO observations using 27 antennas of the ALMA 12-meter array (Salak et al., 2016) virtually deconstructed that galaxy's inner region, confirming, first, that the nucleus is dominated by nonthermal emission (**Figure 20**). Hence, we may be talking about a black hole as the central engine, the mass of which may be on the order of 12 million suns. Four distinct components of molecular gas were also delineated: a compact circumnuclear disk within a radius of 200 parsecs; a 500-parsec ring; a gas-rich galactic bar with a semimajor axis of about 3 kiloparsecs; and kiloparsec-scale spiral arms. Two systematic velocities of 998 and 964 kilometers per second were determined for the circumnuclear disk and 500-parsec ring, respectively. The origin of this velocity offset is not known. One possibility is the bulge is composed of two massive components. One dominates the gas in the circumnuclear disk and a second larger component determines the gas

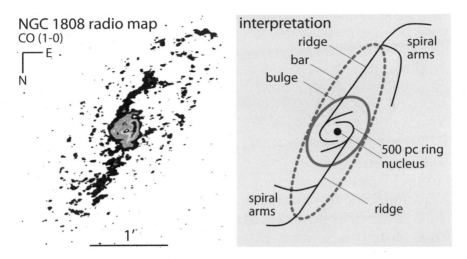

Figure 20: NGC 1808 inner region in radio. An interpretation (right) of a radio map using the Atacama Large Millimeter/submillimeter Array (left), courtesy Salak et al., 2016.

motion in the central two kiloparsecs. In this scenario, neither would possess a single dynamical center, which, again, points to a tidal interaction in the past.

A supernova was discovered in NGC 1808 in November 1993, 220 arcseconds east and 94 arcseconds north of the nucleus. SN 1993af was a Type Ia event. Its maximum brightness was magnitude 17.

Widefield deep images of the region surrounding NGC 1808 bring out numerous faint background galaxies. In the immediate field, we find a magnitude 16 galaxy 3.3 arcminutes away in PA 80° (ENE) from the center of NGC 1808. It is designated 0507-3730 in the Mitchell Anonymous Catalog (MAC). The NASA/IPAC Extragalactic Database (NED) recognizes this as LEDA 622127. Three others may also be found nearby. One, MAC 0507-3732 (LEDA 3098114), shines through the SE outer spiral extension, some 3 arcminutes from the center. Its magnitude is 16.5. Two others, MAC 0507-3728 (LEDA 622698) and MAC 0507-3732A (LEDA 621908), may be found on NGC 1808's NW and western side: the first 4.8 arcminutes away in PA 305°, and the second 4.7 arcminutes away in PA 254°. Their visual magnitudes are 16.5 and 17, respectively. All four have very small angular diameters, with MAC 0507-3730 being the largest at 0.6' x 0.2'.

Proximity in the sky does not indicate proximity in three dimensions of gravitationally bound groups of galaxies. Several of the galaxies discussed here — NGC 1808/1792, NGC 2090, and IC 2135 — are a part of "Low Density Contrast" galaxy group number 384 (LDC 384), identified by Crook et al., 2007, based on the 2-Micron All Sky Survey (2MASS) Redshift Survey. Determining group membership relies on uniform recession velocities (redshifts), and 2MASS offers such a dataset. In 1998, R. Brent Tully identified these galaxies (and NGC 2188 as well) as a northern subgroup of his wide group 53, which he called the Dorado Cloud in his *Nearby Galaxy Catalog*. What we know about the large-scale structure of the universe derives from the latest redshift measurements of galaxies to tease out their respective positions in 3D space. While large well-studied structures like the Coma Great Wall of Galaxies (see next chapter) have widely accepted names, the International Astronomical Union has not seen a need to codify standard naming, so we rely on this mix of individual researchers' catalogs.

NGC 2090

Spiral with bright prominent center

We find NGC 2090 1.5° ESE of Phact in a field sprinkled liberally with 10th- and 11th-magnitude stars; fainter stars (magnitudes 13 and 14) can be seen in and around the disk itself. As mentioned, this galaxy is a member of a triad of galaxies that includes NGC 2188 and ESO 363-29. The most noticeable feature of this object in almost any telescope is its elongated appearance, thanks to a large, bright central region. What is not seen in smaller telescopes is the ghostly outer disk comprising a multiarm spiral. Images reveal these to be flecked throughout with small H II regions (more on this below). James Dunlop discovered NGC 2090 in 1826, describing it as a small, faint nebula "with a ray shooting out on the north side." The last remark is curious, as there is no apparent ray projecting from the galaxy on the north side. Perhaps he was looking at a line of stars or caught a glimpse of a spiral arm, one of which does extend east of the nucleus toward the north.

Hartung doesn't mention NGC 2090 in his compendium of southern deep-sky objects, but Walter Scott Houston mentioned it in his Deep-Sky Wonders column in *Sky & Telescope*, noting that in a 7-inch refractor it looks like a globular cluster, an assumption, Houston says, John Herschel made when he first observed it. According to observers in *The Night Sky Observer's Guide*, in 12- to 14-inch telescopes the galaxy has a moderately bright core surrounded by a faint halo elongated 2.5' x 1' NNW to SSE. At 200x, tiny spiral arcs are visible NE and SW of the center.

NGC 2090's outer disk is bright at ultraviolet wavelengths but has a very low surface brightness (LSB) at longer wavelengths. Near-infrared images, which detect only the older population of stars in the bulge region, render this galaxy as a two-armed grand-design spiral (type Sb) with arms that wrap 360° before fading (Eskridge et al., 2002). Ultraviolet and blue wavelengths, however, show this to be a multiarmed spiral

NGC 2090 ESO 363-23	RA 05ʰ 47ᵐ 01.8ˢ	Dec –35° 15' 02"
Galaxy in Group LEDA 17819	Mag 11.2 SB 13.6	Type SA(rs)c II-III
	Size 4.9' x 2.4'	PA 13

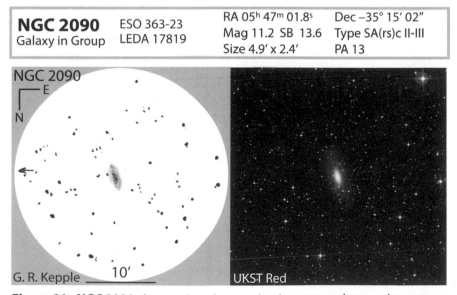

Figure 21: NGC 2090. An eyepiece impression is compared to an observatory survey photograph of this galaxy.

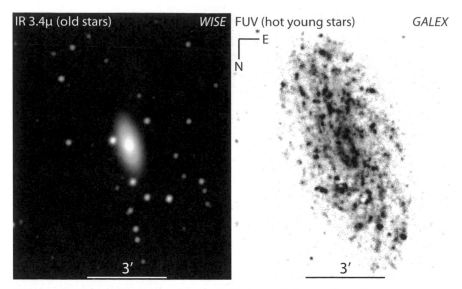

Figure 22: NGC 2090 deconstructed. Old stars (left panel) and hot young stars (right panel) map the structure of this galaxy.

shot through with star-forming hot spots. Astronomers consider this a type 2 disk, one which is rapidly forming stars at a pace that will double its currently low stellar mass in the next billion years, assuming a constant star-formation rate. (A type 1 disk is typical of spirals of all types where star formation is ongoing or near its peak.)

Ultraviolet images taken with the *Galaxy Evolution Explorer* (*GALEX*) show this LSB zone extends over an area more than an order of magnitude larger than the effective size of the old stellar disk (Thilker et al., 2007). This UV-bright LSB zone is considered an example of a disk in formation at the present epoch. The *GALEX* data also show a redder inner disk, surrounded by a bluer, flocculent outer region distinguished by sporadic spiral segments. H II regions are found throughout the disk; in the galaxy's bright inner region, some take the form of a ring structure.

Another study of the stellar populations in the galaxy's outer disk using ultraviolet and mid-infrared imaging with *GALEX* and *Spitzer* (Alberts et al., 2011) racked up 47 star-forming associations in NGC 2090's LSB zone in the disk's NW

NGC 2090

E

N

2′

0.5′ = 30″

Carnegie-Irvine Galaxy Survey

Hubble WFPC2 F606W

Figure 23: NGC 2090 core. The high-resolution image of the core, right, looks a lot like the wider view at left, suggesting that some galaxies are fractal.

quadrant. Their ages ranged widely from 1 million to almost a billion years.

NGC 2090 is rich in Cepheid variable stars. One study (Phelps et al., 1998) discovered 34 with periods ranging between 5 and 58 days. A distance of 12.3 megaparsecs was determined using Leavitt's law of the period-luminosity relationship of Cepheids.

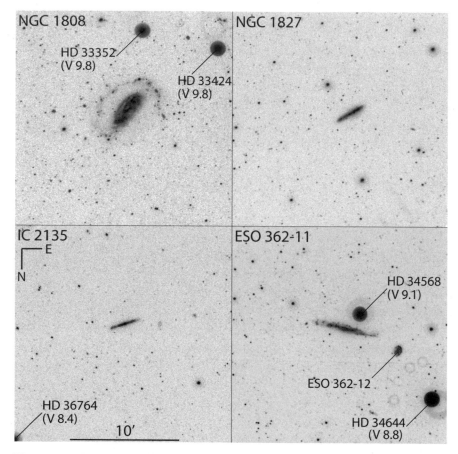

Figure 24: Four near-ultraviolet galaxy images in galaxy group LDC 384.
These images from the *Galaxy Evolution Explorer* (*GALEX*) orbiting observatory
show the galaxies' near-ultraviolet appearances. *GALEX* offered two bands; the
near-ultraviolet displays stars we can see visually and the far-ultraviolet hides
many of these stars, marked here with Henry Draper (HD) labels. Compare the
NGC 1808 image to those in **Figure 18**.

Table 3: Galaxy Group LDC 384

Galaxy	RA h m s	Dec ° ' "	V Mag	SB	Size (')	PA	Typ	Mly
NGC 1792	05 05 14	−37 58 47	10.2	12.9	5.2 x 2.6	137	SA(rs)bc	33
NGC 1827	05 10 05	−36 57 37	12.6	13.1	3.0 x 0.7	120	SAB(s)cd:sp	47
NGC 1808	05 07 42	−37 30 47	9.9	13.3	6.5 x 3.9	133	(R)SAB(s)a	33
NGC 2090	05 47 02	−34 15 02	11.2	13.7	4.9 x 2.4	13	SA(rs)c	39
ESO 362-11	05 16 39	−37 06 09	12.5	13.2	4.5 x 0.6	76	Sbc sp	61
IC 2135	05 33 13	−36 23 56	12.5	12.7	2.8 x 0.6	109	Scd: sp	61

LOOKING TOWARD COLUMBA THROUGH THE MILKY WAY

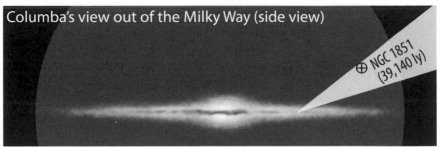

Columba's view out of the Milky Way (side view)

⊕ NGC 1851
(39,140 ly)

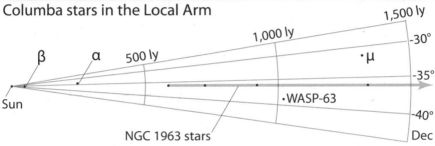

Columba stars in the Local Arm

1,500 ly

1,000 ly

-30°

β α 500 ly

·μ

-35°

Sun

·WASP-63

-40°

NGC 1963 stars

Dec

Figure 25: Columba's view across the Milky Way. All the stars we see are nearby in the Local Arm, including the chance alignment of brighter stars in the "3" asterism of NGC 1963 (gray arrow). The brightest of this asterism, TYC 7067-1021-1, is actually off the page to the right, as are two other stars making up the "3." Far beyond, globular cluster NGC 1851 looks down from the Galaxy's halo.

LOOKING THROUGH COLUMBA: THE EXTRAGALACTIC VIEW

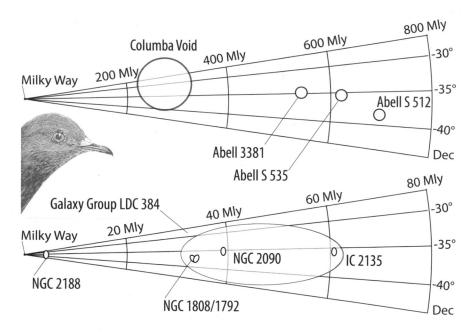

Figure 26: Columba's view out of the Milky Way. As astronomers explored the three-dimensional structure of the universe last century, they sometimes found nearby galaxies (lower panel) in groups. R. Brent Tully collected some of these galaxies in 1988 as a northern subgroup of the "Dorado Cloud," listed as Tully Group 53. Later work (Crook et al., 2007) used the 2MASS dataset to freshly identify Low-Density Contrast (LDC) group number 384, listed in **Table 3, page 106**. Farther out (top panel) Anthony Fairall identified the Columba Void, a large region with statistically few galaxies. Beyond are three Abell (ACO) galaxy clusters, appearing as background to some of the nearer objects discussed earlier in Columba. Note that two of the cluster names include an "S," indicative of the list of "Supplementary" southern ACO clusters too poor or too distant to be included in the main list as Abell 3381 is. According to Harold Corwin, who assembled the ACO list of southern clusters, there are 1,174 supplementary clusters compared to 1,361 in the main southern catalog.

Coma Berenices

Nearly on a line between Denebola and Arcturus, and somewhat nearer to the former, you will perceive a curious twinkling, as if gossamers spangled with dewdrops were entangled there. One might think the old woman of the nursery rhyme who went to sweep the cobwebs out of the sky had skipped this corner, or else that its delicate beauty had preserved it even from her housewifely instinct. This is the little constellation called Berenice's Hair.

— Garrett P. Serviss

The midnight culmination of Coma Berenices occurs in early April in the Northern Hemisphere, but if you wait until late May around 10 p.m., this part of the celestial sphere floats practically overhead. (From latitude 35° south around this time, Coma Berenices crosses the northern meridian at a median altitude of 32°.) This is one of the most important sectors of sky for astronomy research, yet to the naked eye it is unremarkable. It appears as a nearly starless abyss, absent of any prominent features except for a trickle of faint stars barely visible on the darkest of nights running roughly north to south. Nevertheless, we shall spend some time here, not so much for what abides in the Milky Way in this direction, but what lies beyond in what is known as the Realm of the Galaxies.

Coma Berenices, Berenice's Hair	
Abbreviation: **Com**	Pronunciation: **COE-muh-bear-uh-NICE-eez**
Genitive: **Comae Berenices**	Pronunciation: **COE-mee-bear-uh-NICE-eez**
Midnight culmination: **April 2**	
Size on the sky: **386.4 square degrees**	
Bright stars: **None**	
Bright nonstellar objects: **Melotte 111 (in a dark sky)**	
Popular asterisms: **None**	
Note: The North Galactic Pole lies within Coma Berenices at these approximate 2000.0 coordinates: RA 12ʰ 51ᵐ 26.3ˢ; Dec +27° 07' 42". The constellation also contains the Coma Cluster (Abell 1656), a rich, dense assortment of at least 1,000 galaxies.	

Figure 1: Berenice's Hair. Three atlases interpret the shorn locks. Ignace-Gaston Pardies engraved a luxurious tangle with wrapped braids and hints of a head wreath. Johann Bode offers plainer art, with the stars in the foreground. Johann Bayer engraved bound skeins, which can also be interpreted as a sheaf of grain with kernels at the bottom.

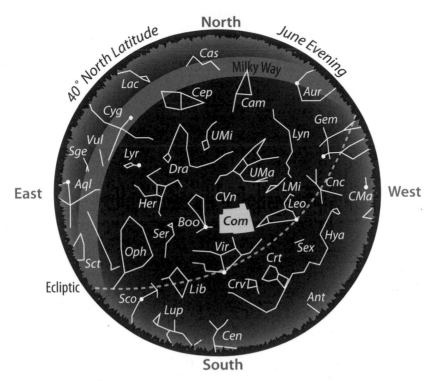

Figure 2: Coma Berenices located on the celestial sphere.

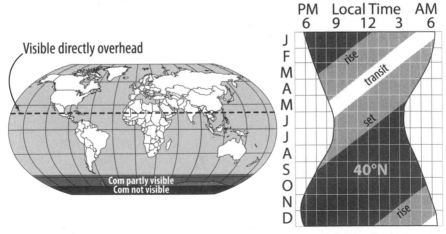

Figure 3: Seeing Coma Berenices from the Earth throughout the year. This constellation is just east of Leo and north of Virgo. The hourglass figure on the right shows the time at which Coma Berenices appears highest in the sky across the months of the year and the duration of night at 40° N latitude. Transit times may be used at any latitude.

Four prominent star groups bracket this dusky region, making it easy to isolate in the sky. To the west is Leo the Lion, just beginning his descent toward the horizon. The eye falls naturally upon the sickle-shaped asterism that forms the lion's westward-facing profile, which is pinned to the sky by 1.4-magnitude Regulus. But our view is also drawn eastward to the (nearly) right triangle hindquarters of the lion, where we find Leo's beta star, Denebola, at its easternmost apex. At magnitude 2.1, this is the brightest star nearest the dusky Coma Berenices border. Meanwhile, to the east flashes ruddy Arcturus in Boötes the Herdsman, brightest star in the northern night sky. High in the north we see the Big Dipper, its bowl always open toward the Little Dipper and the pole region, and its handle like a bent finger pointing back toward Arcturus. Following this arched trajectory past Arcturus and further south, we come across blue-white Spica in Virgo the Virgin, which is approaching the meridian.

A binocular scan offers little in the way of interest, except for that trickle of stars — Melotte 111 — which is nicely contained within a 7x50 field. Careful scrutiny of the region may reveal a woolly object, the globular cluster M53, in the ESE part of the constellation, and the galaxies M64 and NGC 4725. Binocular observers, notably Craig Crossen, point out that quite a few galaxies — including all of the constellation's Messier galaxies — can be glimpsed in 10x50s, albeit some as stellar points.

The reason this part of the sky is so star-poor is that our line of sight passes through the thinnest part of the Galactic plane, in which there are very few stars and little dust to impede our view of extragalactic space. One might describe it as our galaxy's celestial sunroof, though "galactic roof" may be more accurate since the vista in this direction is rich in galaxies both near and far. Hence, an observer really needs a telescope to probe the darkness and appreciate how these remote denizens make this region a worthwhile sojourn.

Two great galactic conglomerations thread through Coma Berenices: the Virgo Cluster, crossing the SW portion of the constellation into Virgo, just SE of the Lion's tail, and the Coma Cluster in the NNE sector, west of Beta (β) Comae Berenices.

The two are often lumped together as either the Coma-Virgo Supercluster or just the Virgo Supercluster. However, when one considers that they are separated by nearly 6,000 kilometers per second in redshift space — a difference of about 80 megaparsecs — one has to conclude the two are separate entities. Despite the unfortunate spatial overlap, we will try to sort them out in the coming pages.

First things first, though: who is the constellation's eponym, Berenice, and why should her hair be so glorified in the heavens? She is based on a very real person, Berenice II of Egypt, daughter of Magus, King of Cyrenaica, and who, in the third century BCE, married her brother, Ptolemy III Euergetes, the third ruler of the Ptolemaic dynasty. Incest was widespread among Egyptian royal families, primarily because their power set them apart from the commoners. It elevated them to the status of gods, who also married each other. On the practical side, incest ensured royal assets would stay in the family. It seemed like a good idea on papyrus. At any rate, the Ptolemaics were not Egyptians but descendents of a family of Macedonian Greek origin that ruled after the death of Alexander the Great. Their dynasty was founded by Ptolemy I Soter (305 BCE) and would end with the death of Cleopatra VII Philopator (yes, *that* Cleopatra) in 30 BCE.

Berenice was an accomplished equestrian who participated not only in the Nemean Games, one of four Panhellenic Games held in ancient Greece to honor Zeus, but the Olympic Games as well. She was obviously a woman to be reckoned with. In mythology, however, her long hair — said to be luxurious and the color of amber — takes center stage. The Greek contemporary poet Callimachus (310–240 BCE) first related the story of Berenice's hair in his poem *Aetia,* in which she dedicates her locks "to all the gods." The Roman poet Catullus (84–54 BCE) translated it into Latin, the text of which survives to this day.

Ptolemy III began his reign in 246 BCE and married Berenice around the time of his accession. According to one version of the story, Berenice was still in their wedding bed when he set out with an army to attack the Assyrians. He left Berenice to act as temporary head of state, but she was far more concerned for her husband's well being. In near despair, she vowed to cut off

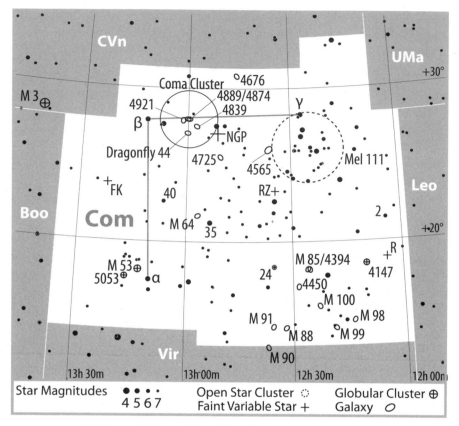

Figure 4: Coma Berenices featured objects.

her long hair and, in Catullus' translation, sacrifice it to the goddess of love and beauty, Aphrodite, if he should safely return. When he arrived victorious, she carried out her pledge and had the priests place the tresses on the altar of the temple of Zephyrium, which was sacred to Aphrodite.

Her lock-loving husband, however, was not pleased. He was even more perturbed, though, to discover her shorn hair had been stolen from the temple (perhaps by a priest who was offended that the offering was made to a Greek deity). Furious, Ptolemy III summoned the priests and threatened to have them executed if they did not reveal the thief's identity. Conon of Samos, a mathematician and astronomer from Alexandria, intervened and told him to wait until nightfall, and he would show Ptolemy what had become of his wife's hair. That eve-

Coma Berenices Featured Objects, North to South

NGC 4676, The Mice: interacting galaxies with remarkable tidal tails (**page 222**).

Gamma (γ) Comae Berenices: not a member of the Coma Star Cluster (**page 123**).

The Coma Cluster: one of the largest galaxy clusters known (**page 227**).

NGC 4889 and NGC 4874: two supergiant elliptical galaxies (**page 228**).

NGC 4921: face-on galaxy with dusty inner ring (**page 243**).

Beta (β) Comae Berenices: nearby sun-like star (**page 119**).

NGC 4839: extensive cD envelope (**page 221**).

Dragonfly 44: ultradiffuse galaxy (**page 243**).

Melotte 111: nearby cluster near the Galactic Pole (**page 148**).

NGC 4565: edge-on spiral; LINER-type nucleus; boxy bulge (**page 177**).

NGC 4725: nearby ringed galaxy (**page 185**).

FK Comae Berenices: rapidly rotating "flip-flop" yellow giant (**page 135**).

RZ Comae Berenices: variable star (**page 143**).

40 Comae Berenices: variable star (**page 143**).

M64: galaxy with prominent nearside extinction (**page 172**).

2 Comae Berenices: fine double star (**page 133**).

35 Comae Berenices: multiple star system (**page 124**).

R Comae Berenices: variable star (**page 143**).

NGC 4147: a young globular cluster (**page 169**).

M85: interacting with neighboring NGC 4394 (**page 210**).

24 Comae Berenices: fine double star (**page 133**).

M53: a first-generation globular cluster (**page 158**).

NGC 5053: globular cluster; may have originated in the Sagittarius Dwarf Spheroidal Galaxy (**page 152**).

Diadem, Alpha (α) Comae Berenices: binary star with edge-on orientation (**page 117**).

NGC 4450: example of an anemic galaxy (**page 198**).

M100: bright grand-design spiral in the Virgo Cluster (**page 204**).

M98: highly inclined spiral galaxy; LINER transition object (**page 188**).

M91: anemic barred galaxy located near the Virgo Cluster core (**page 201**).

M88: bright Seyfert 2 galaxy; double-peaked nucleus (**page 217**).

M99: spiral galaxy just entering the Virgo Cluster (**page 192**).

ning (fortunately it was a clear one), Conon pointed out the mass of stars near the lion's tail. These, he said, were the shimmering skeins of Berenice's Hair, now set among the constellations (presumably by Aphrodite) where they could be appreciated for eternity. Appeased, the gullible Ptolemy allowed the priests to live, Conon was satisfied to have cleverly resolved the incident, and Berenice was immortalized. As Greek myths go, this one turns out pretty well for all concerned.

Of course, that is not the whole story; the end of Berenice's life is a more true-to-form Greek tragedy. Ptolemy III and Berenice had six children, one of whom was Ptolemy IV Philopator, who in his youth was known for indulging in many vices and narcissistic pursuits. Soon after Ptolemy III's death in 221 BCE, Ptolemy IV ascended to the throne. It was during his reign that the decline of the Ptolemaic dynasty began. True to character, he had his mother murdered, probably because he saw her as an obstacle to his way of life as king degenerate. In some versions, she and Ptolemy IV rule together for some time before her assassination, but given Ptolemy IV's disposition, he probably couldn't wait that long. Narcissism trumped his own mother's life.

Thus endeth Berenice. But her constellation lives on, though it took a little time. The asterism was recognized by Greek astronomers Geminus and Eratosthenes, the latter referring to it as seven faint stars visible above the lion's tail in the shape of a triangle, called the "Lock of Berenike Euergetis." Claudius Ptolemy referred to it as "the lock" but did not include it in his list of 48 constellations, considering it, as Eratosthenes had, to be the tufted end of the lion's tail. Berenice's Hair first appeared on a celestial globe by Cologne cartographer and instrument-maker Caspar Vopel in 1536, and subsequently on a globe by Gerardus Mercator, whose reputation ensured its representation on Dutch globes from 1589 onwards.

Tycho Brahe is given credit for elevating Coma Berenices to full constellation status, listing 14 of its stars in his 1602 star catalog. Johannes Hevelius increased the number to 21 and John Flamsteed, in his *Atlas Céleste de Flamsteed*, to 43. The constellation appeared in Bayer's *Uranometria* of 1603 and a few other celestial maps during the 17th century.

Diadem Double or Multiple Star	Alpha (α) Com 42 Com Σ1728AB	RA 13ʰ 09ᵐ 59.2ˢ Dec +17° 31' 46" Mag 4.8 + 5.5 Type F5V + F6V Sep 0.4" PA 193 Epoch 2004

The motion of 42 Comae Berenices, Σ1728 (See, 1896)

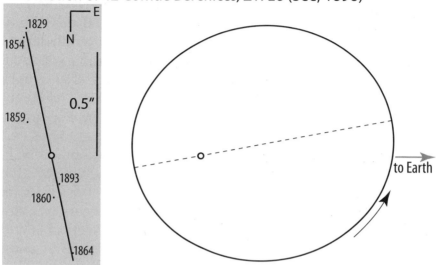

Figure 5: Diadem, Alpha (α) Comae Berenices, a close binary star. Originally thought to be a single star that sometimes appeared double, this star has an orbit that is virtually edge-on as depicted in the left panel (noted by See, 1896) with a derived side view of the orbit, at right. Measurement errors have bedeviled complete understanding of the system.

NOTABLE STARS IN COMA BERENICES

Diadem, Alpha (α) Comae Berenices
Binary star with edge-on orientation

The constellation's alpha star, which demarcates the southernmost point of the inverted L-shaped figure, is actually not quite as bright as Beta. Still, the name Diadem is appropriate for Berenice, given that it refers to a jeweled headband worn as a badge of royalty. Nonetheless, we will refer to the star by its more common identifier, Alpha Comae.

Alpha is a close binary consisting of two yellow-white F-class dwarfs with a combined mass of 2.44 $M_\odot$. They follow an orbit that is virtually edge-on so the components appear to move back and forth along a line, such that the position angle (PA) alternates between NNE on one side and SSW on the other. The visual magnitudes of the primary (4.8) and secondary (5.5) combine to yield a magnitude of 4.3. The challenge is splitting the pair, which can only be done around the time of greatest separation — once every 26 years, and even then only about 0.7 arcsecond. The pair's average separation is 12 AU, but they approach to within 6 AU and recede as far as 19 AU. The distance is about 18 parsecs (58 light-years), so, while not in the solar neighborhood, it is still near enough to make for an interesting study.

Discovered by F. G. W. Struve in 1826–27, the separation at the time was 0.6 arcsecond, near its widest; when in 1833 the star appeared single, Struve and his son Otto Wilhelm took great interest in following its intriguing shifts from being a single to a double star in the course of a few years. Both father and son monitored the star year after year, and after the senior Struve's death in 1864, Otto Wilhelm carried on with the observations. Struve was vexed with determining the period. Both stars appeared so nearly equal in brightness that he couldn't differentiate the primary from the secondary. Moreover, the apparent rectilinear motion made it difficult to decide whether the period was 13 years or twice that. As the observations accumulated, he decided in favor of the second hypothesis and in 1875 published the reduced orbital elements in the *Monthly Notices of the Royal Astronomical Society*. The period he settled on was 25.71 years. Today, the accepted period is 25.9 years, so we see that Struve was very close, indeed.

Since the orbital inclination presents itself nearly edge-on, Alpha Com has long been suspected of eclipsing. Although Struve reported observing "occultations," it isn't clear from his text if they were based on the orbit or a brightness decrease. Any fluctuation would probably have been too slight for the human eye to notice. Speckle interferometric observations (Hartkopf et al., 1989) yielded orbital elements and an inclination that predicted a partial eclipse with a fluctuation of only 0.1 magnitude. Other studies (Hoffleit 1996; Muterspaugh et al., 2010) also suggest Alpha Com is an eclipsing system, but the photometric evidence is lacking. The most recent predicted eclipse date (the week of 24 January 2015) turned out to be erroneous because the position angle measurements for three of the observations from about a century ago were off by 180° (Muterspaugh et al., 2015). That skew meant the eclipse occurred two months earlier than expected, around 18 November 2014. The most recent separation measurement in the *Washington Double Star Catalog* is 0.00 arcsecond (epoch 2015), which closely correlates with the least-separation distance of November 2014.

That leaves two future dates to consider, those of secondary and primary eclipse. Secondary eclipse will occur on or about 11 January 2026, although simulations show that secondary eclipse has only a 5.4 percent probability of happening. The next primary eclipse is predicted to occur around 24 September 2040. Unfortunately, this will not be an optimal observing date, since the constellation will be too near the Sun and sets soon after 8 o'clock. It might, however, be less problematic from distant spacecraft. If not, future astronomers will have to hope for better orientations in subsequent years.

Beta (β) Comae Berenices

Nearby sun-like star

Ever wondered what our Sun would look like from a distance of 10 parsecs, the same benchmark used to calculate absolute stellar magnitudes? You can get a good idea by contemplating Beta Comae Berenices, which occupies the NE juncture of the constellation's L-shaped figure. It is considered by most to be a close solar analog (the spectral type is often given as G0V). It, too, is a hydrogen-fusing dwarf, though slightly warmer than the Sun at about 6,000 K. It is 1.5 times more luminous and 10 percent larger with a slightly greater mass (1.1 $M_\odot$). Most estimates indicate that it is roughly half as old as the Sun. Its distance is approximately 9 parsecs (about 30 light-years), which places it a bit nearer to the Sun than the 10-parsec standard, but it is near enough to make its apparent magnitude close to that of its absolute magnitude (4.4).

Beta (β), Comae Berenices
High Proper Motion Star

HD 114710
HIP 64394

RA 13h 11m 52.4s Dec +27° 52' 41"
Mag 4.2   SpType F9.5V

H-R diagram for Beta (β) and other featured stars in Coma

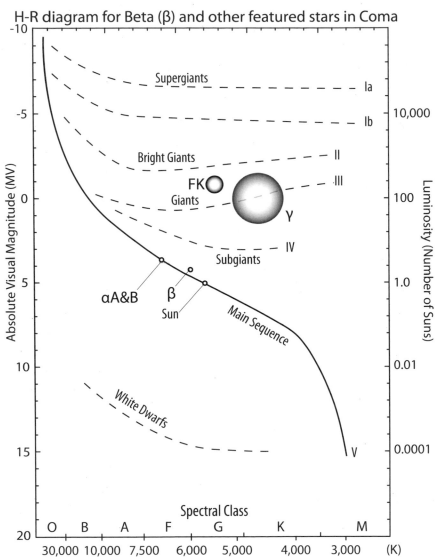

Figure 6: Beta (β) Comae Berenices and other featured stars on a Hertz-sprung-Russell diagram.

Beta Com departs from being a true solar analog in a number of other ways, but only slightly. It is moderately more metal-rich, containing about seven percent more iron. No planets or vestigial dust disks have been detected orbiting the star so far, although there is some evidence for a spectroscopic companion. Beta Com exhibits magnetic activity analogous to the Sun, meaning it must possess starspots, plages, and flares. Its primary magnetic cycle is 16.6 years and it may have a secondary cycle of 9.6 years. (The Sun has a primary cycle of 11 years and a secondary cycle of about 2 years.)

Perhaps Beta Com's biggest differences with the Sun are its equatorial rotation rate and the seasonal behavior of its active regions. The rotation rate, which is about 4 kilometers per second, is roughly twice the solar value, resulting in a rotation period between 11 and 13 days (Gray et al., 1997). This value, while normal for late F and early G stars, does confirm that Beta Com is younger than the Sun by at least half a billion years. We might also mention that, unlike the Sun, Beta is a high proper motion star, with a PM in declination of nearly 0.90 arcsecond per year.

Observations of the star's short-term chromospheric activity over a decade (Donahue and Baliunas, 1992) indicate that Beta Com, like the Sun, rotates faster at its equator than at its poles. In Beta's case, however, active regions are longer-lived than their solar counterparts. A plot of the observed rotation periods versus mean activity suggests the star may have two latitudinal zones of activity, one that is constant in time, and one in which changes in the rotation period appear to follow the starspot cycle.

A comparison of Beta Com's rotation pattern with known solar behavior may be useful here. At the beginning of a solar cycle, activity is low and active regions appear first at high latitudes, and thus have long rotation periods. As solar activity waxes and wanes, the active regions gradually migrate toward the equator where they have the shortest rotation periods occurring at the next solar minimum. For Beta Com, however, the opposite occurs: the rotation period *increases* from cycle maximum through cycle minimum. The finding remains a

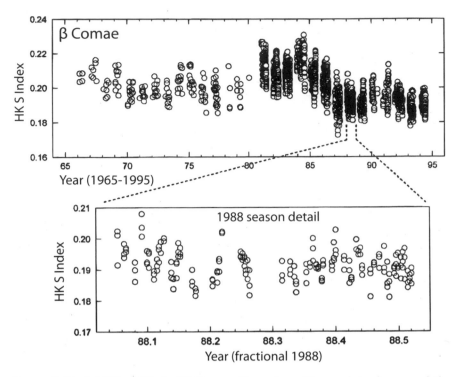

Figure 7: Variability of Beta (β) Comae Berenices. These plots show a subtle variation in the light from Beta, derived from spectroscopic data by Gray and Baliunas, 1997, though it is not considered to be a variable star. These plots depict relative magnitudes of the singly ionized calcium H and K spectroscopic emission lines, represented by the symbol S (hence HK S) over 30 years.

mystery. Perhaps the differential rotation in Beta exerts pole-ward acceleration; alternatively, it could have a solar-like acceleration toward the equator, but the active regions marking rotation migrate away from the equator over the course of an active cycle. Other scenarios have been put forth (Gray and Baliunas, 1997, **Figure 7**) but the bottom line is that Beta Com exhibits decidedly nonsolar behavior, either in the surface acceleration pattern or the progression of mean latitude of active regions during the cycle.

Beta Com may be a solar analog, but only up to a point. Further observations of the star's internal processes, perhaps via asteroseismological analyses, may yield valuable insights into the magnetic cycle variations and dynamo processes within other solar stars as well as our Sun.

Gamma (γ) Comae Berenices Star in Cluster	15 Com HD 108381	RA 12ʰ 26ᵐ 56.2ˢ Dec +28° 16′ 06″ Mag 4.3 SpType K1III

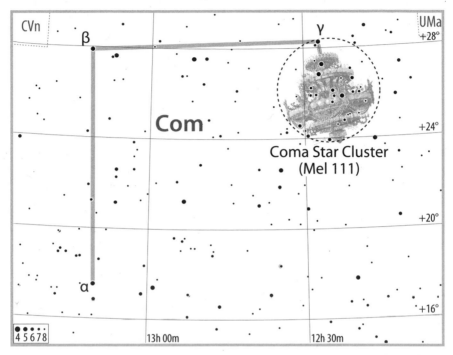

Figure 8: The Coma Star Cluster hanging from Gamma Comae Berenices. The star cluster that represents Berenices' hair is a visual object, inviting our minds to find a pattern. We think it evokes a chandelier (here from the Paris Opera House) or perhaps one of Alexander Calder's mobile sculptures. Calder (1898–1976) was a prolific modern artist, with a notable series called Constellations during World War II.

Gamma (γ) Comae Berenices

Not a member of the Coma Star Cluster

Gamma is the third star in the inverted figure of Coma Berenices, positioned nearly 10° west of Beta. Hanging immediately below (SSE and SSW) of Gamma Com is a throng of stars arranged like a celestial version of an Alexander Calder mobile. This is the Coma Star Cluster, Melotte 111 (Cr 256), an open cluster just discernible to the unaided eye in a dark sky.

The cluster is best appreciated in binoculars, as it is distributed over an angular diameter of about 5°. Gamma Com is often considered part of the cluster, though largely by virtue of its proximity to the cluster's edge. Its distance of 52 parsecs (170 light-years) places it in the cluster's foreground (distance ~96 parsecs, or 313 light-years). Still, SIMBAD lists it as a "star in a cluster." We profile Melotte 111 in the Galactic Objects section.

There is not much else to say about Gamma Com, other than it is a cool K1 giant with a mass of 1.3 $M_\odot$. Interferometric measurements of its diameter (2.7 milliarcseconds) translate into a physical diameter of about 10 times solar.

35 Comae Berenices
Multiple star system

Ensconced near the center of the constellation, 35 Comae Berenices lies 5.4° NW of Alpha Comae, or 54.8 arcminutes WSW of the Black Eye Galaxy, M64. It's a popular triple system (but see below): companion B is 1.2 arcseconds at PA 198° (epoch 2015), and C is more removed at 28.5 arcseconds at PA 127° (epoch 2015). F. G. W. Struve discovered the duplicity of AB in 1828 using the 9-inch Fraunhofer refractor at Dorpat Observatory in Estonia. Since then, the PA of the pair has increased by 173°, though the separation has decreased by only 0.2 arcsecond. William Herschel discovered the more distant visual companion, C, in 1783. Since then, it has shown no significant motion relative to the primary. However, both stars share similar radial velocities and proper motions that have carried them together across the sky for more than 10 arcseconds since their discovery, ensuring that they constitute a physical system. Admiral William Henry Smyth referred to 35 Com as "A delicate triple star, between the Tresses and the Virgin's northern wing." The primary, he wrote, was pale yellow; B was indistinct, and C a cobalt blue. Struve agreed with Smyth on the color of the primary, but deemed the tertiary's color as just blue.

| 35 Comae Berenices
Double or Multiple Star | Σ 1687AB
ADS 8695 AB | RA 12ʰ 53ᵐ 17.7ˢ Dec +12° 14′ 42″
Mag 5.1 + 7.1   SpType G7III+F
Sep 1.20″ PA 198 Epoch 2015 |

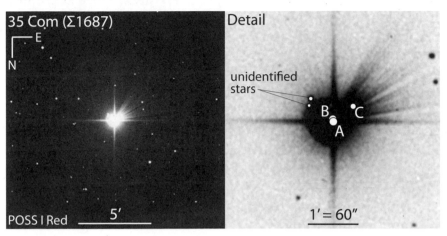

Figure 9: Comae Berenices. The grainy 1956 Palomar Observatory Sky Survey (POSS I) image with artifacts hides the structure of this multiple star (detail at right), which has been well-known for 200 years to visual astronomers. While not useful for double star astrometry, the POSS I produced revolutionary science for decades, including the Abell Galaxy Clusters, discussed later in this chapter.

Beginning in the mid-1960s, the 35 Com system presented a conundrum as astronomers sought to determine the total mass of the AB components. Mount Wilson astronomer Olin C. Wilson utilized the width of the K emission line from ionized calcium to estimate the absolute visual magnitude of 35 Com A, a method he had developed with Indian astronomer M. K. Vainu Bappu. (See the sidebar on **page 127**.) The wider a star's K emission line (in nonvariable stars of spectral types G, K, and M), the more luminous it is. The emission originates in the hot, low-density environment of the star's chromosphere, which overlies the higher density photosphere. In the spectrum, the K emission line (K2) manifests in the center of the broad absorption feature produced by chromospheric gases. The chromosphere, however, is not completely transparent, and at the line's center it can absorb some of its own radiation. This produces an even narrower absorption feature, K3, in the center of the emission line, causing it (the emission line) to appear doubled. This phenomenon is referred to as "self-reversal" or "self-absorption," and is seen among some B stars. Once calibrated for stars of known distance, K-line widths have proven to be a reliable distance indicator, yielding a "spectroscopic parallax" (a slightly misleading name as the method does not rely on the apparent change in a star's position with respect to background stars). For 35 Com, however, there was a problem: the implied spectroscopic parallax derived from the K emission line, when combined with suggested values for the semimajor axis and orbital period, implied a total mass of 7.6 $M_\odot$. As Wilson pointed out, the A component was not sufficiently luminous to justify such a large total mass.

In response, some astronomers speculated that, since the AB orbit has a period of about 700 years, the individual orbital elements were poorly understood. Based on the K-line absolute magnitude determined by Wilson (1967), researchers derived a total mass of 6.9 $M_\odot$. An uncertainty of 17 percent was assigned to the value of the semimajor axis (cubed) divided by the square of the orbital period (Deming and Dykton, 1979).

A decade later, radial-velocity observations (Griffin et al., 1988) revealed the presence of a spectroscopic companion to the primary, raising the total number of components to four. The orbit was reported as eccentric and the period determined to be about 8 years. The observations indicated that the inner companion had a mass comparable to that of the Sun; the close visual companion discovered by Struve (AB) weighed in at about 1.5 $M_\odot$; and the primary, similar in luminosity and other characteristics to the Hyades giants, was close to 2.5 $M_\odot$. Hence, the total mass is about 5 $M_\odot$.

The same study also addressed the mass estimates presented in both the 1967 and 1979 investigations. In the days before the *Hipparcos* astrometry mission, ground-based parallax measurements were limited to only a few tens of parsecs. Beyond that, the angles were too small to confidently measure with any precision. Given this limitation, 35 Com was too distant at the time for any trigonometrical parallax value to be reliable (the Extended *Hipparcos* estimate is 86 parsecs or 280 light-years). At such distances, even a 10 percent error in ground-based calculations introduces a 30 percent error in the total mass. As to the K-line absolute magnitude value, it derives from a number of estimates whose mean deviations are about 0.4 magnitude. Other K-line absolute magnitudes (such as giants in the Hyades) show a spread in the K-line distance modulii that are even larger than the actual spread in distances would produce. Hence, the study concluded, discrepancies that may exist between different mass estimates for the Com 35 system can be attributed to uncertainties in the data concerned.

Modern precision astrometric missions like the *Gaia* space observatory offer the opportunity of determining total mass values of giants in multiple systems at greater distances. The *Gaia* mission is measuring about 20 million stars with a precision of 1 percent or better accuracy, including some 10 million resolved binary systems within 250 parsecs. Astronomers no longer need to be hampered in deconstructing binary systems with long orbital periods and small parallaxes, or, for that matter, from gauging distances to other galaxies. From our little vantage point on Earth, the universe is our oyster.

Olin Chaddock Wilson: Moving Stellar Astrophysics into the Modern Age

American spectroscopist Olin C. Wilson (1909–1994), was known for showing that other stars have cycles of activity similar to the Sun (**Figure 10**). He is eponymized in the Wilson-Bappu effect, a correlation between the measured width of emission lines of ionized calcium (K-lines) and the absolute magnitude of a star. He was, as George W. Preston observed, "a canny practitioner of the art of the possible in observational astrophysics as it flourished in the middle of the 20th century."

Wilson was born on 13 January 1909 in San Francisco, the only child of a family of modest means. When he was 20 years old, his father died, leaving him to support his mother and family until her death in 1961. Despite the financial hardships, he managed to attend the University of California at Berkeley.

Figure 10: Olin Chaddock Wilson. The posed portrait of Wilson was made in the library of the Mount Wilson Offices in Pasadena, California, before a painted portrait of George Ellery Hale (1868–1938) that hangs on the same wall today. Hale, a prolific astronomer and organizer, was one of the founders of the California Institute of Technology (Caltech) and an early leader in establishing the National Research Council, the Huntington Library, and the Palomar 200-inch telescope that was later named in his honor. Hale suffered from depression throughout his life, eventually leading to his resignation as director of Mount Wilson. Olin Wilson and Caltech may have chosen this setting for Wilson's portrait out of respect for Hale's remarkable achievements. Portrait by Caltech staff photographer James McClanahan in 1960, courtesy of the Archives, California Institute of Technology, used with permission.

In 1929, he took an astrophysics course from Donald Menzel. The two struck up a working relationship, and Wilson spent portions of the following summer and Christmas vacations at Lick Observatory helping Menzel analyze W. W. Campbell's solar-eclipse spectra taken in 1922 in Australia. The data provided strong evidence of Einstein's theory of relativity.

Wilson went on to attend graduate school at the California Institute of Technology, drawn to the large telescopes on Mount Wilson and the excited talk of a planned 200-inch reflector on Palomar Mountain. He earned the first Caltech Ph.D. degree in astronomy in 1934 for his work on the comparison of the Paschen and Balmer series of hydrogen lines in spectra.

Wilson became a staff astronomer at Mount Wilson in 1936 and would spend his research career there and at Palomar Observatory. Because his interest was the nature and evolution of stars, he generally worked with the 100-inch during the bright lunar phases, opposite the dark-phase observations of Edwin Hubble and Milton Humason. He observed Wolf-Rayet stars, discovering the first binary member of that class. He also studied the expansion of planetary nebulae, the atmosphere of the cool giant Zeta (ζ) Aurigae, and radial velocities of interstellar neutral sodium and singly ionized calcium lines.

World War II brought Wilson's research to a temporary halt. A number of Mount Wilson astronomers took leave for wartime projects, including Hubble, who left for the Aberdeen Proving Ground to work on the trajectories of bullets, bombs, and rockets. Wilson went to Caltech to work on a rocket project. He would later regale his friends with stories about detonating explosives under questionable conditions in Eaton Canyon, north of Pasadena, and at the foot of Mount Wilson. It was during this period that he met Katherine Johnson, who was also employed in the rocket project. They married in 1943, and a few years later had two sons. When the war ended, he and Katherine moved into a remodeled bunkhouse on Mount Wilson to save money.

Things got back on track when Indian astronomer M. K. Vainu Bappu came to Pasadena in 1951 as one of the first Carnegie Postdoctoral Fellows. His interest was spectroscopy and in collaboration with Wilson, he repeated some 1938 observations Wilson had made in his search for variations of emission features in stars over time. Additional stars were included to extend the investigation to a larger range of luminosities, and the work soon began to bear fruit. Together, Wilson and Bappu found that the width (not the intensity) of the chromospheric emission lines of singly ionized calcium H and K lines in late, cool stars correlated with their absolute magnitudes over a 15-magnitude range: the wider the emission, the brighter the star (**Figure 11**). Based on this relationship, they concluded that the absolute magnitude (and hence the parallax or distance) of any late-type star could be pinned down with a precision of half a magnitude.

To give credit where it's due, Henri Deslandres and V. Burson, who had analyzed the H and K lines in a dozen late-type stars, anticipated the correlation three decades earlier. In a paper published in *Comptes Rendus de l'Académie des Sciences* in 1922, they wrote:

> Those stars which all have chromospheres relatively more luminous and important than the Sun, are all giants...The stars...which have the widest chromospheric lines also have the greatest luminosity; and if on the other hand one notices that the Sun, of absolute magnitude equal to 5.2, is certainly a dwarf star, it seems as if the intensity of the chromospheric lines is closely linked to the luminosity of the star.

The authors further speculated that a new method of measuring spectroscopic parallaxes for late-type stars based on the H and K lines should be possible.

Wilson applied the Wilson-Bappu effect to derive absolute magnitudes of field stars in the solar neighborhood. He showed that the lower-luminosity G- and K-type subgiants coincided with an isochrone corresponding to the oldest known open cluster (at the time), NGC 188. Because the number of very old stars in Wilson's sample greatly exceeded the number of old open clusters, his data strengthened the notion that the age of NGC 188 approximated that of the old Galactic disk.

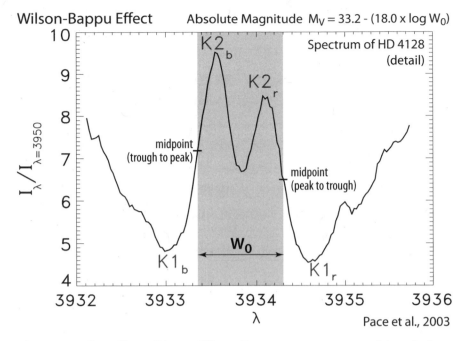

Wilson-Bappu Effect   Absolute Magnitude $M_V = 33.2 - (18.0 \times \log W_0)$

Spectrum of HD 4128 (detail)

Pace et al., 2003

Figure 11: The Wilson-Bappu Effect. Spectroscopy, an essential tool of astronomy, provides a wealth of information about the source of the light analyzed. In 1957, after nearly 20 years of study, Olin Wilson and M. K. Vainu Bappu were able to demonstrate that researchers could estimate a star's absolute magnitude from features in the spectrum, using the H and K emission lines of singly ionized calcium. In 2003, Pace et al. refined the estimate using newer instrumentation, shown here. With this estimated absolute magnitude and the photometric apparent magnitude, it is possible to estimate the star's distance. This simple formula greatly expanded scientific insight into stellar chromospheres and star clusters. Vainu Bappu later returned to India to become a leading astronomer at the Indian Institute of Astrophysics, a research institution with origins in the colonial period of the 1700s.

In 1963, Wilson announced that the average intensity of H and K emission is considerably higher in stars in the Pleiades cluster than those in the Hyades, Praesepe, and Coma (Melotte 111) star clusters; it is weakest generally among local field stars. From these findings, he concluded that the intensity of the H and K lines decreases with stellar age.

Wilson is perhaps best remembered for his seminal 1978 paper in the *Astrophysical Journal* reporting on decade-long observations of H and K emission in 91 Mount Wilson stars.

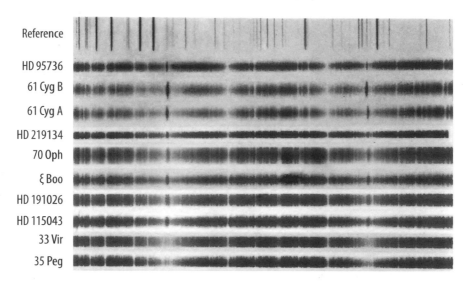

Figure 12: Selected spectra used by Wilson and Bappu in their 1957 paper. Before digital imagery and computers, astronomers collected spectra on photographic plates and analyzed them with microscopes, comparing to reference spectra. Contrast this with **Figure 11**, derived from more recent digital imagery and analysis.

This paper alone was responsible for inspiring the search for stars with variable chromospheric activity similar to the Sun, something stellar astronomers had largely ignored prior to this.

Olin Wilson forged his career in a time of fertile research and advancing theories. A few years before his arrival on the scene, the foundations of the nature of stars were being laid by the likes of Ejnar Hertzsprung, Henry Norris Russell, Albert Einstein, Arthur Stanley Eddington, Hans Albrecht Bethe, and George Gamow. Discussion of Harlow Shapley's Galactic Center and Robert Trumpler's extinction studies helped establish the first models of the Galaxy by Bertil Lindblad and Jan Oort, and the ages of stars and star clusters were continuously being revised. The advent of newer, more sophisticated telescopes spurred research, making some findings obsolete almost before they could be properly recorded. Even in the shadow of war and rumors of war, astrophysics blossomed.

In a sense, not much has changed. Today, in a world often troubled by forces beyond our control, our perspective on the universe continues to unfold with each discovery, providing a striking contrast to the more intrusive affairs of humankind.

2 Comae Berenices and 24 Comae Berenices
Two fine double stars

There is not much in the way of research on these two systems, although they are subsumed in a number of surveys. We include them here because they're excellent telescopic subjects.

We find 2 Com near the border with Leo, 7.8° NNE of Denebola. Smyth described it as a "neat double star" with the primary a pearly white and component B of a lilac tint. Discovered by William Herschel in 1782, it has exhibited no appreciable change in separation or PA since then. So it appears we have a physical pair moving with the same proper motion. The small separation may pose a challenge to observers with small telescopes — especially if seeing is poor, in which case the stars may appear like a figure 8. Try a little more magnification and be patient for those brief moments of good seeing.

Our second offering, 24 Com, lies 8.3° west of Alpha Com. Herschel discovered the pair in 1781. The separation and PA from that epoch very nearly matches the epoch 2015 values, so we seem to be dealing with another fixed pair. And a beautiful pair it is! Smyth gauged the primary to be orange and the secondary emerald while Herschel deemed them whitish and bluish, respectively. The colors, added Smyth, are "very brilliant." Sissy Haas, in her *Double Stars for Small Telescopes,* regards it as a showcase pair in a 60mm at 25x: "A bright, wide and easy pair with pretty colors. The stars are citrus orange and fainter royal blue, and they're attractively close while wide enough to be easy." We agree, in a 6-inch at 100x, the color contrast is remarkably reminiscent of Albireo, beta star in Cygnus the Swan.

2 Comae Berenices Double or Multiple Star	Σ 1596 ADS 8406 AB HD 104827	RA 12ʰ 04ᵐ 16.6ˢ Dec +21° 27' 33" Mag 6.2 + 7.5 SpType F0IV-V Sep 3.7" PA 236 Epoch 2017
24 Comae Berenices Double Star	Σ 1657 ADS 8600 AB HD 109510/11	RA 12ʰ 35ᵐ 07.8ˢ Dec +18° 22' 38" Mag 5.1 + 6.3 SpType K2III Sep 20.4" PA 272 Epoch 2016

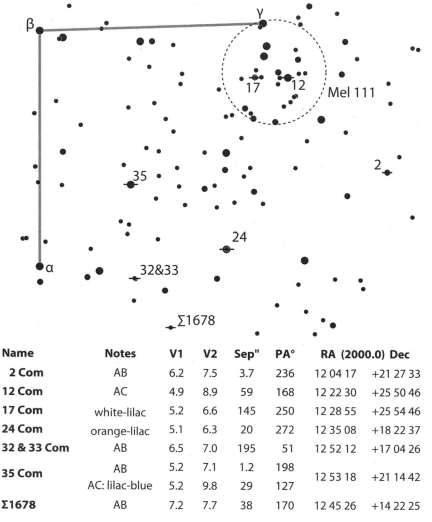

Name	Notes	V1	V2	Sep"	PA°	RA (2000.0) Dec
2 Com	AB	6.2	7.5	3.7	236	12 04 17 +21 27 33
12 Com	AC	4.9	8.9	59	168	12 22 30 +25 50 46
17 Com	white-lilac	5.2	6.6	145	250	12 28 55 +25 54 46
24 Com	orange-lilac	5.1	6.3	20	272	12 35 08 +18 22 37
32 & 33 Com	AB	6.5	7.0	195	51	12 52 12 +17 04 26
35 Com	AB	5.2	7.1	1.2	198	12 53 18 +21 14 42
	AC: lilac-blue	5.2	9.8	29	127	
Σ1678	AB	7.2	7.7	38	170	12 45 26 +14 22 25

Figure 13: Coma Berenices double stars for beginners. The figure at the top is a basic star chart of the easier double stars in Coma Berenices, adapted from *In Starland With a Three-inch Telescope* (1909) by William Tyler Olcott. Stars 12, 17, and 32 have additional fainter companions. Color contrast is subjective, but we offer Olcott's judgement.

FK Comae Berenices

Rapidly rotating "flip-flop" yellow giant

This is a curious object, and a prime subject for reflecting on how a star might take the road less traveled during the course of its evolution. It is challenging to explain the complex phenomena the object displays without also explaining, in gory detail, the instrumentation that brought those phenomena to light. We therefore consider our profile of FK Comae Berenices a review and encourage readers to pursue the references cited herein, should they want to learn more about this rare and unusual star.

Characterized in some science papers as an ultra-fast rotating yellow giant, FK Com has been whimsically dubbed the "Queen of Spin" since it is located in the constellation of Queen Berenices (Trimble et al., 2007). Others, seeing no gender guidance to the FK identifier, prefer "King of Spin" (Ayres et al., 2016). Paul W. Merrill first described its spectrum in 1948, noting a large projected rotational velocity that today is estimated to be about 160 kilometers per second. This star is, indeed, a whirling dervish.

It was once thought that FK stars may have been born with an innately high rotational velocity, but some researchers now believe they represent an intermediate state of a coalesced contact binary, similar to a W Ursae Majoris binary,* in the process of magnetic braking (Webbink, 1976; Bopp and Stencel, 1981). This scenario remains to be confirmed. However, given the large fraction of W Ursae Majoris stars among binary systems, and the rarity of FK Com stars, coalescence either happens rarely or is a very short-lived phenomenon. In fact, both assumptions may be correct.

FK Com is the prototype of a small class of chromospherically active, rapidly rotating G-K giants that vary in brightness as they spin because of numerous starspots. Just like sunspots, FK Com-type starspots are due to local magnetic fields on their surfaces that are strong enough to bottle up the

---

* W Ursae Majoris stars consist of a pair of stars orbiting so close to each other that their outer envelopes are in direct contact.

FK Comae Berenices	HD 117555	RA 13h 30m 46.8s Dec +24° 13′ 58″
Rotationally Variable Star	HIP 65915	Mag 8.0–8.4 SpType G4III
		Period 2.4 days

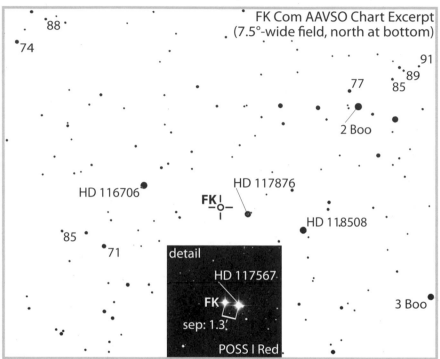

Figure 14: FK Comae Berenices. An irregular variable with a very small (0.4) magnitude variation, FK Com is a difficult star for visual magnitude estimation as there are no nearby trusted reference stars. Shown is an extract of a finder chart produced by the American Association of Variable Star Observers (AAVSO). The closest reference stars are several degrees away. FK Com is in a line of stars from 3 Boo to HD 116706, in a large triangle with 2 and 3 Boo. The AAVSO chooses reference stars (two digit magnitudes, 85 = visual magnitude 8.5) known to be of stable magnitude. FK Com is a wide double with HD 117567, shown in the detail, cataloged as STT 268 A and C in a system of four stars, three of which are visible in the detail image. **Contemplative observing:** With a telescope, locate FK Com and its close companion HD 117567. Consider that FK is a rapidly rotating star with prominent star spots; the surface is shown in later figures, changing over

convective motion that normally transfers energy from the stellar interior to the surface. Consequently, the spots appear as dark sectors poised against the otherwise bright photosphere. Of course, there is no way to see these directly.

Detailed observations of a stellar surface require an indirect means — emission-line Doppler imaging — to bring out inhomogeneous surface features. Simply put, the presence of spots and plages creates distortions in the spectral line profiles. The distortions move across the spectral line profiles due to stellar rotation, allowing them to be mapped.

FK Com's rotational period is 2.4 days, with a peak-to-peak amplitude of about 0.4 magnitude, which the human eye may just perceive. Beyond this single visual observable, much more in the way of magnetospheric activity underlies this star's behavior. For one, it is not just spotted; it is heavily spotted. Long-term photometric studies show the spots can sometimes form belt-like structures, creating an unvarying light curve that is fainter than the star's peak magnitude (Korhonen et al., 2002). Impressive levels of ultraviolet and X-ray emissions, as well as high-energy flares, accompany the starspots. The star's energy output makes it a coronal powerhouse, comparable to such volatile stars as RS Canum Venaticorum binaries.

Another peculiarity is that the active regions perform a periodic "flip-flop," in that the concentrated region of spot activity at one longitude shifts 180° to the other side of the star, where it remains for 6.4 years before returning to the original longitude. FK Com was the first star where the flip-flop phenomenon was observed. A series of photometric observations between 1995 and 2010 (Hackman et al., 2013, **Figure 15**), showed that the flip-flop couldn't be interpreted as a simple phenomenon in which the spot activity springs from one active longitude to its opposite, but rather may be due to differential rotation. In that case, two spot regions may move with different angular velocity and even pass each other (**Figures 16** and **17**). Interestingly, the Sun exhibits flip-flop behavior with a period of about 3.7 years.

Beginning in the 1980s, numerous observing campaigns successfully peeled back the upper layers of FK Com to reveal an astonishing amount of underlying activity from the photosphere to its corona. H-alpha (Hα) observations (Ramsey et al., 1981) detected an "excretion" disk of ejected material surrounding the star. Photometric and spectroscopic observations

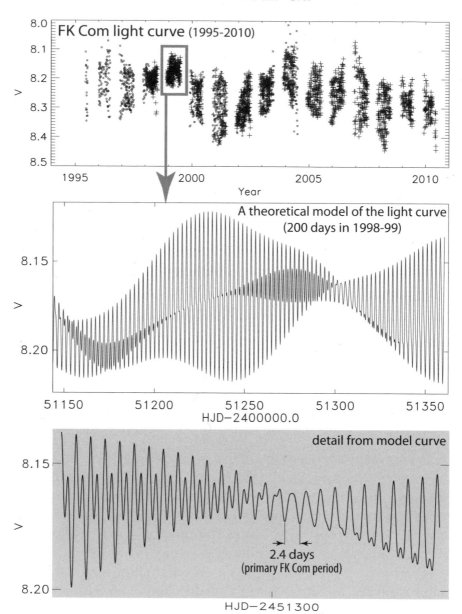

Figure 15: Light curve of FK Comae Berenices. Hackman et al., 2013, studied the 15-year light curve (top) to understand the phenomena known as "flip-flops," slow changes in the shape of the light curve likely due to dramatic changes in surface spots. The authors developed a curve fit model ("carrier fit," middle and bottom panels) to depict the slow, large-magnitude variation superimposed on the primary 2.4-day photometric period.

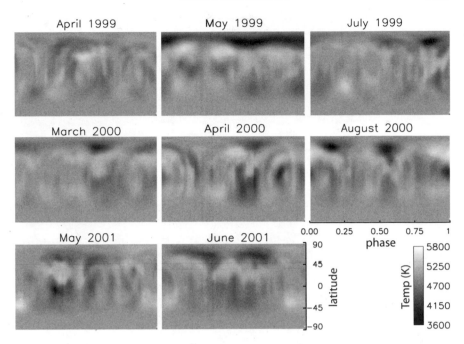

Figure 16: The changing face of FK Comae Berenices. Surface temperature maps of the star over time show dramatic and rapid changes on the surface, courtesy Korhonen et al., 2007. The researchers collected spectroscopic and photometric data over two years' time and developed surface temperature maps using the "Tikhonov Regularization inversion code," which depends on a model of the star derived from other measurements. Starspots are mapped in a variety of ways, including temperature. The maps project the spherical surface of the star on a rectangle, similar to the Mercator world map projection, so the horizontal scale of features near the poles is exaggerated. Also, the image reconstruction process produces vertical striped artifacts (dental X-ray-like features), arising from noise in the measurements. The top row covers the same time period as the middle panel of the previous figure, one of the "flip-flops." Maps from two later years follow in **Figure 17**.

(Huenemoerder et al., 1993, **Figure 18**) indicate that FK Com is a single star with extended matter around it. Long-term Hα observations (Welty et al., 1993) found evidence of co-rotating material around the star within two stellar radii, with lifetimes longer than a few weeks. Additional observations (Oliveira and Foing, 1999) confirmed the complex circumstellar structures.

At the more energetic end of the spectrum, observations made with the *International Ultraviolet Explorer*, the *Far-Ultravi-*

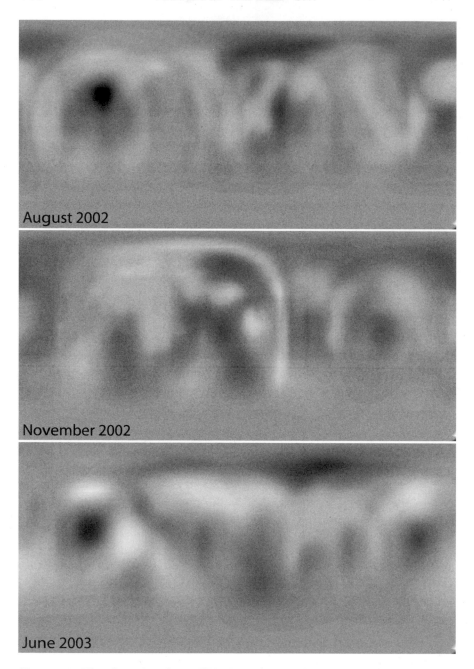

August 2002

November 2002

June 2003

Figure 17: The changing face of FK Comae Berenices, seen in later temperature maps. A closer look at Korhonen's surface temperature maps of the star over time, made later than the images in the previous figure. Some features recur and others move.

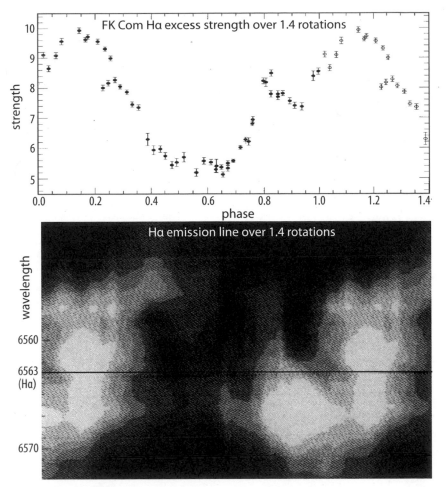

Figure 18: The hydrogen alpha face of FK Comae Berenices. As the surface spots move across the star during its rotation, the brightness varies in Hα. Huenemoerder et al., 1993, used an early CCD echelle spectroscope and other instrumentation to study FK Com in 1989. The Hα relative strength plot (top) confirmed the presence of light and dark Hα emission features on the surface, but the "pseudo-trailed spectrogram," below, tells more of the story. This figure shows the intensity, width, and wavelength of the bright Hα emission line in the spectrogram as the star rotates. As a feature first appears, rotating from the back side, the light is blueshifted, moving the Hα line to a lower wavelength. As it disappears on the other side it is redshifted, moving the Hα line to a higher wavelength — hence a roughly sinusoidal shape but with significant variations in the intensity and width of the emission line. The extreme widening of the emission line at phase 0.2 (repeated at 1.2) suggests a temperature of 10,000 K and turbulence (444 km/sec) where Hα is brighter on the surface, effectively blurring the emission line in the spectrum.

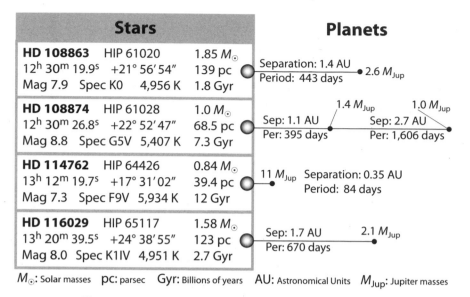

Stars			Planets
HD 108863 HIP 61020		1.85 $M_\odot$	Separation: 1.4 AU ● 2.6 M_{Jup}
12ʰ 30ᵐ 19.9ˢ +21° 56′ 54″		139 pc	Period: 443 days
Mag 7.9 Spec K0 4,956 K		1.8 Gyr	
HD 108874 HIP 61028		1.0 $M_\odot$	1.4 M_{Jup} 1.0 M_{Jup}
12ʰ 30ᵐ 26.8ˢ +22° 52′ 47″		68.5 pc	Sep: 1.1 AU Sep: 2.7 AU
Mag 8.8 Spec G5V 5,407 K		7.3 Gyr	Per: 395 days Per: 1,606 days
HD 114762 HIP 64426		0.84 $M_\odot$	11 M_{Jup} Separation: 0.35 AU
13ʰ 12ᵐ 19.7ˢ +17° 31′ 02″		39.4 pc	Period: 84 days
Mag 7.3 Spec F9V 5,934 K		12 Gyr	
HD 116029 HIP 65117		1.58 $M_\odot$	Sep: 1.7 AU 2.1 M_{Jup}
13ʰ 20ᵐ 39.5ˢ +24° 38′ 55″		123 pc	Per: 670 days
Mag 8.0 Spec K1IV 4,951 K		2.7 Gyr	

$M_\odot$: Solar masses pc: parsec Gyr: Billions of years AU: Astronomical Units M_{Jup}: Jupiter masses

Figure 19: Four stars with planets in Coma Berenices.

olet Spectroscopic Explorer, ROSAT, XMM-Newton, and *Chandra* have all shown that FK Com not only displays a high coronal X-ray luminosity (~1 x 10³¹ ergs) but also robust flaring episodes above its more inactive levels. In 2011, observations of FK Com's photosphere and upper atmosphere using both the *Hubble Space Telescope's* Cosmic Origins and Imaging spectrographs as well as *Chandra's* High-Energy Transmission Grating Spectrometer revealed a highly energetic and more complex picture (Ayers et al., 2016). During a week-long observing campaign, FK Com displayed variability on a wide range of timescales over all wavelengths, including a large X-ray flare, super-rotationally broadened far-ultraviolet lines, and large Doppler shifts suggestive of bright regions on both the advancing and retreating limbs. These features depict a star with a highly extended, dynamic, and hot (about 10 million K) coronal magnetosphere that is interlaced with cooler structures such as prominences, which are continually being regenerated by surface activity and flares. Clearly, FK Com is an excellent stellar laboratory for exploring the boundaries of magnetospheric activity in other stars.

Observers who train their telescopes on FK Com will imme-diately notice a slightly brighter star (magnitude 7.6) and faint (magnitude 13) companion floating just 1.3 arcminutes to the ENE. The bright star is HD 117567 (an F4 or 5 giant or dwarf). Its shy companion is positioned 19 arcseconds in PA 78° (epoch 2015). Both the separation and PA of these components (AB) have changed little since they were measured in 1878. Compo-nent B also possesses a close-in companion (Ba,Bb), 1.3 arcsec-onds away at PA 42° (epoch 2015). Companion C, of course, is FK Com; based on the relative motion of the AC pair, it is not associated with the AB pair, but the trio does form a rather pleasing arrangement. Component A is located at a distance of 60 parsecs, while FK is well behind it, at about 190 parsecs. So far, no FK stars have exhibited pronounced radial velocity vari-ations, indicating that they are probably not binaries — or, if they are, they possess very low-mass companions.

Variable Stars of Interest in Coma Berenices

R Comae Berenices, RZ Comae Berenices, and 40 Comae Berenices

Apart from RZ Comae Berenices, specific research on these variable stars is scant (although they are included in numer-ous surveys). Nevertheless, we encourage observers to con-sider them as a *divertissement*, or, if the spirit is willing, subjects worthy of more serious study.

R Com is located in the western realms of Coma Berenices, 5.5° NE of Denebola. It has a distinctly ruddy color, and its period is just under a year. At minima, it may prove a challenge to identify, so we suggest catching it around maximum. An ephemeris may be obtained from the AAVSO. HD 104785, a 7.7-magnitude K2 giant, floats in the field 3.8 arcminutes to the WNW. A little further afield (some 20 arcminutes to the south) floats the 11th-magnitude spiral galaxy NGC 4064.

If you're looking for immediate results, RZ Com has a quick magnitude turnaround of about 8 hours, thanks to this eclipsing binary's fleet orbital period. It's a contact binary of the W Ursae

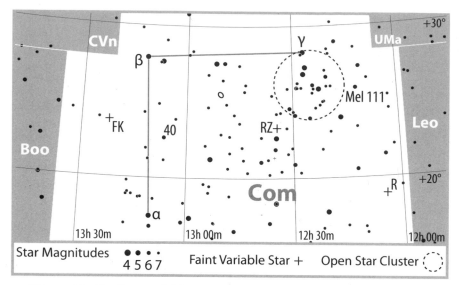

Figure 20: Finding variable stars R, RZ, 40, and FK Comae Berenices.

Majoris type (refer back to FK Com in the previous section). The amplitude of 0.7 magnitude should be easily discernible in most telescopes. If timed carefully, fluctuations might be detected in a single night. Variations in the light curve in recent years are thought to be due to either a dark spot on the primary or an unseen third body in the system (He and Qian, 2008). You will find this object 5.3° south of Gamma Com.

Observers will find 40 Com, also known by its Bayer designation, FS Comae Berenices, 5.1° north of Diadem. HD 113867, a 7th-magnitude F4 dwarf, lies in the field, 20 arcminutes due south. Although SIMBAD categorizes 40 Com as a long-period variable, it is more properly considered a semiregular-late variable. These are typically giants or supergiants of late spectral types that exhibit persistent but poorly defined variability. They are similar to Miras except for their smaller amplitudes, which can range from several hundredths to several magnitudes. 40 Com's fluctuations can be monitored over an interval of just two months. The amplitude (0.8 magnitude) should be apparent in any small telescope. Being a type M5 giant, it has a soft orange tint compared to the field stars. The effective surface temperature for that spectral class typically falls around

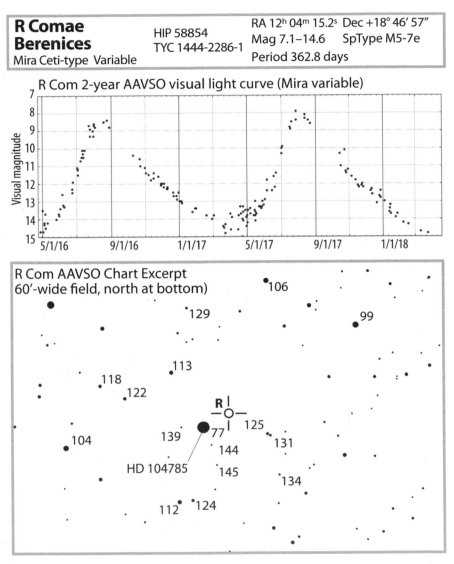

R Comae Berenices	HIP 58854	RA 12ʰ 04ᵐ 15.2ˢ Dec +18° 46' 57"

R Comae Berenices
Mira Ceti-type Variable
HIP 58854
TYC 1444-2286-1
RA 12ʰ 04ᵐ 15.2ˢ   Dec +18° 46' 57"
Mag 7.1–14.6   SpType M5-7e
Period 362.8 days

R Com 2-year AAVSO visual light curve (Mira variable)

R Com AAVSO Chart Excerpt
60'-wide field, north at bottom)

Figure 21: R Comae Berenices. This Mira variable star has a period within a few days of an earth year, so for the next few years its maxima will be in July, shifting to June around 2030. As a Mira, it has a rapid rise from its minimum in March or April, so anyone can easily observe the rapid change in brightness over a few months, by comparison to the nearby magnitude 7.7 reference star HD 104785. Figures courtesy the American Association of Variable Star Observers (AAVSO), used with permission.

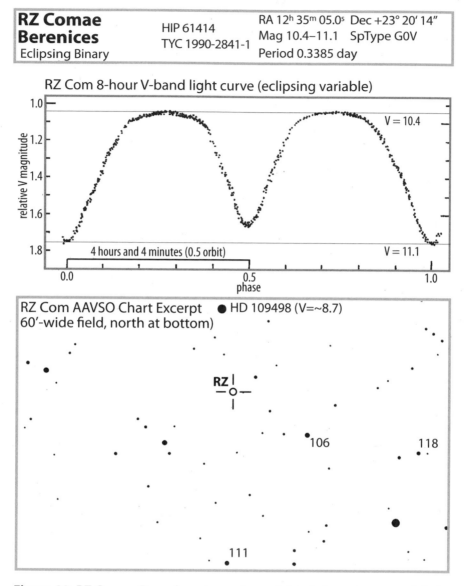

RZ Comae Berenices	HIP 61414	RA 12^h 35^m 05.0^s Dec +23° 20' 14"
	TYC 1990-2841-1	Mag 10.4–11.1 SpType G0V
Eclipsing Binary		Period 0.3385 day

RZ Com 8-hour V-band light curve (eclipsing variable)

V = 10.4

4 hours and 4 minutes (0.5 orbit)

V = 11.1

relative V magnitude

phase

RZ Com AAVSO Chart Excerpt
60'-wide field, north at bottom)   ● HD 109498 (V=~8.7)

RZ

106   118

111

Figure 22: RZ Comae Berenices. In any long night of observing, a careful observer can see the subtle 0.7-magnitude variation of this eclipsing binary star, by comparing its brightness to two nearby stars in a widefield eyepiece, bottom panel, courtesy AAVSO. The light curve is courtesy Rovithis and Rovithis-Livaniou, 1984, who used a dry-ice-cooled photometer in 1982 on the 48-inch Cassegrain reflector at Kryonerion Astronomical Station, near Corinth, Greece. This instrument is part of the National Observatory of Athens, founded originally in 1842 with an observatory on the Hill of Nymphs near the Acropolis.

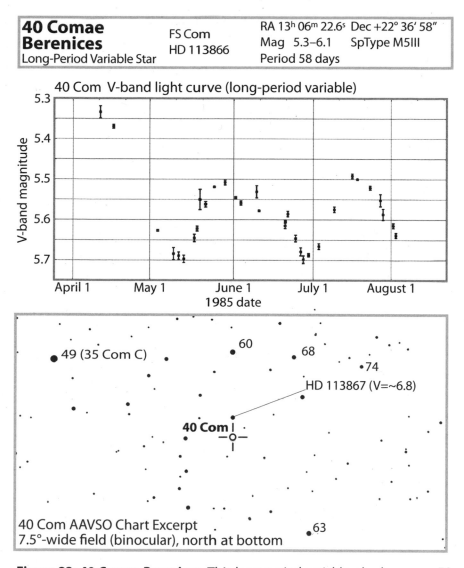

40 Comae Berenices	FS Com	RA 13ʰ 06ᵐ 22.6ˢ Dec +22° 36′ 58″
Long-Period Variable Star	HD 113866	Mag 5.3–6.1 SpType M5III Period 58 days

Figure 23: 40 Comae Berenices. This long-period variable, also known as FS Com, is less dramatic than R Com and not as immediately gratifying as RZ Com, but it makes a fine study of semiregular-late variables with poorly defined periods. Figures courtesy the American Association of Variable Star Observers (AAVSO), used with permission.

2,700 K, though its B-V color index of 1.46 indicates a surface temperature closer to 3,800 K. The radius has been estimated to be some 30 times that of the Sun, and the luminosity, based on *Hipparcos* data, is nearly 700 times that of the Sun.

GALACTIC OBJECTS IN COMA BERENICES

Melotte 111

Nearby cluster near the Galactic Pole

This large, conspicuous cluster is arrayed in the NW section of Coma Berenices just south of Gamma (γ) Com. It covers an area of about 5°; hence, it is best appreciated in binoculars or even finder scopes. Its most notable feature is the two loose chains of stars that extend SSE and SSW of Gamma (the easternmost chain is more pronounced). In ancient times, before the constellation was incorporated into the pantheon of mythological figures, the cluster was often associated with images of hair, threads, flagella of various kinds, and even the tufted tail of Leo the Lion. Eratosthenes first alluded to it as Ariadne's Hair in his entry on the Northern Crown. (In Greek mythology, Ariadne was the daughter of Minos, the King of Crete, and wife of the wine god Dionysus.) In his *Almagest* of 150 CE, Ptolemy described the stellar scattering as a "nebulous mass called the lock." The cluster and the surrounding stars we know as Coma Berenices were first assembled into a "sanctioned" constellation by Dutch cartographer Gerardus Mercator in 1551, and then by Tycho Brahe in 1602.

The cluster almost goes unnoticed in the city and the suburbs, but it jumps out at you in even quasi-dark skies. It is neither in Messier's catalog nor the *New General Catalog* — not because it was overlooked, but probably because it qualified as more of an asterism than a nonstellar object.

And yet, it is a bona fide star cluster made large on the sky due to its proximity to the Sun (90 parsecs, or roughly 300 light-years). It is more distant than the Hyades (45 parsecs) but closer than the Praesepe (186 parsecs) and, hence, makes for a comparative exercise in how distance can affect apparent cluster size. (Although, bear in mind that Melotte 111 has a larger physical size (7 parsecs) than either the Hyades (4.3 parsecs) or the Praesepe (~1 parsec)). The first cluster catalog in which it appears is that of P. J. Melotte (1915), who refers to it as "The large extended cluster in Coma Berenices. Appears to extend

Melotte 111 Open Cluster	Collinder 256 OCL 558.0	RA 12ʰ 25ᵐ 06ˢ Dec +26° 05′ Mag 1.8 Size 300′ 273 stars Bt*Vm 5.0 Type III 3r

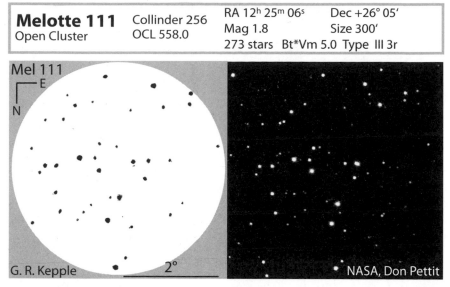

Figure 24: Melotte 111. An eyepiece impression through a finder scope (left) compared to an unusual amateur photograph made by astronaut Don Pettit in 2003 during his rare spare time as a crewmember of the International Space Station (ISS). Pettit used a DSLR camera and telephoto lens, and improvised a mount from available hardware on the ISS.

over an area 6° square." Robert J. Trumpler endeavored to account for the cluster's membership in the late 1930s. Several astronomers (Knut Lundmark among them) had attempted this before using proper motion measurements, but the results were contradictory. Trumpler used three criteria to establish membership: common proper motion, common radial velocity, and their fit on either the giant or dwarf branch of the H-R diagram. He studied stars brighter than photographic magnitude 10.5 within a seven-degree circle centered on the cluster, and established that 37 were group members. Seven fainter stars were selected as possible members based on their common proper motions and radial velocities. Trumpler deemed Melotte 111:

> A typical example of the many galactic star clusters that are poor in stars. Its total mass is probably not much in excess of 70 solar masses and its average mass density is close to the limit of instability.

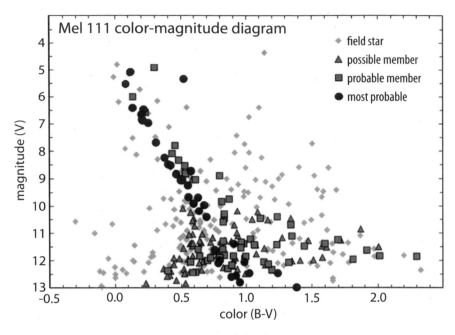

Figure 25: Melotte 111 color-magnitude diagram. Using proper motions and photometry, Guerrero et al., 2015, narrowed down the likelihood of field stars being members of the Mel 111 open cluster. Their main goal was identifying the multiple stars in the cluster, via speckle interferometry. Among the most probable members the scientists found eight binaries and one sextuple star system.

A photometric search for fainter members (down to magnitude 15.5) turned up four stars with the expected proper motions, magnitudes, and colors (Argue and Kenworthy, 1969). Although three of Trumpler's candidate members were rejected by this study, it found that the main sequence of Melotte 111 terminates abruptly where Trumpler had deduced, at a visual magnitude of 10.5 (**Figure 25**).

Given the cluster's large diameter, sparse stellar distribution, low average proper motion, and the fact that the lower main sequence is not well represented, determining a definitive number of members is problematic. We cite a value of 273 stars in our data box above, which comes from the Archinal and Hynes database of open star clusters and is based on images from the Digital Sky Survey. This is probably an outside value, as other sources, which mainly tally the brighter members, cite far lower values: 50 to 60 stars. A definitive population total does not appear anywhere in current literature, which indicates that the census, especially for low-mass members, remains an open question. Moreover, most modern tallies parse candidates into categories of most probable, probable, and possible members (or probability percentages thereof). If you just want to talk about the number of stars visible using binoculars, I made such a count using 8x56 binoculars and came up with about 25 stars, which is not very satisfying either, but at least that estimate will not overly raise expectations.

Candidates for membership are identified both by proper motion data (−11.45 milliarcseconds in RA and −8.9 milliarcseconds in Dec) as well as their average radial velocity, which is nearly zero. The spectral types range from A0 dwarfs to M giants, with the lowest-mass objects being a handful of late M or early L dwarfs, brown dwarfs, and one possible substellar object (Casewell et al., 2014).

The cluster's age, based on color-magnitude diagrams, is between 450 and 550 million years. This is a few hundred million years younger than the Hyades (780 million years); the metallicity is slightly less than solar ([Fe/H] = −0.05). If we assume Trumpler's mass of 70 $M_\odot$ is close, its density must be less than one star per 10 cubic parsecs. Hence, there is not a lot of "there" there, and consequently the gravitational attraction has to be rather weak. Most of the cluster's low-mass stars probably evaporated from its bounds long ago, and now the remaining members are spreading themselves out into interstellar space, like wind-whipped autumn leaves.

Lying near the cluster's center is its brightest member and one of the constellation's brightest stars, 12 Com (magnitude 4.8). It is a spectroscopic binary with a combined spectral type of G0III-IV+A3V. It is also a visual triple system: component B (magnitude 12) lies 37 arcseconds away in PA 57°, and component C (magnitude 9) is about one arcminute away at PA 168° (both measurements in epoch 2012). B is probably a background star, but C, a late F- or early G-type star, is a verified member of the Coma Star Cluster. A fourth component (D) forms an optical pair, as the proper motions of it and the primary are very different.

NGC 5053

Globular cluster; may have originated in the Sagittarius Dwarf Spheroidal Galaxy

Located 1.5° east of Alpha Com, NGC 5053 is a ghost of a globular cluster that to some observers resembles a condensed, granular open cluster. Southern observer E. J. Hartung described it as "a faint luminous haze, irregularly round about 4′ across and very little concentrated to the centre, where 30 cm shows very faint stars and some brighter outliers." Even in a 15-inch at 264x, only about two dozen stars are resolved, mainly along the fringes (as well as an almost-10th-magnitude field star floating 5 arcminutes offshore to the ESE). The core is a slightly concentrated featureless glow covering an area less than 2 arcminutes. Steve Gottlieb, observing with a 17.5-inch, describes it as being similar to a faint, resolved open cluster. William Herschel came across this object in one of his sweeps of March 14, 1784.

NGC 5053 has a mass of about 100,000 $M_\odot$, though its initial mass is thought to have been at least 250,000 $M_\odot$; the age is 12.5 ± 2 billion years (**Figure 27**).

Just 57.5 arcminutes to the NW is the more visually appealing globular cluster M53, which we profile next. The spatial separation between the two is approximately 2 kiloparsecs, making this an unusual pairing in the outer halo of the Galaxy; as we shall see, the two may not only be tidally connected but have a common origin — or not.

One of the biggest mysteries surrounding NGC 5053 is whether it was stripped from the Sagittarius Dwarf Spheroidal Galaxy (Sgr dSph). To date, there are five confirmed members of that system (Terzan 7, Terzan 8, Arp 2, Palomar 12, and M54, the last of which is what remains of the galaxy's core) and at least four additional candidates (NGC 5053, Berkeley 29, Whiting 1, and NGC 5634). If we are to scratch the surface of the nature of NGC 5053, particularly its evolution, we need to examine the evidence for and against its possible relation to Sgr dSph.

Sgr dSph was discovered during a spectroscopic study of the Milky Way's bulge and found to have a space motion of 250

NGC 5053 GCI 23 Globular Cluster	RA 13ʰ 16ᵐ 27.0ˢ Dec +17° 41' 52"
	Mag 9.5 Size 10'
	Bt*Vm 13.8 Conc class XI

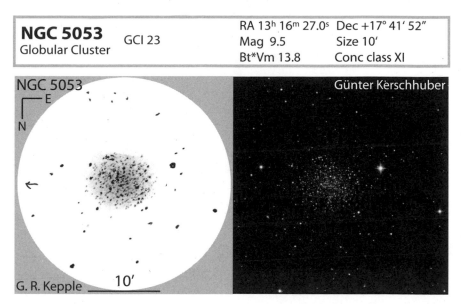

Figure 26: NGC 5053. An eyepiece impression (left) compared to an amateur photograph, courtesy ccdguide.com.

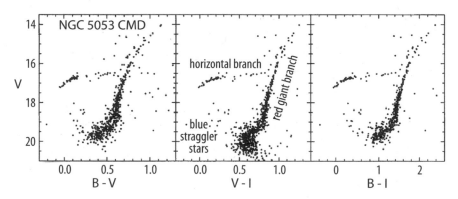

Figure 27: NGC 5053 color-magnitude diagrams. The steep red giant branch and the wide horizontal branch indicate the predominance of metal-poor stars in the cluster in these data collected with the 0.9-m telescope at the Kitt Peak National Observatory and the Whipple Observatory 1.2-m telescope at Mount Hopkins. Sarajedini et al., 1995, also noted the prominent blue straggler stars among the hundreds of stars measured using early CCD cameras and computerized photometry.

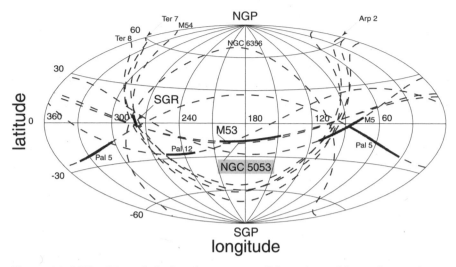

Figure 28: Milky Way globular clusters possibly stripped from the Sagittarius Dwarf Spheroidal Galaxy. In this all-sky Aitoff projection map in galactic coordinates, NGC 5053, along with Messier 53, is one of a number of globular clusters thought to have been captured during a galaxy merger. Palma et al., 2002, noted that a number of globulars appear to orbit around the center of our galaxy, intersecting with the orbit of the Sagittarius Dwarf Spheroidal Galaxy (Sgr dSph) at longitudes 100° and 280°, suggesting that they were stripped off as the Sgr dSph merged with the Milky Way over several orbits. Thick lines are measured motions and dashed lines are extrapolations, so this might not be the final word on this story.

± 90 kilometers per second towards the Galactic plane (Ibata et al., 1994; Irwin et al., 1996). Theorists later suggested the Milky Way might be tidally abrading it. In fact, the dissolution of the galaxy's stars and its globular clusters likely began almost as soon as it fell into the gravitational well of the Milky Way, which could have been 10 billion years ago (the minimum age of its dominant population). The orbital period is slightly less than a billion years, so it could have experienced at least ten perigalacticon passages (Ibata et al., 1997). Published orbits indicate that Sgr dSph passed through perigalacticon within the last 100 million years or so.

Over its numerous passages, the disrupting system has produced a prominent substructure in the Milky Way halo called the Sagittarius Stream. Near-infrared and multi-band photometry (Majewski et al., 2003; Belokurov et al., 2006) has shown that the stream is distributed across the sky in a well-defined arc that stretches around the Galaxy in a near-polar orbit. Models suggest that the most recent tidal debris lies between 10 and 60 kiloparsecs from the Sun, and more than 8 kiloparsecs from the Galactic center. The numerical simulations mentioned above suggest that tidal debris may exist at distances up to 100 kiloparsecs (Law and Majewski, 2010). Observations trace a trailing tidal tail very clearly in the southern Galactic hemisphere as well as a leading arm reaching toward the north Galactic cap. At about this location, the stream bifurcates creating two branches that extend to higher and lower declinations. There are also two southern streams, one more pronounced than the other. The brighter stream consists mainly of metal-rich stars, while the fainter contains largely older, metal-poor stars. Although the cause of the split streams is unknown, astronomers speculate that the Sagittarius Dwarf may have been a binary galactic system, resembling the Large and Small Magellanic Clouds, or that it possessed a smaller dwarf satellite. Hence, the two would have passed together through the halo leaving two trails of stars of different metal abundances in their wake (**Figure 28**).

Such assimilations remind us of the bigger cosmological picture. One of the cornerstones of the Lambda (λ) cold dark matter universe model is that a large fraction of the Milky Way's halo (and other galaxies as well) amassed via the accretion of smaller galaxies and their globular cluster systems. Between 27 and 47 of the globular clusters we observe today may have been absorbed by the Milky Way from as many as eight dwarf galaxies (Forbes and Bridges, 2010).

NGC 5053's membership is based on a number of factors including positional and kinematic properties comparable to the orbit of Sgr dSph (Bellazzini et al., 2003a); the similarity of the chemical abundances of stars in the cluster to those in the dwarf system (Sbordone et al., 2015); and numerical simulations of the tidal disruption of the dwarf galaxy (Law and Majewski, 2010).

Other observations cast doubt as to its former membership, though each comes with counterpoints. For example, the cluster has an extremely low metallicity ([Fe/H] = −2.6), which while consistent with outer halo globular clusters and field stars, may be too low to qualify it as a refugee from the Sgr dSph. The metallicities of three of the confirmed Sagittarius "core" clusters — M54, Arp 2, and Terzan 8 — range between −1.2 and −1.8, while the dominant population of Sgr dSph itself has an unusually high metallicity ([Fe/H] ~ −0.5). On the other hand, there is evidence for a metal-poor tail down to about [Fe/H] = −3.

Putting aside the question of the cluster's origin, a self-consistent picture of Sgr dSph itself is difficult to come by, as there are still other factors to consider. Given its large size (roughly 15° x 7° on the sky), low surface density, and location on the far side of (and near) the Galactic disk, it is a considerable observational challenge to differentiate between its stars and those in the Milky Way. It's unlikely that a complete sample of its stellar populations has been made. One spectroscopic study (Giuffrida et al., 2010) has found evidence for multiple populations in the peripheral zones of the dwarf. Furthermore, based on the stream's velocity dispersion, it is clear that Sgr dSph was probably a much larger and complex galaxy in the past, with an original mass on the order of 60 billion suns (although some estimates cite only a billion suns). In any case, after nearly 10 billion years of continuous tidal stripping, its present incarnation may not represent its original range of properties. Hence, one cannot assume that the kinematics, star-formation history, and chemical composition of the entire system have been thoroughly explored.

As many researchers have pointed out, proper motion measurements for NGC 5053 might help conclusively determine its membership status in the Sgr dSph stream. Numerical simulations predict an apparent proper motion of −2.16 and 1.73 milliarcseconds per year in right ascension and declination, respectively. If NGC 5053 were a genuine member, it would probably have a proper motion similar to −4.2 ± 0.5 milliarcseconds per year in right ascension and −0.1 ± 0.1 milliarcseconds per year in declination (Law and Majewski, 2010). A recent global survey of star clusters in the Milky Way, based on stellar data from the all-sky PPMXL and 2MASS[*] catalogs, yielded values of −5.81 and −2.76 milliarcseconds in right ascension and declination for NGC 5053 (Kharchenko et al., 2013). Given the cited uncertainty in these measurements (0.5 milliarcseconds per year), these values indicate that NGC 5053 is less likely to be associated with the Sgr dSph.

Still other evidence points to a surprising alternative origin scenario. Both NGC 5053 and M53 lie remarkably closer to the Magellanic plane — the orbital plane of the Large Magellanic Cloud (LMC) about the Milky Way — than to the Sgr dSph orbit. This has led some researchers (e.g. Chun et al., 2010) to conclude that both NGC 5053 and M53 are potentially associated with the Magellanic plane rather than the Sgr dSph orbit (**Figure 33**). Indeed, these clusters may have originally been born in the LMC. Moreover, the stream of clusters associated with the Magellanic plane, which includes NGC 5466, M15, M30, M68, and M92, resembles the stellar stream in the halo of M31 that lies along the satellites M32 and NGC 205.

Photometric evidence of a possible extragalactic origin for NGC 5053 is the presence of a tidal tail, indicating that some of its stars have drifted or been drawn out of the cluster (Lauchner et al., 2006). Intriguingly, a tidal bridge extends from NGC 5053 to M53. Similar tidal features have been detected in other clusters in the Magellanic plane (Chun et al., 2010). The NGC 5053 stream corresponds to a projected length of approximately 1.7 kiloparsecs. This structure, however, may not have anything to do with its purported membership with Sgr dSph. Both theoretical models and direct observational evidence have shown that globular clusters are subject to the gravitational potential of their host galaxy, and that cluster-galaxy interactions can cause stars to escape the cluster's gravitation and form tidal tails in front of and behind the cluster's orbit. Circumstantial evidence for this is the cluster's low mass and core concentration, and its relatively small galactocentric distance of about 17

---

[*] PPMXL stands for Position and Proper Motion Extended-L, and 2MASS stands for the Two Micron All Sky Survey.

kiloparsecs. Each of these factors conspires to increase the effect that Galactic tidal forces can have on stars within the cluster. In addition, the NGC 5053 tidal stream's orientation with the Sagittarius Stream suggests a motion with a transverse angle of 60° to the Sagittarius plane. But even this has a counterpoint, as it can be argued that the streams may still be too near the cluster (between 3 and 4 tidal radii) to provide a definitive indication of the cluster's orbital direction.

Finally, a mosaic of Megacam images taken with the Canada-France-Hawaii Telescope revealed complex substructures of clumps and ripples surrounding both NGC 5053 and neighboring M53, as well as a tidal bridge-like structure between the two (Chun et al., 2010). If these structures are real, then one must assume that the evolution of NGC 5053 has been influenced not only by the Galaxy but possibly M53 — never mind Sgr dSph!

Where did NGC 5053 come from? Is it a product of quietly evolving in a backwater of the Galaxy's halo? Or the remnant of a once more massive globular cluster, now a shadow of its former self after being purloined from the Sagittarius Dwarf by the Milky Way? Clearly more observations, including proper motion measurements of the cluster, are needed.

M53

A first-generation globular cluster

M53 is sometimes considered a neglected, moderately bright globular cluster. In both cases, I beg to disagree. Neglected? Hardly. Although it has been the subject of only a modest amount of dedicated research, the SIMBAD database lists well over 600 papers between 1850 and 2018 in which it appears in various studies. These include stellar populations, the search for variable stars (particularly those of the RR Lyrae variety), analyses of stellar chemical abundances, star formation history, and inventories of blue stragglers, to name a few. And moderately bright? True, in terms of visual magnitude it is no Omega Centauri or M13. But in an 8-inch at 150x, it is a standout, and even partially resolved on nights of

M53 Globular Cluster	NGC 5024 GCl 22	RA 13ʰ 12ᵐ 55.2ˢ Mag 7.8 Bt*Vm 13.8	Dec +18° 10′ 05″ Size 13′ Conc class V

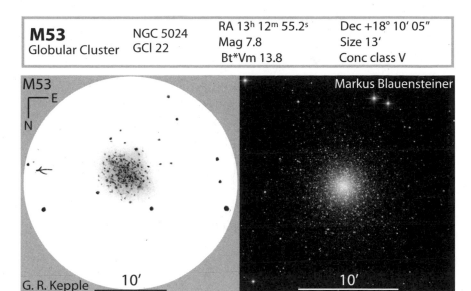

Figure 29: Messier 53. An eyepiece impression (left) compared to an amateur photograph, courtesy ccdguide.com.

good seeing. In larger apertures under dark skies, it is a stunner. As a 16 year-old novice trying to earn my Messier certificate in the late 1960s, I thought M53 was intriguing enough in my friend's 4¼-inch Edmund Scientific "Palomar" reflector: a sizeable nebulous sphere dotted in and around with stars, not quite as large as M13, but impressive enough to present an appreciable visual presence at magnifications of 120x.

A year later, after mowing enough summer lawns, I purchased a 6-inch "Dynascope" reflector made by the Criterion Manufacturing Company and revisited the cluster one pre-dawn morning. I almost couldn't believe what I was seeing: the cluster was no longer hazy but decidedly granular around the edges, and punctuated by at least three dozen stars forming loops and chains that appeared to radiate from the dense core in all directions. Over the years I returned for more stunning views using larger telescopes. Each jump in aperture brought it closer to resolution, and the dark, nearly starless field in which M53 floats made a striking contrast with this effervescent stellar aggregate.

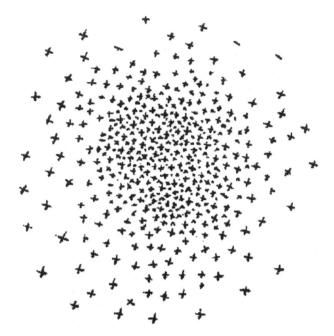

Figure 30: Messier 53, an early drawing. Sir William Herschel resolved the nebula into stars In 1783, publishing this image in *Philosophical Transactions of the Royal Society* in Great Britain in 1784.

Of course, there would be other globular clusters in my future that would be more impressive still. But for someone just discovering the "universe from his backyard," M53 was an enthralling introduction to the species of globular clusters.

M53 lies 56.4 arcminutes NE of Alpha Com and can be discerned as a slightly extended but faint star in 8x56 binoculars. Just 57.5 arcminutes to the SE is the globular cluster we profiled earlier, NGC 5053, glimmering just above the background sky. Johann Bode discovered M53 on February 3, 1775, using a refractor with a focal length of perhaps 7 feet and of unknown aperture. He described it tepidly as "rather vivid and of round shape." Charles Messier compared it to the comet of 1779 (also discovered by Bode). William Herschel observed the cluster in 1783 and proffered an eyepiece impression to *Philosophical Transactions* in 1784 (**Figure 30**).

Other observers since then have been more enthusiastic. Admiral Smyth practically gushed: "This is a brilliant mass of minute stars, from the 11th to the 15th magnitude, and from thence to gleams of star-dust, with stragglers to the *np* [north-preceding], and pretty diffused edges." T. W. Webb, too, referred to the cluster as a brilliant mass of stars, adding, "blazing in the centre." Hartung deemed it "very rich and compact, with rays of outliers about 4' across, rising to a broad center crowded with faint stars which 20 cm will show clearly." Christian B. Luginbuhl and Brian A. Skiff, in their *Observing Handbook and Catalogue of Deep-Sky Objects*, note that a 30-centimeter "shows a 6-arcminute core with most of the outliers on the NW and SE. The cluster is well resolved overall, and in poor seeing the core looks roughly triangular." Walter Scott Houston, although not impressed with the view in a 3-inch, considered the object magnificent in a 12.5-inch reflector, "where faint streams of curving stars run out from the central blaze in all directions."

M53 is among the oldest (12.7 billion years) and most metal-poor ([Fe/H] = −2.10) of the outer halo Galactic globular clusters. It is the second-most abundant in variable stars after M15. It is also richly abundant in blue straggler stars (BSS) with nearly 200 of them, eight of which are SX Phoenicis variables — low-metal versions of Delta Scuti stars, with low-amplitude pulsations and periods on time scales of 0.003 to 0.008 day (0.7 to 1.9 hours). Readers of previous *Annals* volumes are likely already familiar with blue stragglers. They are brighter and bluer (hotter) than normal stars occupying the main sequence, and with up to twice the mass. On the H-R diagram, they lie along an extension of the main sequence a few magnitudes above their turnoff point. For all intents and purposes, they are old stars that should have long ago exited the main sequence and evolved into giants, but instead have somehow been rejuvenated into hot, bright stars. This, plus the fact that they are more massive than normal main-sequence stars, indicates that some mechanism increases the initial mass of single stars. The two most probable are either mass transfer between primordial binaries, or the merger of two single or binary stars via stellar collisions. Both formation scenarios have been shown to have comparable efficiency in producing BSS (Ferraro et al., 2003).

Figure 31: Messier 53, close-up view of the core. Courtesy ESA/*Hubble* & NASA.

High-resolution and widefield multiwavelength observations using the *Hubble Space Telescope*, the Large Binocular Telescope, and the Canada-France-Hawaii Telescope resolved M53's stellar populations from the central regions out to a radius of 0.5°, or about 155 parsecs, assuming a distance from the Sun of 18 kiloparsecs (Beccari et al., 2008). The observations show that the BSS population is bimodal. The blue stragglers are highly concentrated in the cluster center, rapidly decrease at intermediate radii (about 60 arcseconds from the center), and rise to increased numbers at greater radii. The sparsely populated intermediate radii, or "zone of avoidance," correspond well to that part of the cluster where dynamical friction causes the more massive BSS or their binary progenitors to settle to the cluster center.

This bimodal distribution, first detected in M3 (Ferraro et al., 1993, 1997), was thought to be peculiar; however, it has since been found in 47 Tucanae, M55, M5, NGC 6388, NGC 5466, and a number of other globular clusters. Dynamical simulations (Mapelli et al., 2006; Lanzoni et al., 2007) demonstrate that the observed central peak of blue stragglers is built upon stellar collisions in the core as well as mass transfer between primordial binary star systems that have "sunk" to the center due to dynamical friction effects. Concurrently, the external rising branch primarily consists of mass-exchanging primordial binary star systems evolving in isolation in the cluster outskirts.

Not all globular clusters exhibit bimodality. For example, the blue straggler population in M79 in Lepus is highly centrally segregated and does not show an external increase at greater radii; moreover, those in Omega Centauri and NGC 2419 have a radial distribution indistinguishable from that of other "normal" clusters. This is clear evidence that these globular clusters are not fully dynamically relaxed, even in the central regions. It further indicates that the observed BSS are the descendants of primordial binaries, whose radial distribution has not yet significantly been altered by stellar collisions and the dynamical evolution of the cluster (Beccari et al., 2008). The radial distribution of blue stragglers in globular clusters would appear to contain vital information about the dynamical history and evolution of these systems.

As discussed in the previous section (NGC 5053), complex substructures of clumps and ripples surround both NGC 5053 and neighboring M53, and a tidal bridge-like structure stretches between the two. Further, an envelope composed of stars surrounds the cluster system (Chun et al., 2010, **Figure 32**). The tails extend in the east-west direction of M53's orbit, as well as in the direction of the Galactic center for NGC 5053. It is tempting to speculate that we may be looking at a binary globular cluster system; however, none are known in the Milky Way, although one might exist in the peculiar giant elliptical galaxy NGC 5128, Centaurus A (Minniti et al., 2004). And even if the two inter-

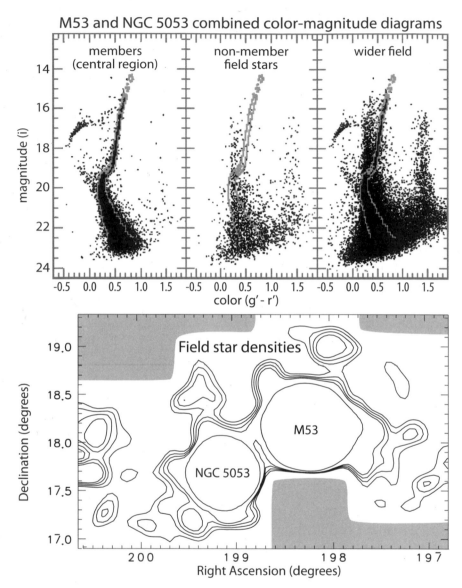

Figure 32: The M53 - NGC 5053 system. Because the two star clusters share a common origin in a galaxy absorbed by our own, their color-magnitude diagrams overlap (top). The jagged gray outline shows the main sequence and red-giant branch of the member stars; the two right panels include field stars unrelated to the clusters. From the same paper (Chun et al., 2010) the researchers estimated the star density in the field, suggesting the clusters are members of a stream of stars stripped from a galaxy whose core might be the Sagittarius Dwarf Spheroidal Galaxy (**Figure 28**). Grayed areas were not measured.

acted in the past, it does not prove that they originated with the same common dwarf spheroidal parent. As noted earlier, there is observational evidence suggesting that NGC 5053 may have been stripped from the Sgr dSph galaxy. But there is also evidence that both M53 and NGC 5053 may have originated in the LMC and been captured by the Milky Way during a near passage, since both clusters are closely aligned with the LMC's orbit around our galaxy (**Figure 33**).

One discrepancy is the radial velocity values of each. For M53 it is 79 ± 4.1 kilometers per second, but for NGC 5053 it is about 44 kilometers per second (Harris 1996). Also, the distance moduli of each indicates the two are separated by some 1.4 kiloparsecs, not an insignificant distance in the Galactic halo, when compared with their tidal radii of 113 parsecs and 67 parsecs for M53 and NGC 5053, respectively. Another disparity is M53's stellar content. Studies of the morphology of its horizontal branch (Caloi and D'Antona, 2011) showed that it might be composed primarily of first-generation stars, a characteristic that puts it at odds with the majority of other globular clusters, which are typically dominated by stars that have recycled gas from previous generations creating more metal-rich abundances. The horizontal branch in color-magnitude diagrams is short, barely reaching a $B - V$ of -0.05 (very blue), with few stars beyond this color.

The question of whether M53 is composed largely of first-generation stars is fundamental to its evolutionary state and mostly defined by the presence of "light-element anticorrelations," specifically oxygen-to-sodium (O-Na), and aluminum to magnesium (Al-Mg). We will spare readers the esoteric astrophysical details of this well-documented relation, but an abridged tutorial is in order.

The O-Na anticorrelation is the primary abundance pattern of stellar populations in globular clusters in our Galaxy and in the Local Group. Generally, first-generation stars have higher oxygen-to-sodium abundances, which resemble those of halo field stars of similar metallicity. The situation is reversed for second-generation stars, which have depleted amounts of oxygen but enhanced levels of sodium due to the carbon-nitrogen-oxygen cycle (the fusion reaction sequence that converts hydrogen to helium) in the hydrogen-burning shells of evolved stars. Although the anticorrelation pattern has not yet been found among field stars in the disk and halo of the Milky Way covering the same metallicity range as Galactic globular clusters, one study (Carretta et al., 2010a) suggests that as many as 1.4 percent of metal-poor field stars could be sodium-rich stars that have evaporated from globular clusters. At any rate, the anticorrelation manifests itself in the presence of at least two stellar generations in every globular cluster. Since hydrogen burning produces helium, second-generation stars are expected to be helium-enriched, which explains the incidence of multiple horizontal branch and main-sequence stars in globular clusters. However, the connection between O and Na anticorrelations, the variation in helium abundances, and the presence of multiple horizontal branch stars is a specialized subject; hence we invite readers to explore it further if they are so inclined (Gratton et al., 2004, 2010).

From a large sample of red-giant branch stars in M53 (Boberg et al., 2016), abundances of elements such as iron, calcium, and nitrogen are consistent with trends seen in Milky Way halo stars. Moreover, the cluster's O-Na anticorrelation is not as extended as other Milky Way globular clusters of similar mass and metallicity. The ratio of second-generation stars to the total number of stars sampled in the cluster is approximately 0.3, with the second-generation stars being more centrally located. This makes M53 a *mostly* first-generation-dominated cluster. As most globular clusters are thought to consist primarily of second-generation stars, those with large numbers of first-generation stars make interesting studies, particularly when drawing conclusions about the chemical characteristics of multiple populations in globular clusters.

As mentioned, M53 possesses a significant population of variable stars, with RR Lyrae stars predominating. The search for these short-period variables in M53 dates back to Harlow Shapley (1920). So far, it has yielded about 60 RR Lyrae stars, many of which exhibit the Blazhko effect, in which the pulsations exhibit periodic modulations of the amplitude and phase

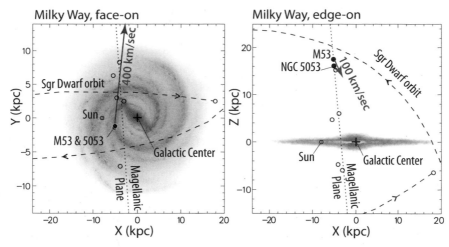

Figure 33: The motions of M53 and NGC 5053 around the Milky Way. Sometimes the orbits of globular clusters in the Milky Way point to their origin in another galaxy. In this figure, adapted from Chun et al., 2010, kinematic evidence suggests that M53 and NGC 5053 are a legacy of our galaxy's interaction with the Large Magellanic Cloud, as they and several other globular clusters (shown as open circles), align with the Magellanic Clouds' orbit. **Contemplative observing:** Observe Messier 53 and its likely fellow traveler, NGC 5053, with any telescope. Consider that both are rapidly moving above the Milky Way in orbits that suggest an origin beyond our own galaxy. We understand what we know from observations and models, though uncertainties remain. Still, M53 continues its orbit through the Milky Way, oblivious to our lingering questions.

of maximum light on timescales of tens to hundreds of days. If you follow the light curve over several Blazhko cycles, it looks like waves whose peaks synchronously rise and fall. The phenomenon is named for Russian astronomer Sergei Nikolaevich Blazhko who discovered the effect in 1907. (For a broader discussion, see M3 in Canes Venatici.)

The average period of M53's RR Lyrae stars indicate that it is a metal-poor Oosterhoff type II globular. In 1939, Dutch astronomer Pieter Theodorus Oosterhoff noted that globular clusters could be sorted into two groups according to the mean period of their of RR Lyrae variables: those that fall near 0.55 days are binned as class I, while those closer to 0.65 days are binned as class II. Oosterhoff class I clusters are metal-rich and contain stars that are hotter and more massive than those of class II. Further, unlike class II globulars, class I clusters are also more likely to follow a retrograde orbit through the Milky Way. The difference in metallicities as well as their space motions suggests that types I and II may have different origins, with the Oosterhoff II clusters forming early in the Galaxy's development and the Oosterhoff I clusters forming at different locations and at later times. It is thought that Oosterhoff I clusters could have been stripped from merging dwarf galaxies.

M53 harbors a 33-millisecond pulsar (B1310+18) discovered in 1989. The pulsar lies within 6 arcminutes of the optical center of M53 and is a member of a very wide binary system with a 256-day orbit. The orbital period is among the longest observed in a globular cluster, with a companion mass of 0.35 $M_\odot$. Conventionally, millisecond pulsars may be spun up through the action of binary companions, although some subsequently lose their companions and appear as isolated pulsars. Interestingly, M53 has a low central density of about 1,000 stars per cubic parsec, so a mass-exchange interaction in such a low-density environment is unusual. When mass transfer began in the progenitor binary, the giant was likely already near the tip of the red-giant branch and rapidly expanding. Its envelope may have been transferred quickly, efficiently spinning up the neutron star. Similar pulsars in the Galactic disk have orbital periods of a few hundred days and spin rates of tens of milliseconds.

In recent years, our perspective on the formation and evolution of globular clusters has undergone a proverbial paradigm shift. The classical view held that globular clusters were stellar "fossils" harboring millions of coeval stars, i.e., all born of the same material at the same time. This static assumption has long been used to trace the kinematic and chemical evolution of galaxies. Over the last few decades, however, a more dynamic picture has emerged, one in which globular clusters harbor two or more distinct stellar populations. It has even been suggested that bona fide globular clusters be defined as stellar aggregates showing the O-Na anticorrelation, as distinct from associations and open clusters (Carretta et al., 2010b). If we are to understand the formation and merger history of the Milky Way and other

NGC 4147 GCI 18	RA 12ʰ 10ᵐ 06.1ˢ	Dec +18° 32' 34"
Globular Cluster NGC 4153	Mag 10.7	Size 4.4'
	Bt*Vm 14.5	Conc class VI

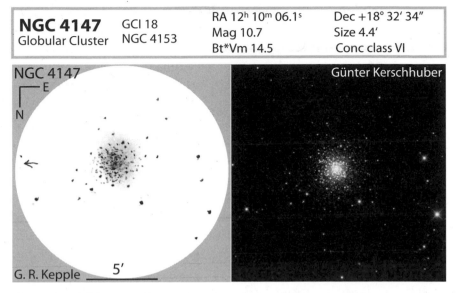

Figure 34: NGC 4147. An eyepiece impression (left) compared to an amateur photograph, courtesy ccdguide.com.

galaxies, we need to delve into the nature of globular clusters and their stellar populations. M53 may provide a continuum between the metal-rich and metal-poor systems, as well as insights into why and how some globulars remain largely dominated by first-generation stars while others are not.

NGC 4147

A young globular cluster

Our third and final globular cluster in Coma Berenices is located nearly 15° west of M53, or 6.4° NE of Denebola. NGC 4147 (with a dual NGC identifier of 4153) is small, faint, and unresolved in 8- to 10-inch telescopes. The view is slightly better in larger instruments, with some fringe stars resolved; the core is bright and compact. At magnifications of around 200x, the inner cluster is irregularly shaped, almost boxy, and slightly elongated NNE to SSW. The immediate field surrounding the cluster is interspersed with 15th- and 16th-magnitude stars, some of which may not be members. One of those masquerading as a member, based on its proper motion, is 13th-magnitude NGC 4147-105, floating 2.6 arcminutes off to the NNE. About 14 arcminutes ENE of the cluster's core is an 8th-magnitude K2 giant, HD 105865, the brightest and most obvious nonmember in the field.

We have here another cluster situated in the outer regions of the Galactic globular cluster system. Its heliocentric distance is 19.3 kiloparsecs, while its galactocentric distance is 21.3 kiloparsecs (Harris 1996). The age, relatively average for a globular cluster, is about 11.5 billion years. Despite its predominantly blue horizontal branch and low metallicity [Fe/H] = −1.8, it is classified as an Oosterhoff type I, one of the most metal-poor globular clusters to be thus classified. (Recall the distinguishing characteristics of the Oosterhoff types I and II described in M53.) The cluster harbors about two dozen blue stragglers and a number of variable stars, including about 20 RR Lyrae stars.

It has been proposed (Bellazzini et al., 2003b) that NGC 4147, like NGC 5053, may be immersed in the Sagittarius Stream, based on its radial velocity and the detection of M-giant Sagittarius stars near the cluster. Deep photometry, however, shows that the heliocentric distance of the northern sector of the Sagittarius Stream in the field is about 20 kiloparsecs greater than the distance to the cluster (Martínez-Delgado et al., 2004). Moreover, numerical models of the disruption of the Sgr dSph (Law and Majewski, 2010) based on observational data indicate that NGC 4147's association with that galaxy is improbable.

Multiband data obtained from Sloan Digital Sky Survey images revealed a number of overdensities in the region surrounding NGC 4147. A close-up view revealed a complex multiple arm morphology, including an S-shaped tidal arm extending over several tidal radii* in northern and southern directions as well as a halo of extratidal stars (Jordi et al., 2010). These extended features are likely the result of past interactions with the Galactic environment, as opposed to being part of the Sagittarius population. Multiple-arm morphology has been predicted for globular clusters on eccentric elliptical orbits close to apogalacticon (Montuori et al., 2007). NGC 4147's current

---

* The tidal radius is the distance from the cluster's center where the gravitational field of the host galaxy has more effect than the self-gravity of the cluster.

position, which is close to apogalacticon, matches the simulations well. The features are likely due to the dissolution of the globular cluster's stars, a result of internal 2-body relaxation and stellar evaporation.

EXTRAGALACTIC OBJECTS IN COMA BERENICES

Practically up to the 1970s, a part of the sky centered on Coma Berenices was referred to as the "Realm of the Nebulae." Now that we know these "nebulae" are in fact assemblages of countless galaxies scattered like windblown confetti north into Canes Venatici, south into Virgo, and east into Leo, we call this region Realm of the Galaxies. This direction leads us out of the Galactic North Pole and into a tangle of various galaxy groups as well as the Virgo, Coma, and Leo galaxy clusters. There are few parts of sky in this region devoid of galaxies. Many are too faint for modest-size telescopes, but brighter ones will keep observers busy. For those with apertures of 15 inches or more, or for imagers who want to "go deep," the Realm of the Galaxies is the threshold to the universe beyond the Milky Way.

Admiral Smyth openly admired it in his *Cycle of Celestial Objects*:

> This is a wonderfully nebulous region, and the diffused matter occupies an extensive space, in which several of the finest objects of Messier and the Herschels will readily be picked up by the keen observer in extraordinary proximity.

One of the more fascinating recent findings in this part of the sky is the existence of a new kind of galactic system, referred to as an "ultradiffuse galaxy" (UDG) or more popularly as a "dark galaxy." The region around the Coma Cluster may harbor 1,000 or more of these mysterious denizens. They can be as large as normal galaxies, and yet are essentially devoid of stars and visible mass. If 99 percent of the mass of our galaxy were removed, the result would be a UDG. The question becomes: how can they maintain a coherent structure, particularly in a galaxy cluster where the hot intracluster medium is

M64 Seyfert Galaxy	NGC 4826 Black Eye Galaxy UGC 8062	RA 12ʰ 56ᵐ 43.7ˢ Dec +21° 40' 57" Mag 8.5 SB 12.7 Type (R)SA(rs)ab Size 10' x 5.4' PA 115

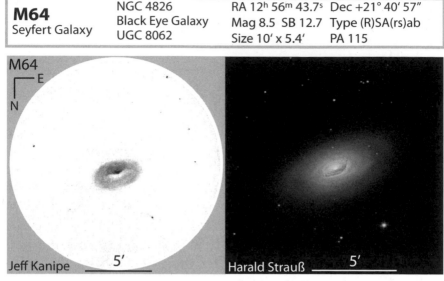

Figure 35: Messier 64. An eyepiece impression (left) compared to an amateur photograph, courtesy ccdguide.com.

notorious for stripping normal galaxies of their gas and dust? Their "glue" must be reservoirs of dark matter, but why and how they formed at all is still a mystery. The first reports revealed 47 such objects centered on the Coma Cluster (van Dokkum et al., 2015). A subsequent search (Koda et al., 2015) turned up nearly 900. We briefly profile one of these objects, Dragonfly 44, later in this section.

M64

Galaxy with prominent nearside extinction

M64 lies 5 degrees NW of Alpha Comae Berenices, and is one of the nearest members of a small group of galaxies referred to by Gérard de Vaucouleurs as the Canes Venatici I cloud.* This famous galaxy, the brightest in Coma Berenices, is renowned for its prominent lidded dust lane just NNE of the galaxy's center (and on the near side), a feature that earned it

---

*This group is noted in Schmidt and Boller, 1992, but not mentioned in R. Brent Tully's *Nearby Galaxies Catalog*; rather, M64 and UGC 8024 (NGC 4789A) are listed as a small group of their own, 14+3+3.

the name Black Eye Galaxy (and sometimes the Evil Eye Galaxy). The swath of absorption is best appreciated in short-exposure images; too long and the galaxy's light swamps the disk, leaving only a trace. This was aptly illustrated in the *Hubble Atlas of Galaxies* in two exposures, both taken in 1910 by George Ritchey with the 60-inch Mount Wilson reflector. In the longer exposure (7 hours and 56 minutes), Allan Sandage notes that the spiral arms exhibit a very soft texture with no resolution into knots (**Figure 36**). In the shorter exposure (4 hours), the dust pattern in the nucleus is very prominent, as are bright filaments that make up the inner spiral structure. A faint dust arm can also be seen "on the inner edge of the last luminous arm" on the north side of the galaxy.

Observer Craig Crossen reports that M64 can be discerned in 10x50 binoculars because of its bright and distinctly elongated disk. It is an easy object in 3- and 4-inch telescopes; an 8-inch renders a smooth, bright oval, with the absorption feature appearing as an amorphous void just north of a nonstellar nucleus. Larger apertures (over 12 inches) resolve this to an almost dramatic extent. Luginbuhl and Skiff describe it as kidney-shaped and obvious in both direct and indirect vision in 30-centimeter apertures. The grainy nucleus appears to be peering out from the very edge of the dust lane. An 11th-magnitude star (TYC 1455-1200-1) lies just offshore, 4.2 arcminutes to the NE.

Variable star pioneer Edward Pigott discovered M64 on March 23, 1779, using "an achromatic instrument three feet long." He described its light as being exceedingly weak. Johann Bode independently came across it 12 days later, desribing it as a small, nebulous star. As sometimes happens, Bode's discovery was the first to be published, followed by Messier's inclusion in his catalog in 1780. Pigott's report, finally published in 1781, was largely ignored until British astrophysicist Bryn Jones retrieved it from oblivion it in 2002.

Apart from the extinction feature, M64's outer disk is relatively free of dust and resembles an S0 galaxy. Fortunately, it also has a medium-high inclination (~60°) that reveals a lot of detail in and around the galaxy's center. The nucleus has been classified as a transition object — a combination of a LINER

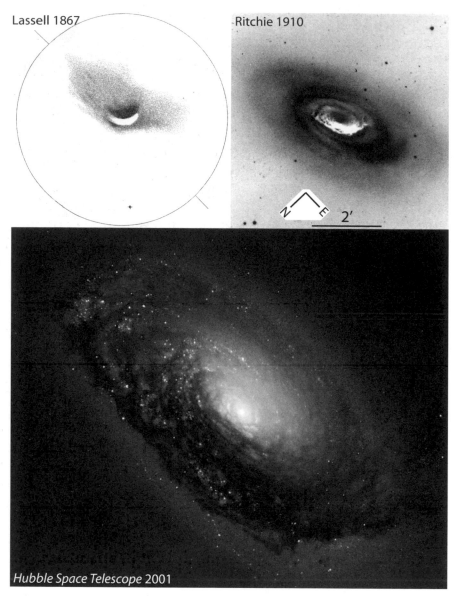

Figure 36: Observatory images of Messier 64. William Lassell used a 48-inch reflector in Malta in 1867 to make the engraving of M64 (upper left) from visual observation. George Ritchie made an early photograph in 1910 from four nights of exposures using the Mount Wilson 60-inch reflector, courtesy Rubin 1994. A more recent *Hubble* image shows rich detail of the dark, black eye dust lanes, courtesy NASA and the Hubble Heritage Team (AURA/STScI); acknowledgment: S. Smartt (Institute of Astronomy) and D. Richstone (U. Michigan).

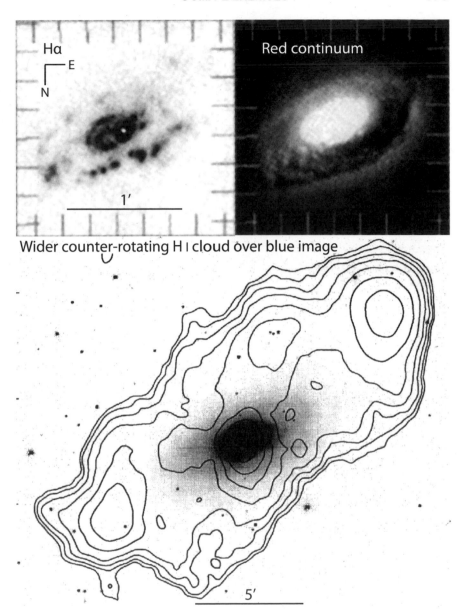

Figure 37: Messier 64 deconstructed. Braun et al., 1994, used the Kitt Peak National Observatory (hydrogen alpha and red continuum) and two radio observatories to map the galaxy; they found a wider cloud (bottom) rotating in an opposite direction to the inner structure, top. **Contemplative observing:** Observe this galaxy with any telescope and consider that its visual disk is rotating in one direction while an unseen cloud of neutral hydrogen gas in which the galaxy is immersed is rotating in the opposite direction.

and a luminous H II region — based on spectra (Ho et al., 1995). As described in *The de Vaucouleurs Atlas of Galaxies* (Buta, Corwin, and Odewahn) it possesses a well-defined inner ring, the morphology of which is greatly shaped by the broad dust feature that partially covers it. Weak spiral structure opening in a counterclockwise direction springs from this ring. Two very diffuse, low-contrast spiral arms form an outer pseudoring that winds in a clockwise direction. Hence, M64 has two counter-rotating gas disks (ionized gas and neutral hydrogen), similar to NGC 4622 in Centaurus. The reversal begins around 30 arcseconds (600 parsecs) from the nucleus. *HST* images reveal that highly active star formation is occurring in the shear region where the oppositely rotating gas disks collide. Smoldering within the turbid dust swath are hot, blue young stars along with ruddy H II regions. Carbon monoxide (CO) observations (Meyer et al., 2013) revealed numerous giant molecular clouds and CO emission clumps within 400 parsecs of the center of M64. The galaxy is also a radio source, likely resulting from the embedded star-forming regions and supernova remnants from central star formation.

A collision/merger with a satellite galaxy, a billion years or so ago, may be responsible for the unusual internal motions. M64 may have originally had an S0 morphology, and the satellite it absorbed may have been an overly dusty spiral. A similar scenario has been proposed for NGC 5128 (Centaurus A), which also possesses a very broad dust belt. Centaurus A may be the relaxed product of a collision between a nearly prolate elliptical galaxy and a small, gas-rich system.

There is some disagreement as to M64's distance; some quote values of 4.1 megaparsecs, which puts it well outside the Local Group; others cite intermediate estimates up to 9.2 Mpc. In any case, it is relatively nearby compared to some of the other galaxies in Coma Berenices.

NGC 4565 Galaxy	The Needle Galaxy UGC 7772	RA 12ʰ 36ᵐ 20.8ˢ Dec +25° 59' 14" Mag 9.6 SB 13.3 Type Sb sp Size 15.8' x 2.1' PA 136

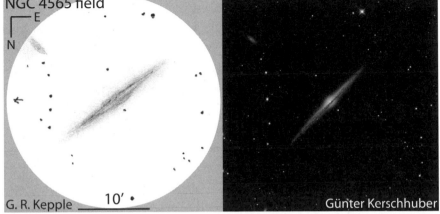

NGC 4565 field

G. R. Kepple   10'

Günter Kerschhuber

Figure 38: NGC 4565. An eyepiece impression (left) compared to an amateur photograph, courtesy ccdguide.com.

NGC 4565

Edge-on spiral; LINER-type nucleus; boxy bulge

NGC 4565 has been called, justly so, one of the most famous examples of a bright, edge-on spiral galaxy. Others include NGC 55, NGC 891, NGC 5907, and NGC 5866. All are unique and tell us much about galaxy formation and evolution, but as we shall see, NGC 4565 is uniquely poised (from a distance of about 12 megaparsecs) to do so. William Herschel discovered this striking system on April 6, 1785, describing it as a "lucid ray" 20 arcminutes or more long, with a very bright middle; "a beautiful appearance." It is an easy find with manual telescopes, being 3° SE of Gamma (γ) Comae Berenices, on the eastern fringes of Melotte 111. Admiral Smyth called it "a curious, long, and streaky object, lying *np* [north preceding] and *sf* [south following] across the field, in somewhat of a weaver's shuttle shape, and preceded by four telescopic stars in a vertical curve.* The parallel appendage [dust lane] to this nebula is a most extraordinary phenomenon" (**Figure 39**).

In the field, there are actually five stars aligned more or less vertically west of the galaxy — the middle three being brighter than those at each end — and if you follow them like stepping-stones southward, you will come across the wispy magnitude-13 spiral galaxy, NGC 4562.

E. J. Hartung was struck with the shape of NGC 4565 and its dust lane:

> I can trace this object for 12′ x 1′ and the absorption lane is prominent, as well as the faint luminosity outside it near the bright centre. This is just visible with 20 cm while 10.5 cm will show the nebula itself as a faint extended haze.

I have observed NGC 4565 through a number of telescopes and found a pleasing view in a 15-inch Dobsonian with magnifications of around 150x. The dark equatorial lane contrasts well with the concentrated light of the edge-on disk, and can be seen along most of the galaxy's flank until it fades into the background on both ends. If you look closely where the dust lane splits the bulge and continues out along the NW extension, you can just make out some mottling. The eye is also attracted to a 13th-magnitude star (2MASS J12362527+2600212) floating 1.2 arcminutes above the bulge to the NE. Another fainter star (magnitude 16?) on the opposite side (SW) often goes unnoticed by observers using larger telescopes. It lies in the foreground of the outer bulge.

NGC 4565 was classified a LINER in 1983 (Keel), with the central 10 arcseconds exhibiting strong forbidden lines of doubly ionized oxygen [O III]. The spectral signature suggests that the core of NGC 4565 contains a blue, metal-rich, and kinematically cold stellar subpopulation, perhaps associated with ongoing star formation (Proctor et al., 2000). Deep imaging reveals bluish regions of young stars in the nibs at both ends of the disk, although one presumes they are distributed throughout the outer disk. Visually, star-forming regions appear entirely absent within the extinction zone, though images made using *HST* and

---

* A weaver's shuttle is a narrow, typically wooden tool that compactly holds the bobbin of yarn used when weaving with a loom.

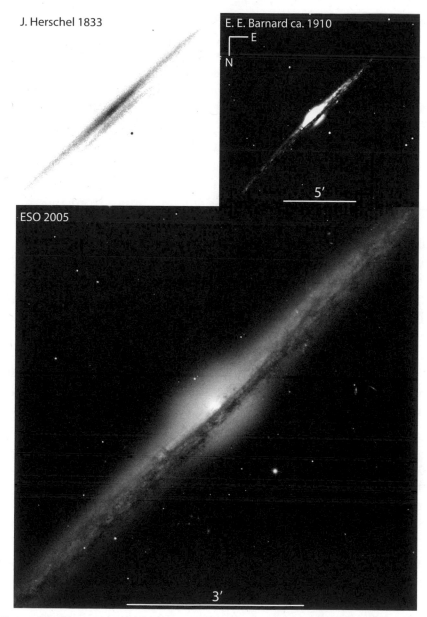

J. Herschel 1833

E. E. Barnard ca. 1910

E

N

5′

ESO 2005

3′

Figure 39: Observatory images of NGC 4565. John Herschel used his father's refurbished 20-foot, 18.2-inch-diameter reflector to make the engraving (upper left) in 1833 from visual observation. E. E. Barnard made an early photograph around 1910, courtesy the Edward Emerson Barnard Papers, Vanderbilt University Special Collections and University Archives. The image of the galaxy's central region was made using the Very Large Telescope at the European Southern Observatory in Paranal, Chile. Note the background galaxies.

ESO's Very Large Telescope reveal numerous stars distributed like blue glacial ice along the edges of the dust belt. At the other end of the stellar evolution ladder, far-infrared observations (De Looze et al., 2012) determined that old stellar populations (about 8 billion years old) supply more than two-thirds of the dust heating in NGC 4565, with localized embedded sources supplying the remaining heating. One can also see that the galaxy is not exactly edge-on, since the core peeks out just SW of the dust lane (the cited inclination is about 87°). Images also reveal something else, though it is very subtle: the very tips of each end of the disk curve very slightly away from the major axis in opposite directions. Neutral hydrogen (H I) maps (Sancisi 1976) show the warp more dramatically, with the most pronounced deformation apparent on the NW side of the galaxy. The warp seen at either end of the edge-on disk implies that it is continuous around its rim, although it is probably not azimuthally symmetric. The calculated mass of the full warp (Rupen 1991) may encompass over 1 billion $M_\odot$, which amounts to about 15 to 20 percent of the H I mass of the entire system.

HST maps of the distribution of young and old stars in the gaseous H I warp of NGC 4565 (Radburn-Smith et al., 2014) found no stars older than about a billion years, but did find a significant population of young stars (less than 600 million years old) within the warped regions. Analysis of the star-formation history indicates that the formation rate in the warp increased, relative to the surrounding regions, at least 300 million years ago. The sustained star formation rate in the warp over this time is ~6.3 x $10^{-5} M_\odot$ per year per square kiloparsec.

Two broad mechanisms are suspected for creating warps: the tidal interaction of nearby galaxies, and the effects of a "misaligned infall" of material. Widefield images show two companion systems to NGC 4565 on the sky: NGC 4562, 13 arcminutes to the SW, and IC 3571 (an "object of unknown nature" according to the SIMBAD database), 6 arcminutes to the north. Based on their radial velocities and redshift values, all three galaxies are in proximity to one another. At a distance of 12 megaparsecs (the mean distance cited by NED), NGC 4562 lies at a projected distance of 46 kiloparsecs from NGC 4565, while IC 3571's sep-

NGC 4565 field in neutral hydrogen (radio)

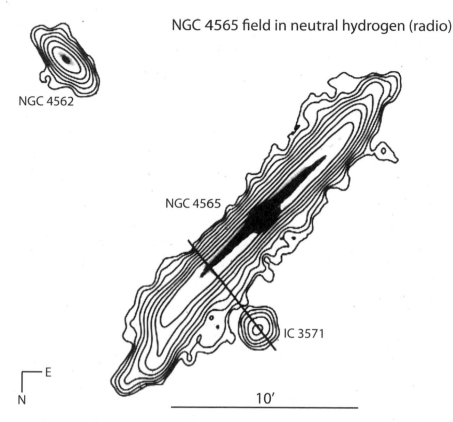

Figure 40: NGC 4565 field in neutral hydrogen. Radio observations, courtesy Heald et al., 2011, tell the story of H I gas extending well beyond the visible galaxies seen in the field. The line across the outer regions of NGC 4565 and through IC 3571 indicates other measurements in the position-velocity domain explored in the paper.

aration distance is 21 kiloparsecs. Of the two, IC 3571 exhibits better physical evidence for a past interaction with NGC 4565, due to its irregular shape. In fact, it may be a satellite. After all, both the Large and Small Magellanic clouds lie at greater distances from the Milky Way. Photometric visual-band observations (Näslund 1995; Näslund and Jörsäter, 1997) detected a faint extension of the NW warp coinciding with the H I warp that appeared to be physically connected to the galaxy. Subsequent deep neutral hydrogen observations (Heald et al., 2011, **Figure 40**) fleshed out the weak bridge between NGC 4565 and IC 3571, which exhibited a smooth change in velocity between the two systems. Perhaps either or both companions to NGC 4565 may, in part, be responsible for that galaxy's warped disk. There are precedents in support of this possibility. The location of the Sagittarius Dwarf galaxy, which has been disrupted in the inner halo of the Galaxy, argues convincingly that it produced the warp in the Milky Way. Similar arguments for tidal interactions inducing warps also have been made for NGC 5907 (Shang et al., 1998).

Simulations in the late 1960s, however (Hunter and Toomre, 1969), showed that galaxy disks are unable to sustain warps, and more recent simulations show that induced warps are not long-lived features and quickly disappear due to the shape of the inner halo realigning itself with the disk (Dubinski and Kuijken, 1995; Binney et al., 1998). Therefore, the long-lived warps observed in roughly half of all galaxies are likely due to ongoing gravitational effects (Bosma 1991).

The lack of old stars in the NGC 4565 warp suggests that the gas has been recently accreted. This leads to the second scenario, misaligned infall. In the Lambda (λ) cold dark matter cosmology, gas constantly accretes from all directions, causing the angular momentum of the host's dark matter halo to continually, and significantly, change over time in random ways. The continual slewing of the orientation of a flattened outer halo due to this misaligned accretion can cause warps in a galaxy's disk. Such warping has been demonstrated in numerical simulations (Jiang and Binney, 1999; Shen and Sellwood, 2006). Hence, rather than torquing an existing disk, the warp itself may have formed from the direct accretion of misaligned material (Radburn-Smith et al., 2014).

The mechanism driving the warp in NGC 4565 remains to be seen, but these observations should help hone analytical models of warp formation by placing constraints on their ages and their longevity. If the warp forms from pristine material, metallicity measurements of the warp may provide insights into the viability of the misaligned accretion model.

The bulge of NGC 4565 has been characterized as "boxy" in that, in profile, it has a rather squarish appearance. Boxy bulges are a fundamental feature in many edge-on galaxies. In some cases they can appear as peanut-like structures or even X-shaped. Whatever their appearance, numerical simulations have shown that they are not bulges, but parts of edge-on bars that have lofted stars vertically above the plane of the disk (Combes and Sanders, 1981). If this were the case for NGC 4565, it would strengthen the boxy-bulges-are-bars interpretation, even though this is something that is pretty well founded already. On the other hand, the inference would be more believable still if a "pseudobulge" were also present in the boxy bulge component.

Readers may recall that we first came upon this term in the profile of M94 in Canes Venatici. As outlined there, a pseudobulge is a dense central component consisting of nuclear bars, disks, tightly wound inner spiral structure or rings, and central star formation. Pseudobulges are the dominant type of central component in disk galaxies and have been found throughout the Hubble sequence. From a face-on perspective, a pseudobulge resembles a classical bulge created in the wake of a galactic merger, except that is not how it formed. Instead, it amassed gradually over time (secularly) out of the galaxy's own disk material. As such, pseudobulges are less spherical and more disk-like in nature.

Archival *HST* and *Spitzer* near-infrared images (Kormendy and Barentine, 2010, **Figure 41**) penetrated the dust lane of NGC 4565, revealing a high surface brightness, central stellar component distinct from the boxy bar and the disk, and surrounded by a dark inner ring. Its brightness profile identified it as a pseudobulge. Now that we know NGC 4565 has a bar and a pseudobulge, we can, in a sense, reorient the galaxy to a more highly inclined angle. Closer to face-on, the box-shaped bulge would morph into a bar surrounded by a ring; in its new incarnation, it would probably appear similar to the SB(r)bc galaxy NGC 2523 in Camelopardalis, which we profiled in volume 3. The bar in NGC 4565 is probably seen almost end-on.

Theories about how galaxies evolved from the earliest epochs in the universe are dominated by the theory of hierarchical gravitational clustering, in which smaller galaxies merged to form ever-larger ones. Some of these, in turn, col-

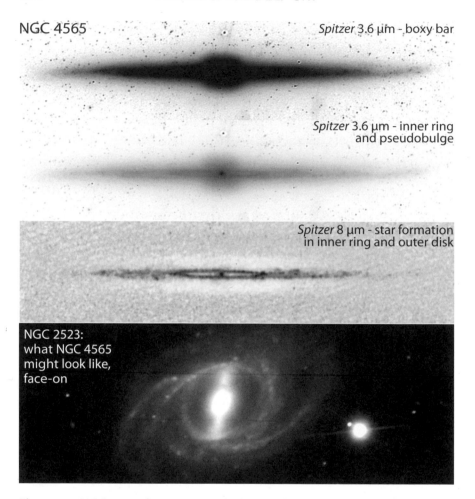

NGC 4565   *Spitzer* 3.6 μm - boxy bar

Spitzer 3.6 μm - inner ring
and pseudobulge

Spitzer 8 μm - star formation
in inner ring and outer disk

NGC 2523:
what NGC 4565
might look like,
face-on

Figure 41: NGC 4565 deconstructed. The top three panels show infrared analysis of the galaxy. The tiny dots at the centers of the middle and lower figures show the inner ring around the galaxy's core. The bottom panel shows another galaxy, NGC 2523 in Camelopardalis, that represents how NGC 4565 might look if seen face-on as an SB(r)bc galaxy. Figure courtesy Kormendy and Barentine, 2010.

lided, and eventually relaxed into the elliptical forms we observe today. Although hierarchical clustering remains well founded, it may be overly biased toward galaxy interactions as a driving force in galactic morphology. Research into pseudobulges shows that this scenario should be augmented by a selection of complimentary evolutionary processes involving rearranging energy and angular momentum to shape isolated galaxies. These would lead to the growth of central structures that, although they look like conventional merger-produced bulges, in general have formed slowly throughout the galaxy's disk. In effect, the existence of pseudobulges implies that galaxies are still evolving, and can dynamically produce unique features on their own without invoking violent interactions.

The distance to NGC 4565 is in question. Minimum distances place it around 10 megaparsecs, while other estimates remove it to 17.5 megaparsecs or more, on par with the Virgo Cluster. Given a distance of 12 megaparsecs (cited above), the visible disk has a projected length of 56 kiloparsecs, and a scale height of about 7 kiloparsecs.

Keen-eyed observers appraising deep images of NGC 4565 may notice a flurry of "fluff" off the SE end of this galaxy. This is a remote cluster of galaxies identified in the *Mitchell Anonymous Catalog*, a database of over 117,000 (very) faint galaxies compiled by Larry Mitchell. The galaxies in this cluster are between 17 and 18 magnitude, so one will need a telescope of between 40 and 48 inches inches to detect the few brightest members! The database is available on the MegaStar Sky Atlas mapping program for Windows, one of our resources.

NGC 4725
Nearby ringed galaxy

The respectable visual magnitude (9.4) of NGC 4725 is largely due to its bright nucleus, which endows it with considerable visual presence. Luginbuhl and Skiff note that it can be seen in a 6-centimeter, and is "very little concentrated except for a small brightening in the center." Larger telescopes reveal a faint extended halo about 5 x 3 arcminutes. A 15-inch at 132x reveals the bright core, elongated SW to NE, and a large diffuse halo over 8 arcminutes along its major axis (some observers estimate 10 arcminutes). Steve Gottlieb, using a 13.1-inch, points out apparent structure with the "WSW edge possibly brighter." The "structure" he alludes to is probably a trace of this galaxy's famed ring, which circumscribes the central

NGC 4725 UGC 7989 Seyfert 2 Galaxy LEDA 43451	RA 12ʰ 50ᵐ 26.5ˢ Dec +25° 30′ 02″ Mag 9.4 SB 13.9 Type SAB(r)ab pec Size 10.7′ x 7.7′ PA 35

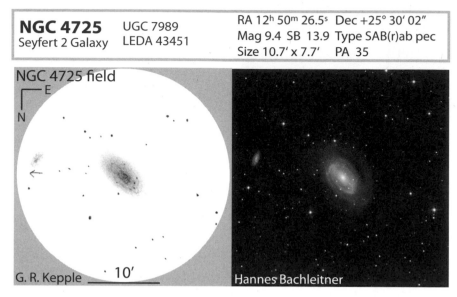

Figure 42: NGC 4725. An eyepiece impression (left) compared to an amateur photograph, courtesy ccdguide.com.

region with a radius of 2.2 arcminutes. Images bring out the ring with dramatic clarity as well as a broad but weak bar. If the image is deep enough, a faint outer arm may be visible wrapping around from the north, through the east, and on to the south and SW, effectively forming an outer pseudoring. An interaction with neighboring NGC 4747 (Haynes 1979; Wevers et al., 1984) is likely responsible for this structure.

NGC 4725 is yet another William Herschel discovery, made in 1785. It is located 5.3° WSW of Beta Comae Berenices within several degrees of NGC 4559 and NGC 4565. Just 12 arcminutes to the west of NGC 4725 lies the emission-line galaxy NGC 4712, which actually sits well behind these three galaxies at a distance of about 72 megaparsecs. The former systems are all members of the Coma-Sculptor Cloud, a filament of the Local Supercluster. The estimated distance to NGC 4725 is about 13 megaparsecs. Although it is categorized as a Seyfert 2, its luminosity is on the low end of the active galactic nuclei limit. The source has not been detected in the radio band, though X-ray images (Cappi et al., 2006) reveal the presence of a nuclear core and of several nearby sources positioned more

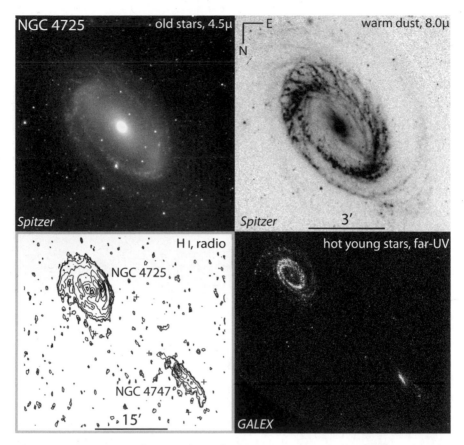

Figure 43: NGC 4725 deconstructed. The top two panels show infrared analysis of the galaxy from *Spitzer*. The lower panels show the fields of both NGC 4725 and NGC 4747 as seen in H I gas (Wevers et al., 1984) and at ultraviolet wavelengths (*GALEX*). The kinematics and distribution of the H I in NGC 4725 and NGC 4747 suggest the two are tidally interacting.

than 30 arcseconds from the nucleus. Again, an interaction with NGC 4747 may have triggered a nuclear starburst.

As pointed out by Ronald Buta (1988), ringed galaxies are of keen research interest, especially considering that ring-like or pseudo-ring-like patterns are evident in up to 50 percent of disk galaxies of early to intermediate Hubble type, and particularly those of the barred variety. They form a distinctive morphological subgroup spanning almost the entire disk galaxy classification sequence (even lenticulars), and thus provide a key constituent for understanding galaxy morphology. More-

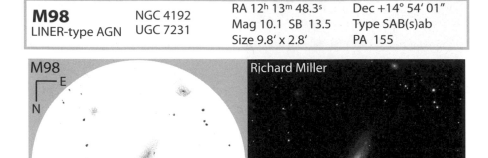

M98 LINER-type AGN	NGC 4192 UGC 7231	RA 12ʰ 13ᵐ 48.3ˢ Mag 10.1 SB 13.5 Size 9.8' x 2.8'	Dec +14° 54' 01" Type SAB(s)ab PA 155

Figure 44: Messier 98. An eyepiece impression (left) compared to an amateur photograph.

over, based on dynamical models, rings make useful probes of galaxy dynamics and structure, particularly when dynamical models are brought to bear. Like most galaxies of this type, the inner ring of NGC 4725 exhibits enhanced star formation compared to regions inside and outside the ring, except most of it is concentrated in broad arcs around the ends of the bar. This indicates that gas is piling up along the bar's major axis and that the ring may be expanding.

To date, this galaxy has been host to two supernovae: SN 1969H and 1940b. The latter event occurred within the NE section of the ring in an environment that contains large OB associations.

M98

Highly inclined spiral galaxy; LINER transition object

M98 is an easy find, lying 6° east of Denebola on the edge of the Virgo Cluster's western boundary. If you begin with this galaxy and slew your telescope east and south, you'll encoun-

Figure 45: Messier 98 in higher resolution. The European Southern Observatory (ESO) released this image using data from their New Technology Telescope at La Silla Observatory in Chile. (ESO acknowledgment: Flickr user jbarring).

ter a host of galaxies of all types. The ones that leap out are M84, M86, M89, and, near Virgo central, the voluminous elliptical M87.

This is another Méchain discovery (March 15, 1781) that was subsequently measured and logged by Messier on April 13, 1781, who deemed it "of an extremely faint light, above the northern wing of Virgo." Smyth called it "a fine and large, but rather pale nebula, between Virgo's left wing and Leo's tail." Heber D. Curtis, in "Descriptions of 762 Nebulae and Clusters Photographed with the Crossley Reflector" (1918), noted: "Bright nucleus; numerous almost stellar condensations. Absorption on east side."

M98 is among the faintest of the Messier objects, but its nearly edge-on appearance helps boost its visual presence in dark skies. I had no trouble finding it in an 8-inch Newtonian at medium magnification — and in suburban skies to boot. It's kicked over from being oriented north to south by about 25° and it appears to point to a small group of faint field stars to the SE (including 14th-magnitude spiral NGC 4186). In telescopes of this size, what you see is its bright inner disk, which makes it seem smaller than it is by three arcminutes along the major axis and nearly one arcminute along the minor. The ansae do not taper but appear nearly squared off. Near the center, and seemingly offset slightly to the SW, is a starlike nucleus. Luginbuhl and Skiff report that in a 30-centimeter it is "rather fainter and less extensive to the SE, and not well concentrated to the center. E and W side[s] of the halo do not bulge as they pass the core: the overall outline is cigar-shaped, and the NE flank is more sharply defined." Still-larger instruments render a stellar nucleus that is slightly diffuse around the edges. Steve Gottlieb, using a 17.5-inch, notes what he thinks is a faint knot near the galaxy's southern tip. I cannot say definitively that I see it in my 15-inch, but it is confirmed in images; even short exposures show a little knot in the SE ansae.

Images also bring out details in the chaotic disk, including chains of blue star-forming regions in the spiral arms, which emerge from a central region that is heavily obscured in occulting dust. The nucleus is considerably reddened, but it is bright enough to just pierce the dust, as if it is peeking out for the first time. Buta, Corwin, and Odewahn in *The de Vaucouleurs Atlas of Galaxies* state that the galaxy possesses a bar, but that the inclination makes it difficult to recognize. The outer arms, they add, form an outer pseudoring; the bar is probably being viewed broadside on, but the dust limits its appearance. To us, the NE arm appears to rise out of the galaxy's plane, but this may be an illusion due to its orientation.

In the same field (at low magnifications) is 6 Comae, some 32 arcminutes to the east. This is a class A3 dwarf lying some 60 parsecs distant. The nearest bright galaxy is M99, 1.3° ESE.

M98 has been classified as a LINER galaxy (low-ionization nuclear emission-line region) based on the spectrum of its nucleus. As the name implies, LINERs have lower luminosities than their more active brethren, Seyfert galaxies and quasars. Rather than exhibiting the high ionization states and broad emission lines of those systems, indicative of hot, fast-moving gas, the LINER spectrum is dominated by emission lines from low-ionization states, particularly oxygen, nitrogen, and silicon, with only weak emission from higher states. The ionizing source is still under debate, although there is no dearth of candidates: photoionization, either by low-luminosity active galactic nuclei or very hot stars, or collisional ionization via fast shocks. More specifically, M98 has been categorized as a transition LINER, i.e., one with a composite nucleus having both circumnuclear H II regions and a LINER component (Terashima et al., 2000). This is another indication of the heavy amount of obscuring dust that envelops the nucleus, preventing it from showing a more definitive LINER face.

The distance to M98 is somewhat contentious. Its radial velocity is 142 kilometers per second in approach, i.e., it is blue- rather than redshifted. As Robert Burnham Jr. pointed out, ordinarily a blueshifted galaxy would be a good candidate for being a member of the Local Group. Distance estimates, however, range between 12 and 19 megaparsecs, the mean of which puts it slightly on the near side of the Virgo Cluster. Its anomalous motion may be a product of internal motions within the cluster itself (infall and random motions due to interactions), which by chance has slung the galaxy in our direction.

As mentioned in the M99 profile, M98 may be responsible for that galaxy's clumpy H I tidal tail — or not. See M99 for more on this curious structure.

M99 H II Galaxy	NGC 4254 UGC 7345	RA 12ʰ 18ᵐ 49.6ˢ Dec +14° 24' 59" Mag 9.9 SB 13.1 Type SA(s)c Size 5.4' x 4.7' PA 51

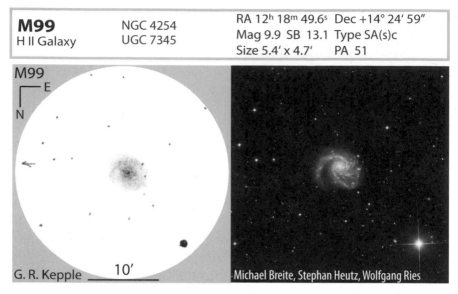

Figure 46: Messier 99. An eyepiece impression (left) compared to a photograph at right, courtesy ccdguide.com.

M99

Spiral galaxy just entering the Virgo Cluster

One wonders why Halton Arp did not include M99 in his *Atlas of Peculiar Galaxies*. It might have gone in the section on galaxies "with one heavy arm," since this system very clearly sports a broad extended SW arm that hooks outward like the claw of a fiddler crab. It resembles NGC 2276 in Cepheus, which *is* in the *Atlas*, except that galaxy's arm is not as pronounced as M99's. The northern arm, too, is prominent, with several indistinct branches seen to the north and east.

M99 is a bright, easy galaxy for observers with small telescopes, and a compelling study in an 8-inch. One may star hop 6.5° east of Denebola to 5th-magnitude 6 Comae, then 50 arcminutes SE, just south of a line between magnitude-6.5 HD 107170 and magnitude-8 HD 106888. In a 5-inch, M99 exhibits a prominent central condensation surrounded by a fainter halo and a smattering of faint field stars; the eastern inner disk is pronounced but cuts off sharply. In larger telescopes (12 to 15 inches) the SW arm is clearly discernible, seemingly detached from the disk — as are two distinct patches, one SW of the nucleus and another near its western extremity. The disk is mottled throughout. Images reveal many massive H II regions embedded in both the major and minor arms in the NE and SW. The central region is also bright with robust star formation.

The galaxy was discovered by Pierre Méchain in 1781 and observed by Charles Messier that same year. He described it as a, "Nebula without star, of a very pale light situated on the northern wing of Virgo, & and near the same star, no. 6, of Comae Berenices. The nebula is between two stars of seventh & eighth magnitude." Lord Rosse noted spiral structure apparent in M99 in April 1846 using the 72-inch "Leviathan" reflector of Parsonstown. On March 11, 1848, one of Rosse's first observing assistants, William Rambaut, telegraphically described M99 as a "spiral with B* [bright star] above, a thin portion of the neb reaches across this * and some distance past it. Principal spiral at the bottom (np), and turning towards the right." Lord Rosse's astonishing (at the time) rendering of M99 was published in *Philosophical Transactions* of 1850 alongside his sketch of M51 (**Figure 47**).

In 1921, Lowell astronomer Carl O. Lampland announced that he had observed slight changes in the "form and structure" of the nucleus of M99 on photographic plates, though he stated that the observations were uncertain. In 1967, Merle F. Walker of Lick Observatory reported that a reexamination of plates taken by Lampland between 1916 and 1948 seemed to confirm his claim. Walker speculated that the object causing the variability might be a grouping of O and B stars (based on spectroscopic and photometric observations) or that it might be a peculiar variable star of extreme luminosity and early spectral type. "If so," he wrote, "it is *very* much brighter than the brightest variables found by Hubble and Sandage in M31 and M3 which have photographic absolute magnitudes at maximum light of about −8.43." Walker estimated that the object in M99's nucleus had a photographic absolute magnitude of −14.

Because of its brightness, proximity, and morphological asymmetry, M99 has been the subject of a number of studies

Rosse 1850   Lassell 1867

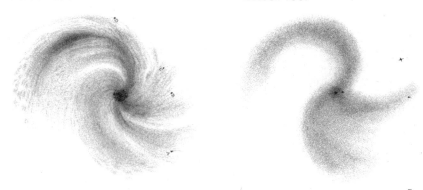

Figure 47: Observatory images of Messier 99. Early engravings from visual observations compared with an ESO Very Large Telescope image; circles in this image are Wolf-Rayet stars.

aiming to understand its lopsided appearance, particularly in the absence of a bar or obvious companion. Explanations for its asymmetry include induced spiral modes via global gravitational instability, asymmetric gas accretion onto the disk, ram pressure stripping[*], a lopsided distribution of dark matter with respect to luminous matter, or a close high-speed encounter with an unknown companion.

The galaxy's heliocentric distance is about 15.5 megaparsecs. On the sky, it lies 3.5° NW of M87 and the center of the Virgo Cluster. In three-dimensional space, it has a projected separation of 1 megaparsec from M87 for a Virgo Cluster distance of 16.7 megaparsecs (Mei et al., 2007). The galaxy's heliocentric velocity of 2,407 kilometers per second implies a velocity of about 1,300 kilometers per second with respect to the overall cluster.

M99 has no close neighbor, but a clumpy tail of neutral hydrogen (H I) trailing to the NNW links the galaxy with a massive H I source, VIRGOHI21, with a mass of about 100 million suns and a velocity gradient of 220 kilometers per second (Minchin et al., 2005 and 2007). The H I tail can be traced over 50 arcminutes, which, at a Virgo cluster distance of ~17 megaparsecs, amounts to a physical length of about 250 kiloparsecs. VIRGOHI21 is one of the larger condensations within this tail. Given its mass and velocity, the H I source has been interpreted as a starless "dark galaxy," a family of objects that consists of a disk of normal matter (baryons) rotating in a dark-matter halo. However, dark galaxies would differ from normal galaxies by being free of stars, having all their baryons in the form of gas. As such, they would be "dark" at most wavelengths but visible at radio wavelengths through their H I emission.

The formation of low-mass dark galaxies is actually predicted by cosmological cold dark matter models, although some theoretical arguments counter that no galaxy could remain indefinitely stable against star formation, unless they are of very low mass, at least a factor of 10 below that of classical dwarf. Hence, if they exist, dark galaxies would have a low dynamical mass and H I content.

---

[*] As a galaxy passes through the dense, hot intracluster medium of a galaxy cluster, it experiences a "wind," much like passengers feel when moving rapidly through the air in an open car. Ram pressure stripping can occur if the wind is strong enough to overcome the galaxy's gravitational potential, thus abrading its neutral hydrogen gas content and redistributing its dust.

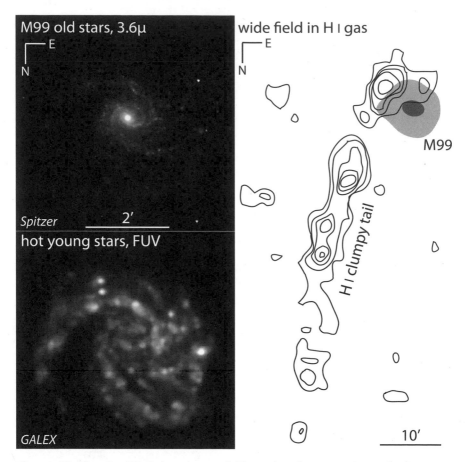

Figure 48: Messier 99 deconstructed. The galaxy has experienced robust star formation, which is evident by comparing the old and young star distributions (two left panels) at identical image scales. A long clumpy tail of hydrogen gas is mapped to the north in radio, courtesy Haynes et al., 2007; the tail is shown with isophote lines and the stronger emission around the galaxy is shown in gray. **Contemplative observing:** Locate Messier 99 using any telescope and consider that there is a stream of gas stretching out of the frame of a wide-field eyepiece. Consider that this stream contains information important to understanding the dynamics of the Virgo Galaxy Cluster.

This dark galaxy scenario has since been challenged via numerical models that indicate the H I tail is the result of simple streaming motions of tidal debris (Duc and Bournaud, 2008). According to these simulations, a high-speed flyby (1,100 kilometers per second) of M99 by a massive companion

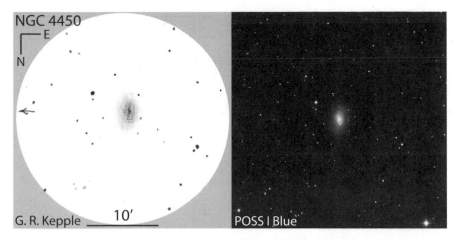

Figure 49: Messier 99. An eyepiece impression (left) compared to a photograph at right.

750 million years ago extracted the debris. The interloper was possibly M98 (although there are other credible candidates within a megaparsec).

But another inescapable oddity that swings the argument back to this being a dark galaxy is its shortage of baryons compared to visible galaxies (Minchin et al., 2017). Typically, 10 percent of the dynamical mass of visible disk galaxies is in the form of stars and gas. If VIRGOHI21 had this abundance of baryonic mass, it would contain at least two billion solar masses of H I spread evenly across the disk. This, in turn, would yield a column density well above the threshold to form stars. Since VIRGOHI21 seemingly contains no stars, its minimum dynamic mass in baryons must be ten times lower. In other words, 90 percent of the normal matter one would expect to find in a typical galaxy is apparently missing from VIRGOHI21. This makes it difficult to explain how this "galaxy" can be anything *but* dark. According to the authors of the study, "[T]he new observations show a long drawn out tidal feature which has an abrupt velocity change and we cannot find a candidate galaxy to have caused it. Tidal interactions between optically bright galaxies often draw out stars as well as gas. We have … used *HST* to search for stars associated with VIRGOHI21 and find none down to very faint surface brightness levels."

The characteristics of the H I tail — its unequivocal association with a disturbed galaxy, its overall length, modest mass (6 x 10^8 $M_\odot$), and roughly sinusoidal velocity field — are consistent with a high-speed interaction called galaxy harassment. These are known to occur in the crowded environs of galaxy groups or clusters, but M99 may be just beginning its harassing flybys. Compared to many spirals of similar linear size found within 1.5 megaparsecs of the inner regions of the Virgo Cluster, M99 has a normal H I content and disk metallicity gradient. Therefore, one can conclude that it is just beginning to enter the Virgo environment at high speed for the first time. Once it takes its initial plunge, it will suffer significant gas removal and star formation quenching, as have other established cluster members.

M99 has been host to at least four known supernovae, the most recent being 2014L, a type Ic event. It was located 14 arcseconds west and 16 arcseconds south of the nucleus.

NGC 4450

Example of an anemic galaxy

In a 1976 paper in the *Astrophysical Journal*, Canadian astronomer Sidney van den Bergh proposed a new galaxy classification system designed to address some of the biases and less elegant aspects of the Hubble-Sandage sequence, as well as to establish a more natural framework for different galaxy types. In particular, van den Bergh argued the Hubble scheme primarily focused on giant galaxies without taking into account the effects of differing galaxy luminosity. He also noted that the large sample of galaxies photographed by the Palomar Sky Survey in the 1950s clearly showed that the appearance of many galaxies in rich clusters differed from that of field galaxies of similar Hubble type. Van den Bergh wanted to bring these discordances into balance within the Hubble-Sandage scheme. Normal spirals, he pointed out, differed from type S0

| **NGC 4450**
 LINER-type AGN | UGC 7594
 LEDA 41024 | RA 12ʰ 28ᵐ 29.3ˢ
 Mag 10.1 SB 13.2
 Size 5.4' x 4.1' | Dec +17° 5' 6"
 Type SA(s)ab
 PA 175 |

lenticulars "primarily in their total gas content and hence in the mean age of their stellar populations. The existence of both highly flattened gas-free systems and similarly flattened gas-rich galaxies suggests that there might exist a class of flattened objects with characteristics that are intermediate between those of S0 galaxies and normal spirals." Van den Bergh coined the name for such gas-poor objects, in which not much star formation is taking place, "anemic spirals." Star formation in these types of galaxies has been suppressed by ram pressure stripping as the galaxy rapidly passes through the hot intra-cluster environment.

NGC 4450 is just such a galaxy. Note that in photographs it has a medium inclination (~42°) and soft spiral arms. There is not much in the way of contrast between the spiral arms and disk, although it does have a very bright LINER-type active galactic nucleus (AGN).

What Méchain and Messier missed was left to the indefatigable William Herschel to discover in 1784. He described it as bright, large, and round, with a gradually brighter center and a bright star in the field. In 15- to 18-inch telescopes, these features translate into a rather diffuse disk, elongated north to south and affixed to the sky by a bright, mottled core. Some observers (Luginbuhl and Skiff and *The Night Sky Observer's Guide*) report that the stellar nucleus is off center to the east. An orange magnitude 9 star (BD+17 2485) lies 4 arcminutes to the SW. The galaxy is classified in NED as an ordinary spiral with an S-shaped inner ring, although Buta, Odewahn, and Corwin give it an SAB designation, as they recognize a weak bar oriented north to south across the central region. A faint dust lane crosses the northern half of the bar, making the bar difficult to discern. Sandage, in the *Hubble Atlas of Galaxies* (**Figure** 50), also noted that the most conspicuous arm, wrapping around the east side of the galaxy from the north, begins not in the nuclear region but some distance from the center, a feature he considered "unusual."

Apart from the low contrast of their spiral arms, anemic galaxies are also poor in H I content, redder than normal spirals, and have fewer star-forming regions. They also tend to

NGC 4450

E
N

3'

Hubble Atlas of Galaxies, 1961

Old stars, 3.6μ

Spitzer, 2017

Hot young stars, FUV

GALEX, 2007

Figure 50: NGC 4450 deconstructed: NGC 4450 shows dramatic differences per wavelength. The top image, made in 1947, was taken with the 100-inch on Mount Wilson after the war, and the lights from Los Angeles (bright even then) washed out faint outer detail. Old stars (lower left) give the galaxy a smooth appearance while younger stars (lower right) give it a decided coarser appearance.

have chaotic circumnuclear dust spirals within the central kiloparsec. In NGC 4450, these structures have been brought out in *HST* archival images using unsharp-masking techniques (Elmegreen et al., 2002). Dust spirals do not have associated star formation, unlike nuclear spirals in other galaxies, which suggests the galaxy's inner gas disk is not strongly self-gravitating.

The dust spirals are also very irregular, with both leading and trailing components that become darker as they approach the center but decrease in contrast with increasing radius. Analyses of these properties suggest that the circumnuclear dust spiral in NGC 4450 is an indication of turbulence in the inner gas disk. Such turbulence dissipates orbital energy of the gas and possibly drives accretion to power the galaxy's low-luminosity AGN. The increase in dust opacity in the central region of NGC 4450 is consistent with the amplification expected for inward motions. Bolstering this interpretation are spectroscopic observations showing that the galaxy exhibits double-peaked broad Balmer emission lines (Ho et al., 2000). This type of line profile, seen in some nearby LINERs, may be interpreted as the kinematic signature of a relativistic accretion disk.

The mean distance is 16 megaparsecs, though estimates range as high as 24 Mpc.

M91

Anemic barred galaxy located near the Virgo Cluster core

Like NGC 4450, M91 is another anemic galaxy in the Virgo Cluster, although this one exhibits a prominent bar and two spiral arms that split off into multiple sub-branches with increasing radius. It lies 50 arcminutes ENE of M88 or, if you prefer to begin with a larger canvas, 8.8° WSW of Alpha Comae.

In small telescopes (3 and 4 inches), M91 manifests as a small round patch with a star-like center. In larger telescopes, the galaxy's halo amounts to 2.5' x 1.5' and is elongated from NNW to SSE (PA 150°). Steve Gottlieb, using a 17.5-inch, notes the galaxy is "bright, moderately large, elongated 3:2 SW-NE, 3'x2', [and] gradually increases to a bright core and a very small nucleus." If you know that it's there, observers using larger telescopes might also look for a sudden cutoff in brightness NNW of the central region. This is where the western arm arches over the bright inner hub toward the ENE, creating an inner void between the two. Averted vision may show this best.

Charles Messier discovered M91 in 1781, but afterward he inadvertently mislaid it. For this reason, it is known as one of

M91	NGC 4548	RA 12^h 35^m 26.4^s	Dec +14° 29' 47"
LINER-type AGN	UGC 7753	Mag 10.2 SB 13.4	Type SB(rs)b
		Size 5.2' x 4.2'	PA 150

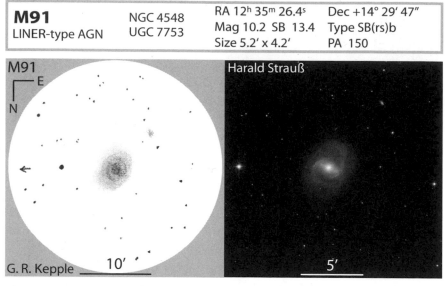

Figure 51: Messier 91. An eyepiece impression (left) compared to a photograph at right, courtesy ccdguide.com.

the "missing Messier" objects, since no object was visible at the 18th-century coordinates Messier provided. To make a long story short, it seems that he made a duplicate observation of another object in the vicinity, thought to be M58, which had the same right ascension as Messier's position for M91 (NGC 4548) but differs by nearly 2° in declination (Gingerich 1960). In 1969, amateur astronomer William C. Williams discovered that Messier probably measured M91's position from M89, which he thought was M58, and thus plotted it incorrectly. The two also have similar right ascensions and are separated on the sky by 54 arcminutes.* Given the crowded conditions of galaxies in this region, such an error on Messier's part is understandable.

Morphologically, M91 is a classic example of a barred spiral with a broken or pseudo-inner ring: SB(rs)b. Looking closely at deep images, one discerns that the pseudoring consists of two inner spiral arms that spring from the bar's minor axis, arch around the ends of the bar, and broaden and fade as they trail away from the galaxy's main body. The bar is well defined,

---

*See *Sky & Telescope*, December 1969, p. 376, for Williams' letter on the matter.

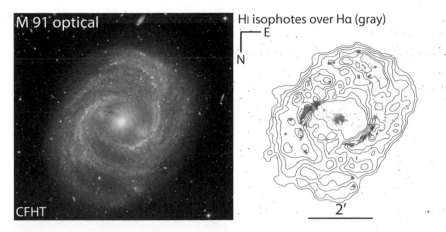

Figure 52: Messier 91 deconstructed. The image at right, courtesy Vollmer et al., 1999, shows H I limited to the visible parts of the galaxy, left, and the ring of hydrogen alpha around the core. Optical image courtesy Canada-France-Hawaii Telescope / Coelum, © 2014 CFH.

with a noticeable dust component at the SW terminus along the inner arm.

Neutral hydrogen and CO observations (Vollmer et al., 1999, **Figure 52**), coupled with previously obtained Hα data, revealed some intriguing substructure in the M91 system. Once again, the H I content does not extend very far beyond the visual disk, but the atomic gas distribution reveals a ring-like structure that is distorted along its northern and NW edges, which are nearest to the observer. Moreover, there is a warped and partially detached low-intensity arm in the north with no optical counterpart. It is possible that in this direction, ram pressure stripping is responsible for the gas removal and perturbations, and that the ram pressure may be either fading after the galaxy's close passage to the cluster's center, or increasing again due to a second approach. Meanwhile, maps of the Hα emission show strong star formation ongoing at both ends of the bar, indicating that it supplies the nucleus with an inflow of gas, thus triggering the starburst activity.

M91 was part of a survey conducted by the *Hubble Space Telescope* Key Project on the Extragalactic Distance Scale (Graham et al., 1999), which aimed to refine the Hubble constant to within 10 percent accuracy. Observations of 24 probable Cep-

| **M100**
Active Galaxy Nucleus | NGC 4321
UGC 7450 | RA 12ʰ 22ᵐ 54.9ˢ Dec +15° 49′ 20″
Mag 9.4 SB 13.4 Type SAB(s)bc
Size 7.4′ x 6.3′   PA 30 |

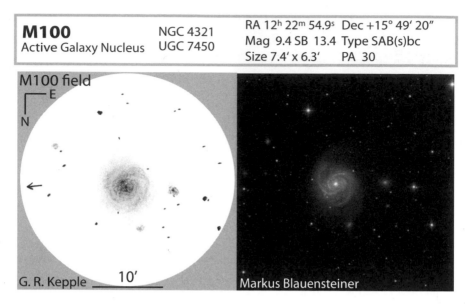

Figure 53: Messier 100. An eyepiece impression (left) compared to a photograph at right, courtesy ccdguide.com.

heids in the galaxy indicated a distance of about 16 megaparsecs (give or take 2 megaparsecs), which is very near that of the putative center of the Virgo Cluster, anchored by the giant elliptical M87 (16.5 megaparsecs). As is typical, there is some disagreement as to the actual distance. Other estimates range from 14 to 21 Mpc. Given its anemic appearance from ram stripping and its proximity to M87, only 2.4° to the SSW, it is likely near the Virgo Cluster core.

M100

Bright grand-design spiral in the Virgo Cluster

Roughly a third of the way along a line drawn from Denebola to Alpha Comae Berenices we find one of the brightest galaxies in the Virgo Cluster, M100. Discovered by Méchain in 1781, and its position subsequently determined by Messier, this grand design spiral is one of the finest objects in telescopes of all sizes. William Parsons, the third Earl of Rosse, or as he is more commonly referred to, Lord Rosse, included M100 in his list of spiral nebulae in his 1850 paper for the *Philosophical Transactions of the Royal Society of London*, describing observations of nebulae using three-foot and six-foot reflectors at Birr Castle, Parsonstown.

M100 consists of two prominent spiral arms springing from an oval central whorl, which forms a weak bar. If the image is deep enough, one can perceive a split in the northern arm as it begins wrapping around on the east side, where it declines into a tenuous extension toward NGC 4323 (often identified as NGC 4322), which lies 5.3 arcminutes to the NNE. A number of other galaxies grace the field, the most prominent being NGC 4328, some 6 arcminutes to the east; the nearly edge-on NGC 4312, 18 arcminutes to the SSW; and IC 783, about 19 arcminutes to the WSW. Wilhelm Tempel saw other nebulae in the immediate field, but at least two of them (NGC 4322 and NGC 4327) are spurious. NGC 4327 appears not to exist except, perhaps, as a 16th-magnitude star at Tempel's position. And according to Harold Corwin, NGC 4322 was probably a star further west of NGC 4323 that has the same coordinates as Tempel's. NGC 4323 is often identified as NGC 4322 in catalogs, atlases, and papers. In WikiSky and SIMBAD, for example, the same galaxy shares both identifiers.

Admiral Smyth described M100 as "a round nebula, pearly white," but "of little character, though it brightens from its attenuated edges towards the centre; and is therefore proved to be globular." Hartung deemed it a "large diffuse luminous haze about 4' across, rising broadly and then suddenly to a small bright nucleus with no visible structure."

In 6- to 8-inch telescopes, M100 has a pronounced visual presence in the field when it suddenly swims into view. At 80x it appears as a 4 x 3 arcminute oval with a bright, granular nucleus. The outer disk is smooth and diaphanous, but some mottling can be detected nearer the halo, particularly on the east side. Luginbuhl and Skiff note that with a 30-centimeter aperture, the halo extends to 5' x 4' in PA 60°. "The small bright core is 20" across and elongated in PA 60° with little wings on the NE and SW." In a 15-inch under very dark skies, one begins to see shadowy contrasts in the disk that indicate the presence of spiral arms. Steve

Gottlieb, observing with a 48-inch telescope, notes that the galaxy is "sharply concentrated with an intensely bright circular nucleus. Two prominent, high-contrast arms (fairly narrow) each rotate ~ 270° and can be clearly traced to within 1′ of the center." He adds that numerous H II regions may be discerned in some segments of the main spiral arms.

At a Virgo Cluster distance of 16.5 megaparsecs, the galaxy's radius amounts to about 18 kiloparsecs. In *The de Vaucouleurs Atlas of Galaxies*, Buta, Corwin, and Odewahn observe that its two spiral arms dominate the galaxy's structure. "The spiral pattern is 'grand design' and very regular. In the center, a small nuclear pseudoring is seen that is patchy and has a somewhat boxy appearance. This feature stands out as a distinct ring-shaped region of star formation in the $B - R$ color index map, which also reveals the complex dust structure and some indication that the dust lanes follow the concave sides of the spiral arms." In the *Hubble Atlas of Galaxies*, Allan Sandage published two images of M100: one showing the entire galaxy (**Figure 54**), and another zooming in on the nucleus. Sandage notes in the latter image that the spiral arms emerging from the core are dust arms, and that the luminous arcs are separated by gulfs of obscuring dust. "Continuations of these dark lanes form the two principal dust arms which wind out through the lens and end on the insides of the two most luminous outer arms." The image in James D. Wray's *Color Atlas of Galaxies* is telling in terms of star formation. The inner region is bright (indicating mild star-forming activity) but is surrounded by a yellow circumnuclear ring (indicating older stars). Beyond, the two main spiral arms are festooned with bright blue star-forming knots. One of the brightest appears in the southern spiral arm, about 1.6 arcminutes from the nucleus in PA 141°.

Over the years, numerous multiwavelength observations (**Figure 55**) have deconstructed M100's complex nuclear region. Optical, Hα, infrared, and CO images delineate a nuclear bar nearly perfectly aligned with a large-scale bar within the circumnuclear ring. Several H II regions lie on the ring crossing the long stellar bar, and two bright spots near the nuclear bar's termini dominate at 6.75 and 15 μm, emission

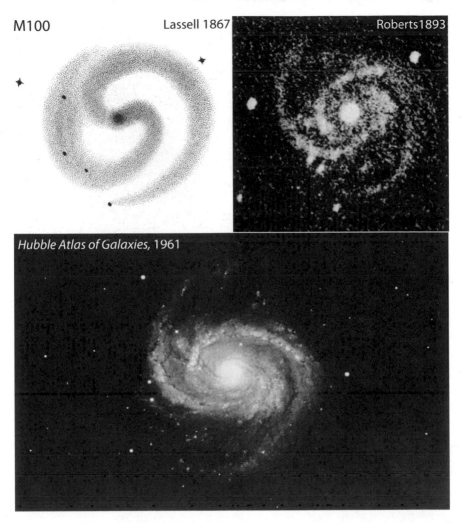

Figure 54: Observatory images of Messier 100. A pointillist-style engraving of M100 by Lassell tracks the spiral structure seen in an early photograph by Isaac Roberts. Below, a wide field from the *Hubble Atlas of Galaxies*, taken in April 1954 near the peak sophistication of photographic emulsion astrophotography. In their time, each image was considered to be among the best scientific depictions of this object.

possibly created by hot dust from the winds of Wolf-Rayet stars (Wozniak et al., 1999). Some 57 H II regions have been resolved within the ring itself. A kinematic study of the gas and stars in the circumnuclear region shows that it is fed by gas flowing in

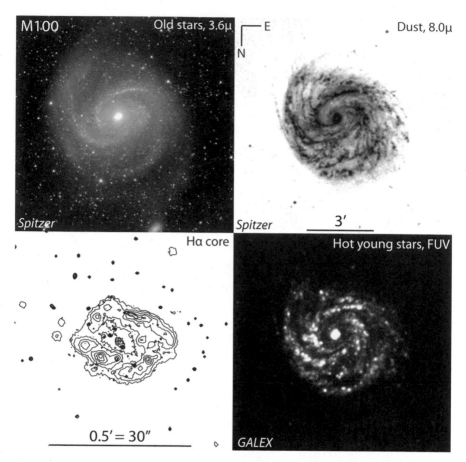

Figure 55: Messier 100 deconstructed. Four images in different wavelengths reveal different aspects of the structure of this grand design spiral. At lower left is a close up of the galaxy's core revealing a swirling inner ring of H II regions apparent in the light of hydrogen alpha, courtesy Rozas et al., 1998.

from the disk due to the resonance action of the bar. The youngest star clumps are found between the ring and dust lanes, perpendicular to the bar's major axis, where inflowing gas causes gravitational collapse and massive star formation (Ryder et al., 2001; Allard et al., 2006). Stellar population models indicate the underlying bulge and disk formed several billion years ago and that the nuclear ring began forming stars around 500 million years ago in a stable succession of bursts. Clearly, bars and nuclear rings are not ephemeral in nature, but stable, long-lasting structures.

Far from the center, all is not symmetrical bliss. As mentioned, a portion of the northern arm is drawn out forming a wispy bridge extended toward NGC 4323. Moreover, the northern arm is weaker than the southern arm both in CO and Hα emission. This should come as no surprise considering the galaxy-rich environment in which we find M100. The cause of the asymmetry may be due to tidal forces from NGC 4323, ram pressure from the Virgo Cluster's intracluster environment, the weak central bar, or all three factors. Given that a bridge of material appears to link M100 with NGC 4323, it might have played a larger role in disturbing M100.

The Virgo Cluster has also left its imprint on M100. Far-infrared observations in the 250 to 300 μm range with the *Herschel Space Observatory* (Pohlen et al., 2010) mapped the galaxy's distribution of gas and dust, and found that compared to H I, dust can be found almost out to the H I edge. This is not expected in isolated galaxies, whose H I footprint generally extends far beyond the optical disk; in this case, however, it is not surprising, as M100's outer quota of H I has probably already been stripped by its interaction with the cluster environment. The study of gas and dust distribution is important in understanding galaxy formation and evolution. The rate at which gas amasses and precipitates into stars regulates both the star formation history and chemical evolution of galaxies. Dust plays a key role by acting as a cooling "shade," shielding gas from ultraviolet radiation and providing the site at which H I can be converted into molecular hydrogen that then collapses into stars.

Amateur observers would do well to monitor M100 for supernovae. The galaxy has been host to at least five: 1901B, 1914A, 1959E, 1979C, and 2006X, the last one occurring inside the inner arm, SSW of the nucleus. Optical spectroscopic and photometric observations made between 10 days before and 91 days after the explosion showed that it had one of the highest expansion velocities ever recorded for a Type Ia, nearly 20,000 kilometers per second (Yamanaka et al., 2009).

In 1994, M100 earned the distinction of being the first galaxy to be imaged by the optically corrected Wide Field and

M85 Interacting Galaxy	NGC 4382 UGC 7508	RA 12ʰ 25ᵐ 24.1ˢ Dec +18° 11′ 28″ Mag 9.1 SB 12.9 Type Type SA(s)0⁺ pec Size 7.1′ x 5.5′ PA 5

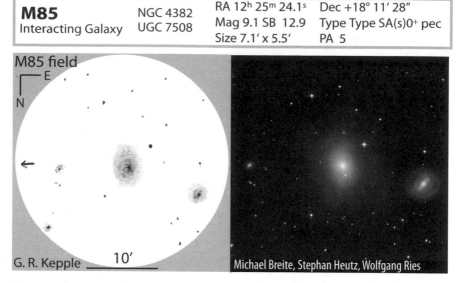

Figure 56: Messier 85. An eyepiece impression (left) compared to a photograph at right, courtesy ccdguide.com. The barred galaxy to the ESE is NGC 4394. IC 3292 lies on the opposite side.

Planetary Camera installed on the *Hubble Space Telescope*. The modified optics allowed *HST* to resolve the galaxy to an unprecedented level of clarity and sensisitivity. The space telescope went on to do the same for thousands of objects in the universe, both near and far.

M85
Interacting with neighboring NGC 4394

The general location of M85 is 10.6° west of Alpha Comae Berenices; more specifically, it is 1.2° NE of 11 Comae (magnitude 4.7), where it forms a physical pair with the barred spiral NGC 4394, just 8 arcminutes to the ENE. In 1781, the year Méchain discovered it, Messier described M85 as a "nebula without star" (one of his often-used descriptives). Follow-up observations by William Herschel in 1784 describe it and its neighbor to the east as "two resolvable nebulae." John Herschel observed it on at least three occasions, each time calling it very bright, round, and brighter toward the middle. As Robert Burnham Jr. points out, T. W. Webb referred to it as a "fair specimen of the many nebulae in this region." Hartung was a bit more expansive: "M85 is a conspicuous hazy ellipse with faint envelope about 3' x 2' in pa. 25°, the central parts much brighter and showing a broad band in the prism. Large instruments show traces of spiral structure." Heber D. Curtis first noted the spiral structure Hartung refers to in photographic plates taken with the Crossley reflector at Lick Observatory (Curtis 1918).

In small telescopes (6 inches or less), M85 is a small ovoid with a stellar-like nucleus, elongated north to south and punctuated by a magnitude 12 star situated just NNE of the nucleus. NGC 4394 appears in the same field to the ENE as a chalky bar with a flattened halo, elongated NW to SE. Telescopes of greater aperture render M85 as a disk embedded in a translucent halo but nothing in the way of outer disk features. Some 3 arcminutes SE of the nucleus floats a magnitude 10.4 star (BD+18 2609). Steve Gottlieb, using a 17.5-inch, describes the galaxy as "very bright, moderately large, with a small very bright core." I would add that, in a 15-inch, the core has a decided granular appearance and is, perhaps, slightly brighter to the NE. Deep images tell a more intriguing story by revealing a disturbed halo, particularly to the NE and SW. In the *Reference Catalog of Bright Galaxies* (1964), Gérard de Vaucouleurs wrote: "Extremely bright, diffuse nucleus. Weak, smooth whorls in a lens. Very faint diametric distortion toward the south." He classified it as peculiar.

M85 is a northern outlier of the Virgo Cluster, the center of which lies 6° south. It is a luminous lenticular system, some 16 to 17 megaparsecs distant and has clearly interacted with neighboring NGC 4394, which lies at a projected distance of about 40 kiloparsecs from M85. Evidence for an interaction comes in a number of forms. Although classified a lenticular, the galaxy exhibits some vague swirly spiral structure just outside of its bright central region (**Figure 57**). Photographic surface photometry (Burstein 1979) showed that NGC 4394 and M85 share a common envelope and that M85 is tidally distorted by its smaller companion. M85's major axis rotates with increasing distance from its center until some of the outermost isophotes are diamond-shaped (King 1978), with one edge touching NGC 4394. Their line-of-sight velocity differences are essentially zero, indicating that the two form a bound double galaxy.

An imaging search for structure in elliptical and S0 galaxies (Schweizer and Seitzer, 1988) delineated about a dozen irregular arc-shaped shells in the galaxy's outer envelope as well as a northern plume. These ripples are similar to those seen in NGC 474 (Arp 227) in Pisces. They probably do not originate with the galaxy but consist of extraneous material deposited by a merging galaxy. Images show that the ripples are bluer than the underlying galaxy and that they tend to overlap on opposite sides of the nucleus with increasing radius. Such an overlapping pattern is at odds with spiral arms induced by circulating density waves (such as those in M51). Numerical simulations based on accretion, however, provide a more natural explanation. Moreover, the observed ripples pitch in the opposite direction from inner spiral arms. In other words, while one ripple may approach the nucleus clockwise, the diffuse spiral arm may approach the nucleus from the opposite direction. The capture and accretion of a smaller galaxy several billion years ago could have induced a ring-like vibration in the disk as a series of rebounds of the intruder's stellar material as it sloshed back and forth in the galaxy's gravitational potential. We encountered this phenomenon, called phase wrapping, with NGC 5128 in Centaurus.

Might there be incontrovertible evidence for a remnant of this accreted galaxy? Searches of photometric and spectroscopic data from the Sloan Digital Sky Survey (Sandoval et al., 2015) turned up an "ultracompact dwarf" (UCD), M85-HCC1, floating 0.6 arcminute (3.3 kiloparsecs) SSW of M85 (in the galaxy's halo) with a similar recession velocity. The object's size is comparable to a typical globular cluster (1 to 2 parsecs in radius) but is much more luminous ($M_V \sim -12.5$). It is by far the densest free-floating stellar system known and is equivalent to the densest known star clusters. (Another UCD was found in M60, in Virgo.)

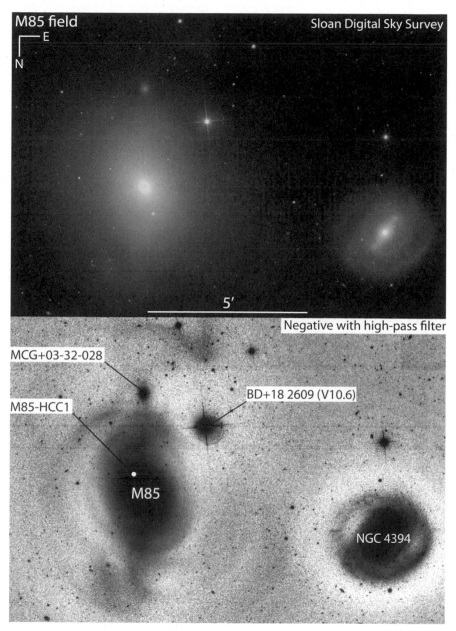

Figure 57: Messier 85 field. Sloan Digital Sky Survey (SDSS) images reveal subtle structure in the region around M85, including the ultra-compact dwarf M85-HCC1, suggesting past interactions with other galaxies.

The formation process of UCDs is unknown, although a number of scenarios have been proposed. Some astronomers suggest that they are the high end of the globular cluster mass function observed around galaxies with rich globular cluster systems. Another idea is that they are dwarf ellipticals stripped by tidal interactions leaving only their central nuclei, a mechanism referred to as threshing. The nearest example of a nucleated dwarf elliptical is NGC 205, companion to M31 in Andromeda. Although they are rare, they are typically found in the crowded environs of galaxy clusters. M85-HCC1 is relatively young (about 3 billion years) and exhibits a metal abundance resembling those of galaxy centers. Given that M85 exhibits large-scale perturbations, it is possible that this dense object is the remnant nucleus of a recently accreted galaxy.

There is some debate as to whether M85 harbors a central black hole. The surface brightness profile as a function of radius indicates a core at the center and a possible black hole of 100 million solar masses (Kormendy and Bender, 2009). *HST* images do show the nucleus to be double (similar to M31), which suggests the presence of a nuclear eccentric stellar disk resulting from a recent merger. But the velocity dispersion profile of the nucleus, which would indicate the orbital velocities of stars in the immediate vicinity of a high-mass object, does not support a black hole (Gültekin et al., 2011). Another study, this one searching for radio emissions of a central massive black hole (Capetti et al., 2009), was also unable to detect the telltale signature of a black hole's beating heart in M85. If one does abide in the galaxy's core, its mass would probably not exceed 65 million solar masses.

On January 7, 2006, a curious object turned up in an optical image of M85 made by the Lick Observatory supernova search team (Kulkarni et al., 2007, **Figure 58**). The unfiltered magnitude was about 19.3 at a projected 2.3 kiloparsecs (about 30 arcseconds) from the center of the galaxy. It was christened Optical Transient 2006-1 (OT2006-1). The object peaked at an absolute *I*-band magnitude of about −13. The light curve, with a plateau of 60 days, was unlike that of a type Ia supernova, and its duration was too short for a luminous blue variable outburst like Eta Car-

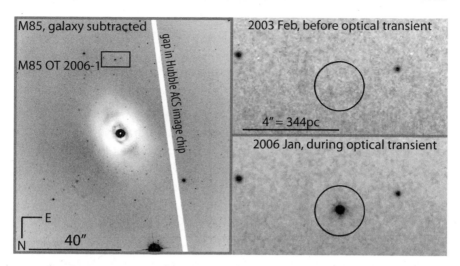

Figure 58: M85 OT (Optical Transient) 2006-1. In 2006 the Lick Observatory Supernova Search discovered an optical transient in M85, though it was not a supernova. Later, Ofek et al., 2008, studied the field with the *Hubble Space Telescope* and compared it with a pre-transient, high-resolution image in the *Hubble* ar-

inae. The following day a spectrum was obtained, though no emission features were detected; a spectrum taken February 3 was similarly featureless, though it unfortunately, did not cover Hα. By February 23 and 24 a number of emission lines were readily detected, probably because of increased sensitivity. The strongest lines were Hα and Hβ, with a peak recession velocity each of about 880 ±130 kilometers per second, in agreement with that of M85 (about 730 km/s). An interesting characteristic of the transient was its strong infrared excess that developed in the eruption's aftermath, with the peak emission evolving toward progressively longer wavelengths. Six months after its discovery, *Spitzer* observations (Rau et al., 2007) showed it to have a 1,000 K blackbody spectral energy distribution and bolometric luminosity some 300,000 times that of the Sun.

The transient's age, based on its stellar environment, was estimated at over a billion years and its progenitor mass less than 2 $M_\odot$ (Ofek et al., 2008). The age estimate resonates well with the age determined for M85. A study of the UBV colors of galaxies in de Vaucouleurs' *Second Reference Catalogue of Bright*

Galaxies (Schweizer and Seitzer, 1992) showed that M85 is somewhat bluer than typical S0 galaxies, and therefore possibly younger. This assumption was supported by a spectroscopic study (Terlevich and Forbes, 2002) that yielded a relative age of 1.6 billion years for M85.

The spectral and temporal properties of OT2006-1 resembled that of two other objects known at the time: M31-RV (1988) and V838 Mon (2002), a small class of objects collectively referred to as luminous red novae (LRN).[*] On average, their total energy output falls into a range between 10^{45} and 10^{47} ergs, greater than a nova but just below that of type Ia supernovae. This excess infrared emission is attributed to condensation of newly formed dust in the expelled envelope around the progenitor star. The startling *HST* images of V838 Mon beginning in 2002 showed light from the outburst echoing off surrounding dust. By 2009, the star's B3 dwarf companion was totally engulfed in opaque dusty ejecta.

For a number of years, astronomers mused upon several theories to explain LRN: a merger of two stars, mass accretion onto a main-sequence dwarf from an asymptotic giant branch star, or some unusual supernova mechanism. The mystery was apparently resolved by the V1309 Sco outburst in 2008. This object was observed before its outburst and found to be a contact binary; afterward it was a single object, indicating a merger had occurred. Still, not everyone is on board with this idea and more observations are needed (Pastorello et al., 2007; Todd et al., 2008).

In the last decade or so, many other similar eruptive events have been observed and the list of LRN is growing. The estimated Galactic rate for mergers is fairly common: 0.1 a year for fainter events like V1309 Sco, and 0.03 a year for brighter events like V838 Mon (Kochanek et al., 2014). Observers take heed. The discovery of an LRN may be in your future.

---

[*] They are also referred to as intermediate luminosity red transients, intermediate luminosity optical transients (ILOTs), V838 Mon-like events, and supernova impostors.

M88 Seyfert 2 Galaxy	NGC 4501 UGC 7675	RA 12ʰ 31ᵐ 59.0ˢ Dec +14° 25' 11" Mag 9.6 SB 12.8 Type SA(rs)b Size 6.7' x 3.7' PA 140

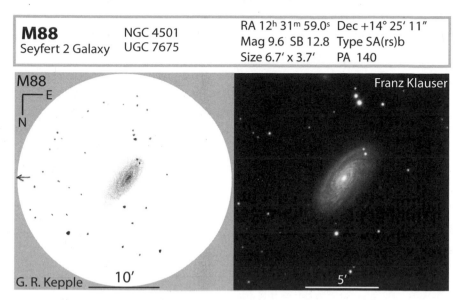

Figure 59: Messier 88. An eyepiece impression (left) compared to a photograph at right, courtesy ccdguide.com.

M88

Bright Seyfert 2 galaxy; double-peaked nucleus

M88 lies in the thick of the Realm of the Galaxies, 51 arcminutes west of M91. Evidence of this may be appreciated if you slew a little over a degree south and west to Markarian's Chain, a procession of galaxies that form a graceful arch across the sky. The brightest members consist of two galaxies in Coma Berenices (NGC 4477 and NGC 4473) and several systems in Virgo (NGC 4461, NGC 4435, NGC 4438, M86, and M84).

M88 is among the brighter spiral galaxies in the Virgo Cluster, with a compact central region out of which swirls a complex multiarmed spiral structure. It's a fascinating study in telescopes of all sizes. Luginbuhl and Skiff note that the halo is distinctly elongated in a 6-centimeter telescope. A 10-inch telescope shows a 6-arcminute outer disk with brighter oval nucleus; both are elongated NW to SE. Averted vision shows the outer disk brushed in subtle contrasts, particularly on the NE and SW sides; these features are greatly enhanced in a 15-inch, endowing both disk and nucleus with much better visual presence. The core is well-defined and bright. Steve Gottlieb, observing with a 48-inch telescope, notes, "A thin spiral arm was clearly visible extending along the entire western flank of the halo and stretching 4.5' from NW to SE. This arm separates more cleanly from the central region as it extends south, reaching a wide double star . . . that is superimposed on the southeast end. A fainter, very thin, straight arm was also visible along the east side of the galaxy, extending towards the northwest. This arm hugs pretty close to the east side of the core, and separates a bit on the north side." Incidentally, the fainter southern component of the wide double star Gottlieb mentions has a close companion (magnitude 16) discovered by Brian Skiff in 2007. At the time, the position angle was 257° and the separation 2 arcseconds.

Charles Messier discovered M88 in 1781, chalking it up as another "nebula without stars." R. J. Mitchell, one of Lord Rosse's stable of observing assistants, noted on March 9, 1855: "Another spiral? dark spaces p[preceding] Nucl, others also, especially one s f [south following] Nucl." Eight nights later he wrote, "Thought I could trace a dark passage from south end down past the Nucl. Saw but the one branch of neby outside this passage." Smyth deemed it a long elliptical nebula, on the outer side of Virgo's left wing. "It is pale-white, and trends in a line bearing *np* and *sf*; and with its attendant stars, forms a pretty pageant. The lower or N. part in the inverted field is brighter than the S, a circumstance which, with its spindle figure, opens a large field for conjecture." The nature of spiral nebulae would baffle astronomers well into the twentieth century.

If we accept a distance estimate of 19 megaparsecs, the visible disk is about 38.5 kiloparsecs across its major axis. It is inclined at an angle of about 30° and dominated by dust all the way to the center, where it exhibits the hint of an open inner pseudoring. The outer arms on the galaxy's SW side are examples of "fossil" spiral arms, remnant features containing mostly old or spent stars that are gradually beginning to disperse hundreds of millions of years after a massive burst of star formation. The nucleus is classified as a Seyfert 2, one whose spectrum shows narrow emission lines — as opposed to the spectrum of

Seyfert 1 galaxies, which also shows broadened emission lines indicative of rapidly moving hot gas. (Both Seyfert 1 and 2 galaxies may essentially be the same type of object except viewed from different vantage points. Whereas our line of sight allows us to observe the broadline region of type 1 Seyferts, with type 2 Seyferts, the galaxy's inclination or obscuring dust prevents this.)

Being immersed in the Virgo Cluster environment, M88 manifests evidence of ram pressure stripping and compression of its interstellar medium. Radio maps of the galaxy's CO footprint (Nehlig et al., 2016) found strongly polarized emission in the SE region due to its plunge through the dense intracluster medium. The compressed region is oriented toward M87, indicating this is the galaxy's first penetration into the cluster (**Figure 60**). Unlike gravitational tides, ram pressure does not always disturb the galaxy's stellar disk, but the resulting compression can stimulate star formation on relatively short timecales. (On longer timescales, several billion years, the dense cluster environment quenches star formation.)

The central region of M88 has long been of interest since it is known to have a high degree of gas condensation for a galaxy without an apparent visual bar (but see below). Spectroscopic observations found chemically distinct metal-rich nuclei in both M88 and NGC 4216 in Virgo (Silchenko et al., 1999). The solar magnesium-to-iron ratios measured in their galactic nuclei suggest that a prolonged interval of secondary star-formation bursts produced the chemically distinct stellar subsystems. In another study (Merloni et al., 2003), analysis of archival radio and X-ray data found that M88 possesses a supermassive black hole with an estimated mass of nearly 80 million suns.

High-resolution interferometric observations of the CO emission in the central 5 kiloparsecs of the galaxy reached even deeper by revealing a nuclear concentration within a radius of 390 parsecs that is double-peaked and has a gas mass of 130 million $M_\odot$ (Onodera et al., 2004). The double peaks are being supplied by inflow from the spiral arms but have a low star-forming efficiency, since no star-forming ring is seen near the double peaks. The inefficiency may arise from the gravitational

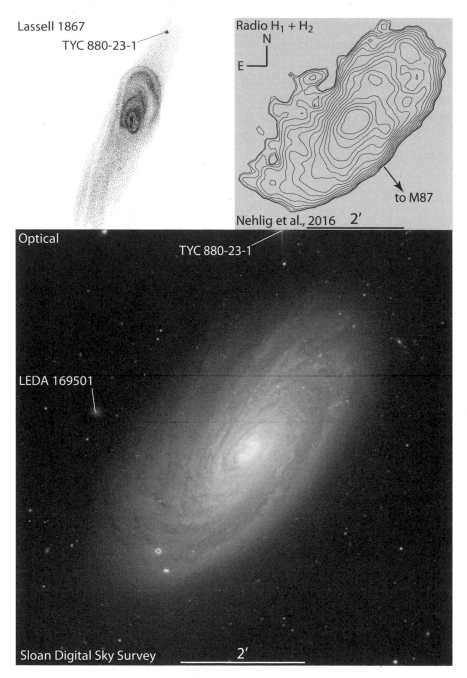

Figure 60: Three other views of Messier 88. A Lassell engraving, a radio map showing the ram pressure stripping of the Virgo Galaxy cluster from the southwest, and a Sloan Digital Sky Survey image. It clearly shows the dual nature of the companion in the wide double star in the SE part of the disk.

stability of the gas, owing to a low gas-to-dynamical mass ratio. The peaks are separated by 4.7 arcseconds (about 370 parsecs) and are located on the roots of the nuclear spiral dust lanes imaged by *HST* (Carollo et al., 1998). The dual peaks may be related to a small, 15-arcsecond bar revealed in near-infrared K-band images (Elmegreen et al., 1999).

M88 has one of the higher recessional velocities of bright Virgo Cluster galaxies, over 2,200 kilometers per second.

NGC 4839

Extensive cD envelope

Being situated between a magnitude 11.6 star 2.7° to the NE and a magnitude 14 star 2.4 arcminutes to the SW helps a little in pinpointing this Coma Cluster galaxy for those without computer control. Its location some 43 arcminutes from the cluster's center, however, is unusual. Even in large telescopes, the galaxy presents a small (1-arcminute) elongated concentration in a diffuse halo. Images reveal the presence of a curious knot 26 arcseconds SW of the nucleus. This is actually a faint back-

NGC 4839 Radio Galaxy	LEDA 44298	RA 12ʰ 57ᵐ 24.4ˢ Dec +27° 29′ 51″	
		Mag 12.1 SB 14.3	Type cD
		Size 4.0′ x 1.9′	PA 65

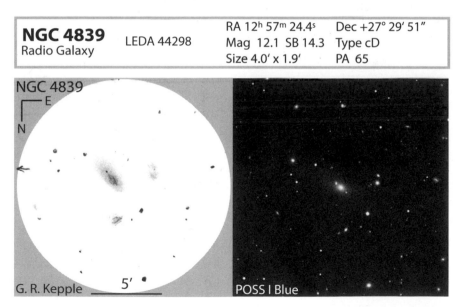

Figure 61: NGC 4839. An eyepiece impression (left) compared to a photograph at right.

ground galaxy. Brightness profiles show that the galaxy has a prominent extended cD envelope. NGC 4839 lies adjacent to NGC 4842A and NGC 4842B, just 2.6 arcminutes to the east. The surrounding field contains a scattering of fainter galaxies. Multiwavelength analyses and velocity studies indicate this galaxy and its surrounding group is falling into the Coma Cluster (Adami et al., 2005) at a distance of 93 megaparsecs. X-ray observations (Neumann et al., 2001) found indications of a bow shock and ram pressure stripping around the system. The infall produces merger-induced turbulence, which in turn endows this galaxy with a radio tail.

NGC 4676, The Mice

Interacting galaxies with remarkable tidal tails

William Herschel discovered NGC 4676 in 1785, describing it as faint and much extended. Neither he nor John Herschel, who made a single observation, apparently recognized the system's dual nature. Russian astronomer Boris Vorontsov-Velyaminov nicknamed this strongly interacting pair of spiral galaxies "the Mice" in 1958, and the name has stuck ever since. The tail of the northern galaxy, NGC 4676A, is narrow, nearly straight, and punctuated with knots of star formation, while that of NGC 4676B is more diffuse. The dust lane arcs from 4676A into 4676B, where it amasses along that galaxy's northeastern flank in a knot before sweeping toward the south in a mane of blue stars. The pair was one of Alar and Juri Toomre's first computer simulations of a galaxy interaction (1972). They deduced that the most telling feature was 4676A's tail: "Its straightness, together with its near collinearity both with the ragged dust lane and the major axis of its parent galaxy, indicates not only that we must be viewing hulk* A almost equatorially but also that the encounter must must have [been] one of low inclination to that galaxy itself. Hence our view of the combined 4676 seems, fortuitously, to be from a direction that lies nearly in the orbit plane as well."

---

* "Hulk" is a term used to define the remnant galaxy.

NGC 4676 AB Interacting Galaxies	Arp 242 IC 819 + IC 820	RA 12ʰ 46ᵐ 10.7ˢ Dec +30° 43′ 39″	
		Mag 13.1/13.8 SB 13.5/14.2	Interacting pair
		Size 2.3′ x 0.7′ / 2.2′ x 0.8′ PA 0° / 2°	

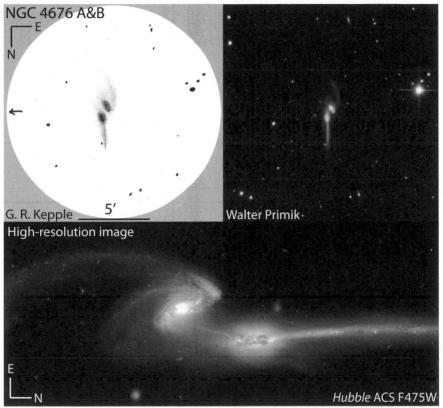

Figure 62: NGC 4676 AB, The Mice galaxies. An eyepiece impression (left) is compared to a photograph at right, courtesy ccdguide.com. A high-resolution Hubble Legacy Archive image shows richer detail (bottom). The galaxies are also known collectively as Arp 242 (see **Figure 63**).

The Toomres point out that the dust lane should not deceive observers into thinking that the straight tail attaches to the near side of A. As demonstrated by Geoffrey and Margaret Burbidge (1961) and others, the opposite is true: 4676A is edge-on (or nearly so) with its north end receding and south end approaching, relative to the galaxy's velocity. Spectroscopic observations confirm that 4676A rotates in that sense, while 4676B's axis points nearly at the observer and the disk rotates in a counterclockwise direction, with the northeastern edge receding.

At a distance of 95 megaparsecs, the Mice represent a nearby example of a major gas-rich prograde merger, where the roughly equal mass of both galaxies, and the coincidence of the sense of rotation and orbital motion, have led to lengthy tidal tails (Wild et al., 2014). The presence of these tails and an obvious bridge between the two galaxies indicates that the impact of the first passage, which occurred some 170 million years ago (Barnes 2004), significantly transformed the morphology, creating strong bars in both galaxies. Optical spectroscopy shows that the barred spiral NGC 4676B exhibits a strong twist in both its stellar and ionized gas disk, while 4676A, which appears to be bulge-free, has a strong bar that endows it with a boxy light profile. Strong outflows, similar to superwinds from ultraluminous infrared galaxies, have been detected issuing from 4676A, even though it has a modest infrared luminosity of $3 \times 10^{10} L_\odot$. Apparently, energy beyond what is provided by star formation appears to drive the outflow. In fact, simulations show little enhancement in star formation during and following the first passage, which is in agreement with observations. Perhaps the outflow is provided by a source that has since "switched off," like an active galactic nucleus or more intense starburst activity during the first passage.

The magnitudes of these two galaxies are not very inviting to observers with apertures less than about 20 inches, which may explain the dearth of available visual observations. Some observers report that even in a 17.5-inch, the tails of either galaxy cannot be seen. Barbara Wilson, using a 20-inch, could easily distinguish both galaxies as luminous ovals, with the southern component's nucleus appearing stellar. She could also see the long, straight tail from 4676A but not 4676B. In a 25-inch, Dave Tosteson notes that 4676B is smaller and brighter than 4676A, but the latter galaxy's tail is more noticeable. Steve Gottlieb, viewing the pair in a 48-inch, reports that the northern tail has a high surface brightness and extends some 80 arcseconds before fading entirely. The southern tail, he adds, was not clearly resolved. Hence, even in a telescope with that aperture,

Arp's *Atlas of Peculiar Galaxies* images in Coma Berenices

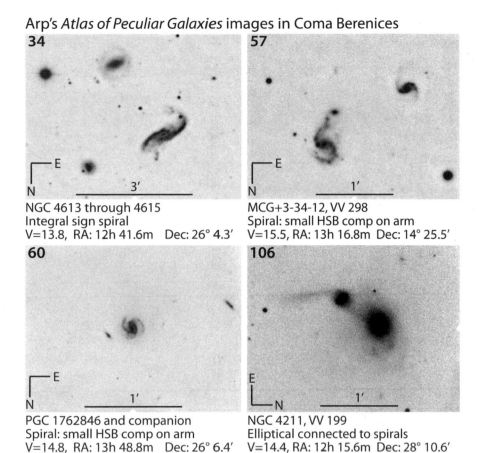

34

E
N   3'

NGC 4613 through 4615
Integral sign spiral
V=13.8, RA: 12h 41.6m   Dec: 26° 4.3'

57

E
N   1'

MCG+3-34-12, VV 298
Spiral: small HSB comp on arm
V=15.5, RA: 13h 16.8m Dec: 14° 25.5'

60

E
N   1'

PGC 1762846 and companion
Spiral: small HSB comp on arm
V=14.8, RA: 13h 48.8m   Dec: 26° 6.4'

106

E
N   1'

NGC 4211, VV 199
Elliptical connected to spirals
V=14.4, RA: 12h 15.6m Dec: 28° 10.6'

Figure 63: Arp galaxies in Coma Berenices. In 1966, Halton Arp published his *Atlas of Peculiar Galaxies*, including these fields. Fourteen fields from the *Atlas* are in Coma Berenices, a constellation rich in bright galaxies. Arp sought to collect and organize images of peculiar galaxies in the hope that they might provide insights into the nature of galaxy evolution; consequently, his collection has been exhaustively studied. The Arp catalog number appears at the upper left in each panel with additional identifying information appearing below each image. Readers interested in learning more about Arp galaxies and the *Atlas* may refer to *The Arp Atlas of Peculiar Galaxies: A Chronicle and Observer's Guide*, by Jeff Kanipe and Dennis Webb (Willmann-Bell, 2010). *Atlas* images are courtesy Barry Madore

the Mice are problematic. The system may be a subject best left to imagers or armchair amateur astronomers.

Arp Galaxies in Coma Berenices

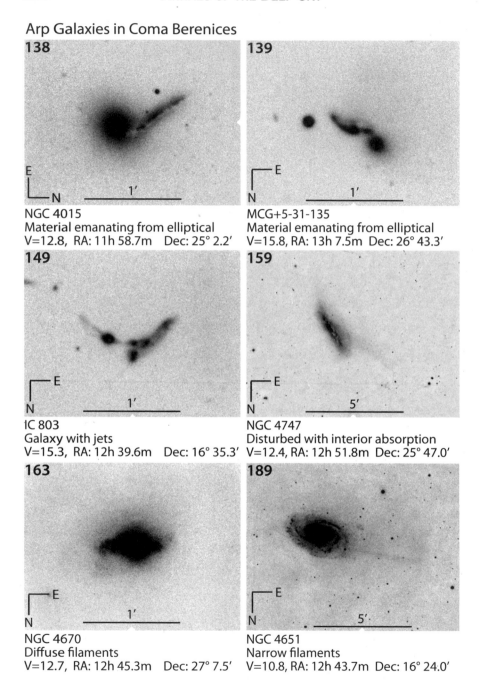

138

NGC 4015
Material emanating from elliptical
V=12.8, RA: 11h 58.7m   Dec: 25° 2.2'

139

MCG+5-31-135
Material emanating from elliptical
V=15.8, RA: 13h 7.5m Dec: 26° 43.3'

149

IC 803
Galaxy with jets
V=15.3, RA: 12h 39.6m   Dec: 16° 35.3'

159

NGC 4747
Disturbed with interior absorption
V=12.4, RA: 12h 51.8m Dec: 25° 47.0'

163

NGC 4670
Diffuse filaments
V=12.7, RA: 12h 45.3m   Dec: 27° 7.5'

189

NGC 4651
Narrow filaments
V=10.8, RA: 12h 43.7m Dec: 16° 24.0'

Figure 64: More Arp galaxies in Coma Berenices. Arps 159 and 189 are larger fields, amenable to imaging. *Atlas* images are courtesy Barry Madore of Caltech.

Arp Galaxies in Coma Berenices

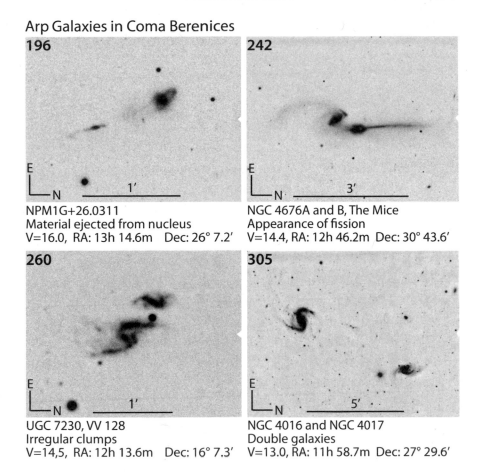

196

NPM1G+26.0311
Material ejected from nucleus
V=16.0, RA: 13h 14.6m   Dec: 26° 7.2'

242

NGC 4676A and B, The Mice
Appearance of fission
V=14.4, RA: 12h 46.2m Dec: 30° 43.6'

260

UGC 7230, VV 128
Irregular clumps
V=14,5, RA: 12h 13.6m   Dec: 16° 7.3'

305

NGC 4016 and NGC 4017
Double galaxies
V=13.0, RA: 11h 58.7m Dec: 27° 29.6'

Figure 65: Still more Arp galaxies in Coma Berenices. Arps 242 (The Mice) and 305 are larger fields, amenable to imaging. *Atlas* images are courtesy Barry Madore of Caltech.

The Coma Cluster

One of the largest galaxy clusters known

Also known as Abell 1656, the Coma Cluster is our next stop as we venture into a more remote realm of the cosmos, some 100 megaparsecs from the Sun, still a minuscule percentage of the span of the observable universe. The general part of the sky we'll be exploring lies 2.7° east of Beta Comae, very near the North Galactic Pole. We profile two of the most prominent galaxies in the Coma Cluster as our introduction to this vast structure, which plays an essential role in understanding the formation of large-scale structure in the universe.

NGC 4889 and NGC 4874

Two supergiant elliptical galaxies

NGC 4889 is the brightest galaxy in the Coma Cluster, and, along with NGC 4874 just 7.2 arcminutes to the west, marks the center of the galactic conglomerate. Two magnitude 7 field stars, HD 112734 and HD 112887, point SE directly between the two galaxies and thus make good pilot stars. Both galaxies are easily visible in telescopes of all sizes, but if any region of the sky benefits from large apertures, this is the place. A 15-inch renders NGC 4889 as small, bright, and slightly elongated, while NGC 4874 is decidedly fainter and more spherical. These two galaxies attract the eye immediately, but take a careful look around. Both fields are suffused with a swarm of noticeable fluff of surrounding galaxies (**Figure 66**). With increasing aperture, more of these galactic snowflakes rise above the background. Some of the brightest in the immediate vicinity include NGC 4921 and NGC 4911, 19 arcminutes to the SE; NGC 4944, 54 arcminutes to the ENE; NGC 4841A and B, 41 arcminutes to the NW; and NGC 4839, 43 arcminutes to the SW.

Because these two dominant galaxies are in such proximity to each other, and as the distribution of X-ray gas shows, Coma is classified as a binary cluster. Both galaxies are classified as type cD, meaning extra large elliptical galaxies in clusters. Such voluminous systems are often referred to as "brightest cluster members," or BCMs, particularly when morphology is not taken into consideration. BCMs are of intense interest for a number of reasons, though two stand out. First, their high luminosities enable them to be used as standard candles in cosmological studies. Second, their large masses and locations near the centers of galaxy clusters mean they are sites of interesting evolutionary and dynamical phenomena, which we will get to later.

NGC 4889 Galaxy in Group	UGC 8110 LEDA 44715	RA 13h 00m 08.0s Mag 11.5 SB 13.3 Size 2.8' x 2.0'	Dec +27° 57' 36" Type cD4 PA 80
NGC 4874 Radio Galaxy	UGC 8103 LEDA 44628	RA 12h 59m 36.1s Mag 11.7 SB 13.1 Size 1.9' x 1.9'	Dec +27° 57' 35" Type cD0 PA –

NGC 4889 & NGC 4874 field

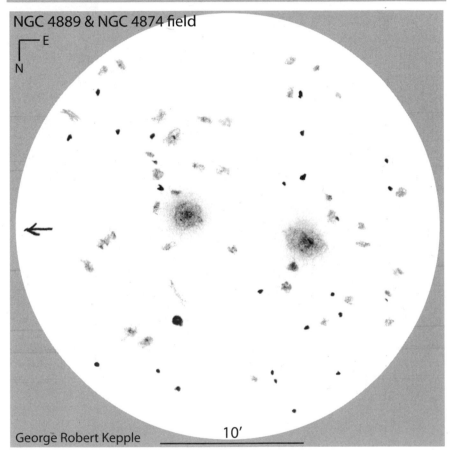

George Robert Kepple   10'

Figure 66: Coma galaxies surrounding the field of NGC 4889 and NGC 4874. An eyepiece impression using a large Dobsonian telescope shows a field rich with galaxies.

Discovered by William Herschel in 1785, NGC 4889 was mistakenly observed as a different object, NGC 4884, by Heinrich Louis d'Arrest in 1865. Harold Corwin tells us that, apart from the offset in right ascension measured on one night,

NGC 4889 & NGC 4874 field

Walter Primik

Figure 67: NGC 4889 and NGC 4874 near the center of the Coma Galaxy Cluster. Photograph courtesy ccdguide.com.

d'Arrest's description is essentially correct: "brightest of a multiple nebula...." The confusion is understandable, considering Coma's rich, dense field. D'Arrest is sometimes credited with recognizing the Coma Cluster as being a physical assemblage; in an 1865 paper in *Astronomische Nachrichten*, his description comes very near to calling it as such. Under favorable conditions, d'Arrest wrote, he could see an extraordinary number of nebulae in his telescope in this region:

> The nebulae . . . are incredibly numerous and dense, and although very faint, they have a diversity that one cannot imagine a priori. Sometimes, in the most favorable moments, I have

Wolf's Image of the Coma Galaxy Cluster (detail)

HD 112734
HD 112886
plate artifacts
HD 112887
NGC 4889
NGC 4874
NGC 4921
10'
N
E

Figure 68: Wolf's image of the core of the Coma Galaxy Cluster. Max Wolf used the Bruce double astrograph, in Heidelberg, Germany, in 1901 to photograph the dense area of "nebulae" known from the *New General Catalogue*. He found many new small, faint nebulae across the 24x30-cm plate. Here, we see a small region of this plate, which Wolf labeled "nebelhaufen" or cluster of nebulae. He made two plates simultaneously, as the purpose of a "double astrograph" is to produce two images to rule out plate defects. This plate, B165a, was not annotated, but the other, B164a (next figure) was exhaustively marked to show the newly discovered nebulae that we now know to be galaxies in a cluster. Image courtesy Heidelberg Digitized Astronomical Plates (HDAP), which was produced at Landessternwarte Heidelberg-Königstuhl under grant No. 00.071.2005 of the Klaus-Tschira-Foundation.

had the very definite impression that the nebulae, often only a few arcseconds in diameter, are intermingled with larger, round, oblong, star-shaped or cometary ones, like oysters packed together in a barrel.

In professional literature, however, credit for the discovery usually goes to German astronomer Max Wolf, who in March

1901 was the first person to capture the Coma Cluster's jumble of galaxies in a photographic survey using the 16-inch Bruce double astrograph at the Heidelberg Observatory (**Figure 68**). He cataloged 108 galaxies in what he called a "nebelhaufen" (see sidebar on Max Wolf, page 243).

This entire region has long been recognized as a veritable galactic cornucopia. William Herschel called it "the nebulous stratum of Coma Berenices," adding that "I have fully ascertained the existence and direction of the stratum for more than 30 degrees of a great circle and found it to be almost every where equally rich in fine nebulae." There was no way for him to know that he was dimly perceiving one of the first of many large-scale structures in the universe stretching across space for hundreds of millions of light-years.[*] Heber D. Curtis expanded Wolf's 108 members to over 300 in 1918. Shapley (1934) thought it might be associated with "an extensive metagalactic cloud," though others (Shane and Wirtanen, 1954) argued that it was an isolated structure that blended into the background sky at a radius of 2°. Fritz Zwicky (1957), who doubted the existence of super-large-scale structures, nonetheless estimated the cluster extended to a projected radius of 6°, corresponding to a distance of about 10 megaparsecs. George Abell (1961) followed up with his measurements and suggested that the cluster is one of six members comprising a supercluster extending nearly 64 megaparsecs. The actual distance is on the order of 100 megaparsecs.

The Coma Cluster is one of the most-often studied galaxy clusters in the sky; the SIMBAD database lists over 3,800 references between 1850 and 2018. It is also one of the richest, with at least 650 confirmed members. If you include dwarf systems, the population surpasses 2,000; and if you include the recently discovered population of ultra-diffuse galaxies (which we will get to), one may include at least 1,000 more. It has long been considered the archetypal rich cluster, one that appears regular and roughly spherical with a strong central condensation. Its shape and regularity suggest that the cluster has achieved

---

[*] To be clear, Herschel was referring to the northern part of the Local Supercluster, which is much nearer than the Coma Cluster. Hence the Coma Cluster itself actually plays no role in Herschel's "stratum" of nebulae.

Wolf's annotations on the other plate, B164a

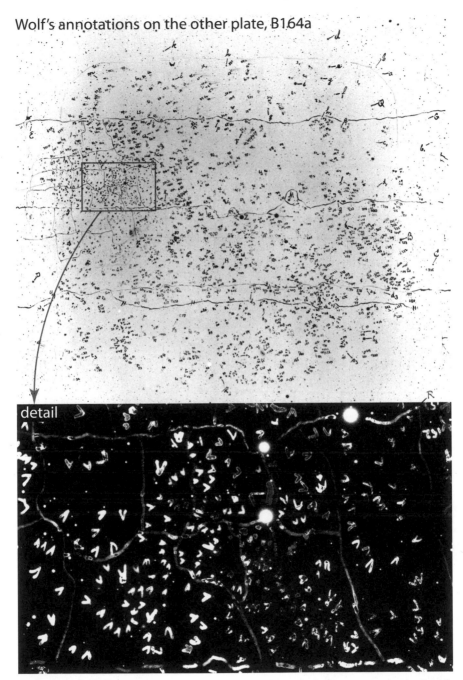

Figure 69: Wolf's annotated plate B164a. Objects of interest are marked with a ">" symbol. Positive detail at the bottom includes the field of the previous figure. Image is also courtesy HDAP.

dynamical equilibrium, and is therefore accessible to straight-forward theoretical analysis. Studies over the last few decades, however, have shown the cluster is far from relaxed. Research into the complexity of this dynamic system has led to many insights into the process of cluster formation and the nature of matter at the largest scales. Zwicky showed in 1933 that the motions of some of the visible members of the Coma Cluster were too rapid to remain bound based on their apparent mass alone. The mass had to be many times greater than what their luminosity suggested. This was the first inkling that the cluster contained vast amounts of dark matter, an idea that would not be accepted for at least a half century.

Overall Structure

Subclusters are common in many galaxy clusters, and there are at least four in Coma. NGC 4874 and NGC 4889 comprise two. The third most dominant galaxy in the cluster, NGC 4839 (another cD system), constitutes yet another subcluster. A fourth has been identified with the giant spiral NGC 4911. NGC 4839 exhibits a radio tail that points away from main cluster, indicating that it may be entering Coma for the first time from the direction of the nearby cluster Abell 1367 and is passing through a dense region of the intracluster medium (Neumann 2001).

The distribution of these subclusters — the basic units that make up the larger cluster — reflects the associated filamentary distribution on a supercluster scale. Coma is the most conspic-uous cluster concentration situated in an elongated filament of galaxies that extends along a projected position angle of between 70° and 80°. Toward the SW, the filaments extend toward the nearby cluster Abell 1367, and to the NE the fila-ment can be traced to Abell 2197/2199.

A pioneering redshift survey published in 1978 (Gregory and Thompson) showed a definite bridge linking Coma with Abell 1367 (**Figure 70**). Their observations revealed the so-called "fingers of God," ridges in the galaxy redshifts that appeared to be pointing directly at the observer. Then, in 1986,

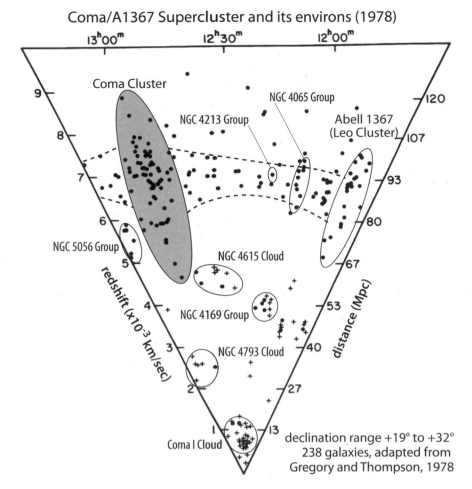

Coma/A1367 Supercluster and its environs (1978)

Coma Cluster

NGC 4065 Group

NGC 4213 Group

Abell 1367
(Leo Cluster)

NGC 5056 Group

NGC 4615 Cloud

NGC 4169 Group

NGC 4793 Cloud

redshift (x10⁻³ km/sec)

distance (Mpc)

Coma I Cloud

declination range +19° to +32°
238 galaxies, adapted from
Gregory and Thompson, 1978

Figure 70: The large-scale structure of the universe around the Coma Cluster. Throughout the 1970s and '80s, astronomers amassed increasingly larger data sets of redshift measurements that revealed greater large-scale structure. This diagram from 1978 shows the Coma Cluster embedded in what a decade later would be recognized as the Great Wall of Galaxies. Groups, clouds, and clusters of galaxies in Coma Berenices are labeled, including foreground structures; some such groupings do not have a standardized nomenclature, as there is uncertainty in the third dimension. Note the elongated "Finger of God" effect on the Coma Cluster and Abell 1367, a product of peculiar motions of individual galaxies that could not be factored out of the redshift-distance relation.

the Harvard Center for Astrophysics (CfA) bowled over the astronomical community with its redshift survey featuring 1,100 galaxies (de Lapparent, Geller, and Huchra). The iconic map showed the galaxy distribution arrayed into the shape of a bandy-legged stick figure superimposed on the Coma Cluster with "arms" extending for over 200 megaparsecs through the survey region (**Figure 71**). As more and more galaxies were surveyed, there was no doubt that the cluster was embedded in a decidedly filamentary skein punctuated by voids (Geller and Huchra, 1989).

The map prompted a wave of descriptives. Some proposed the cluster was a network of filaments of galaxies; others speculated that the galaxies were arrayed on the surface of bubble-like structures (and the filaments were artifacts produced by viewing slices through the bubbles). And of course, there was the "Great Wall" of galaxies, so named by Margaret J. Geller and John P. Huchra in *Science* (1989). They estimated this structure, which they characterized as "sheet-like" or "sponge-like," had dimensions of 7 by 85 by 214 megaparsecs. Whether the structures were filamentary, bubble-like, or planar in nature was up for grabs. It was, however, important to know since the topology of large-scale matter distribution is an important test of different models for the formation of structure in the universe (West 1998).

In a 1997 conference on the Coma Cluster,[*] astronomer Michael J. West made an interesting argument that the Great Wall in the CfA redshift survey was a filament of galaxies by comparing the axial ratios of the Great Wall to its namesake, the Great Wall of China. The Great Wall of China, he noted, is about 6,000 kilometers long, 7 meters high, and roughly 9 meters wide, for an approximate axial ratio of 1,000,000:1:1. The most prominent large-scale feature in the CfA survey extends at least 200 megaparsecs, yet is only 7 megaparsecs in projected thickness in its densest regions and 7 megaparsecs along the line of sight, corresponding to an approximate axial ratio 30:1:1. "Hence," West concluded, "a plausible argument can be made that, despite their names, both the Great 'Wall' of China and the Great 'Wall' of the Coma cluster are in reality highly elongated filamentary type structures!"

---

[*] *Untangling Coma Berenices: A New Vision of an Old Cluster*, proceedings of the meeting held in Marseilles (France), June 17–20, 1997, Eds.: A. Mazure, F. Casoli, F. Durret, and D. Gerbal, World Scientific Publishing Co Pte Ltd.

The Great Wall of Galaxies and the Stick Man (1989)

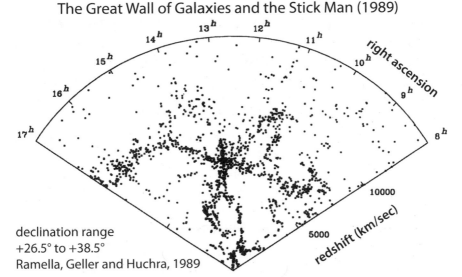

declination range
+26.5° to +38.5°
Ramella, Geller and Huchra, 1989

Figure 71: The CfA Great Wall of Galaxies and the Stick Man. The Harvard-Smithsonian Center for Astrophysics (CfA) measured redshifts of 1,766 galaxies and identified the Great Wall supercluster of galaxies, including a rough human-shaped stick figure, whose torso and head delineate the Coma Cluster; compare to the previous figure. The Great Wall is a filamentary structure perhaps 750 Mly long, 200 Mly wide and 16 Mly thick. **Contemplative observing:** On an early summer night, trace a path from Castor and Pollux in Gemini, through Cancer, Leo and Leo Minor, Coma Berenices, Boötes, Corona Borealis, and into Hercules. Consider that we have mapped a filament of galaxies along this distance, one of the largest structures we have detected in the observable universe.

The filamentary nature of the supercluster environment is also evident in the remarkable tendency for the major axes of rich clusters to point toward neighboring clusters over separations of 20 megaparsecs or more (Binggeli 1982). This is readily seen in the Coma Cluster, whose major axis lies along the same 70° to 80° position angle as the prominent filament that surrounds it. These alignments also seem to be imprinted on the cluster's galaxies at small scales. Studies have shown that the dominant central galaxies tend to share the same axial orientation as their parent cluster (Porter et al., 1991; West 1994). In the Coma Cluster, the orientations of NGC 4874 and NGC 4889 share the 70° to 80° PA with the Abell 1367 filament. Moreover, these alignments can sometimes be traced all the way to sub-kiloparsec distances from the galaxy center.

Modern observations and redshift surveys have gone a long way toward sorting out the Coma Cluster's environs and overall structure, as well as throwing light onto how clusters and superclusters form. Computer simulations show that, like elliptical galaxies, mergers build galaxy clusters from the anisotropic infall of material shepherded along the cluster's filaments, i.e. along preferred directions. In theory, this sort of infall may be a general phenomenon of numerous models of structure formation. It is therefore likely that over the course of the next few billion years, the Coma Cluster will continue engulfing a number of sizeable galaxy groups.

Morphological and Gaseous Inventory

As in most clusters of this size, the core consists of mostly elliptical and lenticular galaxies, with predominantly spiral galaxies along the outskirts. For the brightest 200 galaxies in the cluster, the assortment amounts to E:S0:Sp = 30:55:15 percent (Colless 2006). Variations in the morphological assortment can be seen in the galactic colors, with red galaxies amassing around the center and blue ones along the fringes. Some galaxies show evidence of recent star formation, which may have been triggered by interaction with the tidal field of the cluster or the intracluster medium as objects fell into the cluster.

It is difficult to discuss NGC 4889, the cluster's most luminous galaxy, without mentioning NGC 4874, since each comprises one nucleus of a binary cluster and is likely in the process of merging. But there are differences. NGC 4874 has an extended halo and is a strong radio source, while NGC 4889 possesses a modest halo and is radio quiet. NGC 4889's lack of a halo means that it has been tidally stripped in the merging process, and that NGC 4874's halo is probably in the process of being abraded as well.

Spectroscopic analysis (Coccato et al., 2010) found evidence for different chemical and star formation histories for stars near the center and in the halo of NGC 4889. Data for the inner galaxy are consistent with a rapid, dissipative merger early in the galaxy's formation, followed by one or a few "dry" mergers (mergers between gas-poor galaxies). Data for the halo indicates later

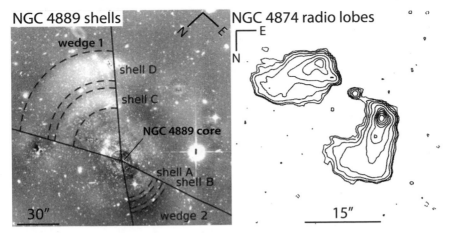

Figure 72: Inner structures of the Coma Cluster's core galaxies. NGC 4889, left, harbors faint shells, likely remnants of a merger with another galaxy, courtesy Gu et al., 2013. Its partner, NGC 4874, features two radio tails, a product of jets emerging from the inner core, courtesy Feretti and Giovanni, 1987.

accretion of stars from old systems with more extended star formation histories. Complimenting this study are photometric observations (Gu et al., 2013) that revealed four stellar shells (**Figure 72**) within NGC 4889, each well aligned with the major axis and bluer than the underlying stars. The shells A, B, C, and D lie at radii of 14, 17.5, 23, and 35 kiloparsecs from the center, respectively, with the first two shells located NE of the galaxy and the latter two on the SW side; the innermost shells are thinner than the outer ones. The unique environment within the central region, as well as the lack of dust features, suggests that the shells formed through a nondissipative merger event, probably with a small satellite galaxy. The mass from the disrupted satellite remains in the shell structures.

High-resolution radio observations of NGC 4874 obtained with the Very Large Array at 20 and 6 centimeters (Feretti and Giovanni, 1987) found a wide-angle dual tail structure on a very small linear scale, embedded within the optical galaxy boundary. In the 20-centimeter map, there is a gap of radio emission between the core and the SW lobe, while a faint jet connects the core to the NE lobe. At 6 centimeters, both jets appear after gaps of about 3 arcseconds on either side of the core, or 1 kiloparsec at the galaxy's distance (about 95 megaparsecs). The lobes are bent by nearly 90° with respect to the jet direction. What we're probably seeing is a a foreshortened source, with the bending occurring where the protective interstellar medium leaves off and the intergalactic medium begins, creating turbulence that interrupts the flow of the jet.

NGC 4921

Face-on "anemic" galaxy with dusty inner ring

NGC 4921 is considered the largest and brightest spiral galaxy in the Coma Cluster and is the prototype of the "anemic" spiral class (van den Bergh 1976). This giant, face-on barred spiral harbors an active LINER-type nucleus and exhibits a perturbed gas distribution, with most of the H I emission in this system distributed along the SE spiral arm, while the NW arm appears depleted (Bravo-Alfaro et al., 2000). Deep, high-resolution *HST* images reveal a rich population of blue globular clusters in its halo, and a number of extended star clusters in the spur region of the arms (Lee and Jang, 2016). The galaxy is just visible in 6- and 8-inch telescopes, but it takes instruments twice that size to bring out its concentrated core (thanks to an active nucleus) and its misty surround.

Another *HST* image (**Figure 73**) shows a remarkable sinuous ring of filamentary dust encircling the central region, with embedded clusters of young stars on the western side of the ring. A ghostly dwarf companion can be seen along the northern periphery of the disk. Galaxies also can be seen through and around the disk. The distance is estimated to be 91 megaparsecs.

Ultradiffuse Galaxies: A New Class of Objects

In the spring of 2014, widefield (3° x 3°) images of the Coma Cluster (van Dokkum et al., 2015) reached down to magnitude 29.3 and revealed a population of 47 extended, low surface brightness galaxies with effective radii in the range of 3 to 10 arcseconds and a central surface brightness of between 24 and 26 magnitudes per square arcsecond in the *g*-band. Spectroscopic analysis confirmed that these are located in the direction of the Coma Cluster. Further searches for these objects,

| **NGC 4921**
 Active Galaxy Nucleus | UGC 8134
 LEDA 44899 | RA 13ʰ 01ᵐ 26.1ˢ   Dec +27° 53′ 08″
 Mag 12.2 SB 13.6   Type SB(rs)ab
 Size 2.4′ x 2.1′   PA 165 |

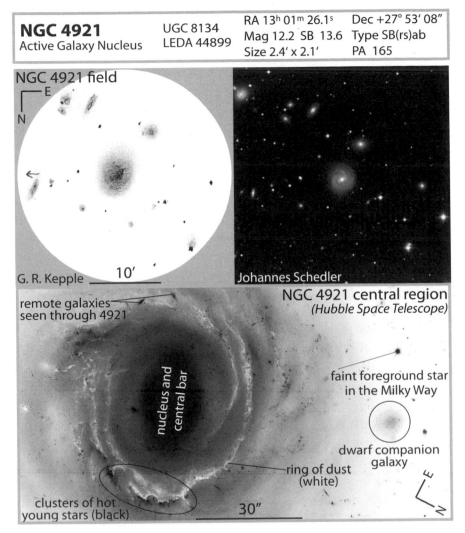

Figure 73: NGC 4921. An eyepiece impression and a photograph, courtesy ccdguide.com, at top. Below is a high-resolution *Hubble Space Telescope* image, courtesy NASA, ESA, and K. Cook (Lawrence Livermore National Laboratory, USA), showing the structure of dust lanes, young star clusters, a dwarf companion galaxy, and many background galaxies visible through this remarkably transparent

christened ultradiffuse galaxies (UDGs), soon turned up over 800, with the prediction that the cluster probably harbors as many as 1,000 (Koda et al., 2015). UDGs have also been spotted in the Virgo Cluster, as well as other clusters and groups.

UDGs are very odd objects. They are considered a subset of the low surface brightness galaxies that have been studied for decades. Some UDGs have effective radii of 1.5 kiloparsecs, but many have sizes comparable to the Milky Way with only 1 percent as many stars. Some 99 percent of their mass may consist of dark matter, since they have been able to survive the tidal fields inherent in the Coma Cluster. Astronomers are stumped as to how such objects could form in the first place, much less endure intact over the age of the universe. Their spectra provide no clues, other than confirming that they have an early-type spectrum and no significant ongoing star formation. Are they the failed equivalents of more massive galaxies that were prevented from assembling a normal stellar population due to feedback from supernovae and young stars? Perhaps they are puffed-up (tidally stretched) versions of low luminosity galaxies, or galaxies that were tidally "flogged" by others in the Coma Cluster. The consensus appears to favor the failed-galaxy scenario, especially since other near low surface brightness analogs are known (Brodie et al., 2011). Still, the fact that such massive objects exhibit exceedingly low luminosities and lack both a classical disk and bulge makes UDGs anomalous in the extreme.

The discovery of such unusual objects required an unusual instrument as well as a new approach to imaging. Both are embodied in the Dragonfly Telephoto Array, located at New Mexico Skies observatory. Dragonfly is a robotic imaging system consisting of (in 2014) eight Canon 400mm f/2.8 telephoto lenses coupled to eight science-grade commercial CCD cameras. The lenses are mounted on a common framework and coaligned to image the same area of sky. An upgrade to 48 lenses in two clusters in 2016 made the array equivalent to an f/0.4 refractor with an effective aperture of about 1 meter, similar to the Yerkes 40-inch telescope. The multiple lenses, which are designed to mimic a dragonfly's compound eye, are very effective at reducing scattered light and unwanted diffraction patterns, which plague large reflecting telescopes due to the secondary mirror obstruction. The telephoto lenses used in the array contain many optical elements, which is not ideal, but utilize "nano" fluorite coatings and are excellently baffled. The

	SDSS	RA 13ʰ 00ᵐ 58.0ˢ	Dec +26° 58′ 35″
Dragonfly 44	J130057.99+	Mag 19.4 SB 16.4	Type –
	265839.7	Size 20″ x 15″	PA 150

array can technically reach a limiting magnitude of about 32 magnitudes per square arcsecond.

One of the objects discovered with the Dragonfly Array was identified as number 44 among the first 47 UDGs found — and thus we have Dragonfly 44.

Dragonfly 44

Ultradiffuse galaxy

Dragonfly 44 lies submerged in the sky background some 50 arcminutes SSE of the NGC 4874/4889 pair. It is one of the largest UDGs in the Coma Cluster, but at magnitude 19.4, don't expect to see it in any telescope. Images with the Gemini-North 8-meter telescope (van Dokkum et al., 2016) render the galaxy as a rounded greenish thumbprint with a very slightly brighter center, punctuated throughout with an unusual number (about 100) of globular clusters, a characteristic that may provide a clue as to how this galaxy formed. The mass is estimated to be 1 trillion $M_\odot$, comparable to the Milky Way, but only one-hundredth of 1 percent of that mass is in the form of stars and normal gas and dust. The rest consists of dark matter.

The hope is that if nearby UDGs are found — Dragonfly 44's distance is assumed to be in excess of 100 megaparsecs — they may provide significant insights into the nature of dark matter, perhaps even providing the first direct detection.

Maximilian Franz Joseph Wolf
Father of Heidelberg Astronomy

Max Wolf (1863–1932) is considered an innovator of applied astrophotography for research, developing several new photographic methods for observational astronomy. His passion was asteroids and comets, but he was also a prolific observer of nebulae and star clusters. He was born in Heidelberg, Ger-

Figure 74: Dragonfly 44, an Ultra Diffuse Galaxy (UDG). Dragonfly 44, located at 13^h 00^m 58.0^s $+26°$ $58'$ $35''$, is a faint galaxy at 24.5 magnitudes per arcsecond, and is the same size as our own Milky Way. The Dragonfly Photo Array, below, discovered DF 44 and the Keck II 10-meter telescope followed up, courtesy von Dokkum et al., 2016. Dragonfly's astronomers are, left to right, Roberto Abraham (University of Toronto), Shany Danieli (Yale University), Lamiya Mowla (Yale), Deborah Lokhorst (U of T), Jielai Zhang (U of T), Allison Merritt (Yale), and Pieter von Dokkum (Yale), photograph by Pieter von Dokkum. Courtesy University of Toronto's Dunlap Institute for Astronomy and Astrophysics.

many, on June 21, 1863, the son of Franz Wolf, a well-known medical doctor, and Elsie Helwerth. He began his astronomical career at age 16 with a small observatory his father built for him in the family's garden, and from which he discovered his first comet in 1884, one with a six-year period. Wolf was educated at Heidelberg University, earning a PhD in mathematics at age 25. He spent two years of post-graduate study in Stockholm, after which he returned to Heidelberg with the position as a lecturer in astronomy. Although he would receive offers from other universities, he turned them all down; he would live the rest of his life in his home town.

His career rapidly advanced. In 1893, he was appointed to a special professorship in astrophysics as well as director of a new observatory being constructed atop the Königstuhl (King's Throne), a hill a few kilometers east of Heidelberg. Wolf secured funding for a new telescope from American philanthropist Catherine Wolfe Bruce, after which he designed and ordered a 16-inch double astrograph refractor (**Figure 75**) with a fast focal ratio of $f/5$ from Pittsburgh astronomer and telescope maker John Brashear. Considered a mechanical genius, Brashear manufactured many astronomical research instruments as well as smaller telescopes for amateurs. Many are still in use today. The telescope, known as the Bruce double astrograph, was completed in 1900 and is still housed in a dome at what is now called the Heidelberg-Königstuhl State Observatory.

Wolf was the first to use time-lapse photography, which was useful in detecting asteroids, and brought the "dry plate" technique to astronomy in 1880. In 1900 he introduced the blink comparator, a device that could examine two plates taken days or months apart to detect objects that had moved in the interim. The blink comparator figured large in Clyde Tombaugh's discovery of Pluto in 1930, but many astronomers also used it to study double and variable stars. During Wolf's tenure at Heidelberg, he produced a list of about 1,500 new large proper motion stars, and discovered more than 200 asteroids and three comets. He used the Bruce telescope's wide field to make a photographic survey of the sky and Milky Way, which yielded great numbers of nebulae, including about 5,000 new objects as

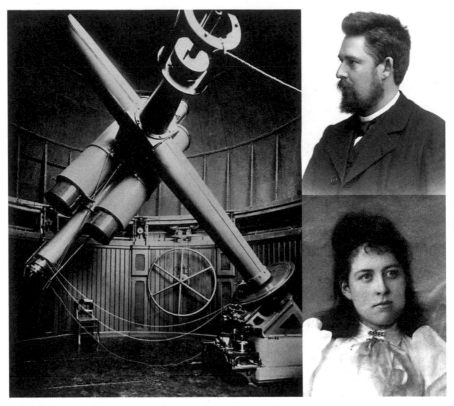

Figure 75: The Bruce double astrograph, Max Wolf, and Catherine Wolfe Bruce. Catherine Bruce, a reclusive American heiress, lower right, funded the Bruce double astrograph (optics by John Brashear) for the Heidelberg Observatory, left. Max Wolf, upper right, used this system to make groundbreaking astrophotographs including his detailed images of the Coma Cluster of Galaxies, the "nebelhaufen," **Figures 68** and **69**. Wolf portrait and telescope image are courtesy Walter Stephani.

well as myriad examples of dark nebulae. Using statistical star counts, he went on to show that dark nebulae were clouds of opaque interstellar dust that were often associated with bright nebulae. In 1901, he photographed and cataloged a cluster of 108 nebulae in a space only 30 arcminutes across. He termed the strange mass a "nebelhaufen," or cluster of nebulae. This turned out to be the Coma Cluster of galaxies.

Wolf enjoyed many other accomplishments, including the discovery of variable stars in the Orion Nebula, as well as several new stars. One named for him, Wolf 359, is the fourth-nearest star system to the Sun. He was the first to observe the return of Comet Halley in 1909, which, due to its close approach, created much excitement and unscrupulous ballyhoo. In 1912, in his role as an advisor for the Deutsches Museum in Munich, he proposed that the Carl Zeiss optical company develop a modern projection planetarium. Unfortunately, World War I intervened and Zeiss was unable to develop and install the planetarium until after peace had been restored. It went into permanent operation on May 7, 1925.

Wolf became a Bruce Medalist (awarded annually by the Astronomical Society of the Pacific) in 1930, an award for which he thought he was unworthy. "The work which I have done was the work of a poor, simple workman," he wrote when he learned he would receive the medal.

> But your medal is destined for an ingenious thinker — And the men who got it before, were and are great Astronomers, from what I am very far. Therefore I fear you will bring a discontinuity in your splendid Series, and therefore I should have preferred to be passed over by your board.

The Society, of course, did not agree, but admired his letter as the work of not only a great astronomer but also a modest man.

Wolf died unexpectedly on 3 October 1932, leaving behind a wife and three sons. By all accounts, he was a gifted teacher and respected by both professional astronomers and amateurs, whom he helped with their own astrophotographs. Today, he is often referred to as the "Father of Heidelberg astronomy."

"Uncle John" Brashear: Scientist, Telescope Maker, Educator

The science of the stars must always remain an unfinished science. There are infinite areas of unexplored wonders that will never come within the compass of the eye of man until the glass through which he now sees darkly shall be needed no more.

–John A. Brashear

The reputation for making fine astronomical telescopes in the US in the 19th century often goes to Alvan Clark & Sons, makers of the 36-inch Lick and 40-inch Yerkes refractors, as well as the 26-inch objectives and mounts for the refractors at the United States Naval Observatory and the University of Virginia. By the turn of the century, the firm had gained worldwide fame and prestige.

Too often overlooked — though not by professional astronomers and connoisseurs of antique telescopes — is another telescope maker of that period, John Alfred Brashear. His life was marked by hard work, struggle, and traumatic setbacks, but it is also an example of how perseverance toward a sense of purpose can lead to gratifying success.

Brashear was born in Brownsville, Pennsylvania, the son of a skilled saddle maker, Basil Brown Brashear, and a schoolteacher, Julia (née Smith). He was the oldest of seven children. He revered his maternal grandfather, Nathaniel Smith, a horologist who taught him the names of the brighter stars and constellations. Smith took his grandson, at age 9, to look through the telescope of an aquaintance, Joseph P. Wampler. The sight of the Moon and Saturn so impressed the boy that he decided he would study astronomy and one day have a telescope of his own. Wampler, too, set an example for the impressionable Brashear, as he (Wampler) had fashioned the flint element of the lens of his telescope from glass that he found among the ruins of the Bakewell Glass Works factory, destroyed in 1845 by the great Pittsburgh fire. Wampler's resourcefulness would be a life lesson as Brashear grew older.

He received a common school education in a two-room brick building, which, combined with his family's meager means, put him at a disadvantage in gaining both a solid foundation in astronomy and a telescope. When the Civil War broke out, Brashear's father enlisted in the Union Army, and Brashear took a job in a steel mill in Pittsburgh's South Side to help support his family. Despite the circumstances, Brashear continued studying mathematics, physics, and astronomy in the streetcars on his way to and from work. On Saturday nights, when the mills were quiet and the smoke had cleared

1862
wedding portraits

John A. Brashear   Phoebe Stewart Brashear

John A. Brashear, in 1913, standing in front of his first optical shop

Figure 76: Brashear's early years. John and Phoebe married in 1862, portraits courtesy University of Pittsburgh, and he pursued his vision of making optics in a shed behind their home, revisited many years later courtesy Bart Fried. The smaller extension behind Brashear housed a steam engine used to drive a lathe and grinding machine, before he moved the operation to larger quarters when he became more successful.

from the air, he spent long hours studying the stars from the cinder-covered Monongahela riverbank near his home.

He married Phoebe Stewart of Pittsburgh on September 25, 1862 (**Figure 76**). Phoebe would become Brashear's chief aide and inspiration behind his work throughout her life. With the help of friends from the mills, they built a home and installed a little coal shed in back, which he converted into a workshop. It was here that he struggled to build his first telescope, a 5-inch refractor, taking two years to grind and figure the lens. When it was at last complete and he was inspecting the finished product, it slipped from his hands and broke into two pieces on the floor. Brashear was sickened by the accident, but a friend who was visiting offered to purchase a replacement, since he didn't have the money to buy another one. Two months later, the new glass arrived and Brashear began again. The telescope, completed in three years' time, was a success.

Brashear showed his new lens to Samuel Langley, director of the Allegheny Observatory. Impressed, he encouraged Brashear to try his hand at building a reflecting telescope. Langley loaned Brashear Henry Draper's book, *On the Construction of A Silvered Glass Telescope* (1864). He also consulted a British magazine, *The English Mechanic and World of Science*, on the procedure. A year later, the mirror was nearly ready for silvering when it broke in his hands! This second accident nearly devastated Brashear, but Phoebe coaxed him into starting over with another mirror. This time, working with a friend who had a chemistry background, he devised a new variation for silvering that did not require heat. It became known as the Brashear process and would remain the standard for 50 years.

Between 1877 and 1879, he made mirrors for several local amateur astronomers. Then, in an effort to bring in a little more money, Brashear placed an advertisement in *Scientific American*, the headline of which read "Silvered-glass specula, diagonals and eye-pieces made for amateurs desiring to construct their own telescopes." The result was beyond his wildest expectations as hundreds of orders poured in. Despite the success, he was reluctant to give up his secure job at the steel mill. Two years later, however, the hard work in the mills cou-

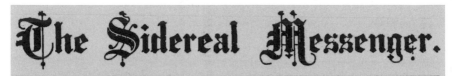

The Sidereal Messenger.

"In the present small treatise I set forth some matters of interest to all observers of natural phenomena to look at and consider."—GALILEO. *Sidereus Nuncius*, 1610.

Vol. 1	MAY, 1882	Nos. 2 and 3

SILVERED GLASS REFLECTING

TELESCOPES

AND SPECULA.

I am prepared to make the above instruments at most reasonable rates. The Specula are of the best quality, being tested and corrected by a modified form of Foncaults method. The plane mirrors are tested and corrected by Dr. Hasting's process, and are warranted correct. The telescopes are all mounted equatorially unless otherwise desired. Speculæ made for those for who desire to mount their own telescopes. For testimonials and further information, address

I. A. BRASHEAR,
No. 3 Holt street. Pittsburg, S, S. Penna

Figure 77: Brashear's advertisement in 1882. As his business grew, Brashear advertised his services to the community. This ad from 1882 appeared in the *Sidereal Messenger*, a monthly American publication claiming to be "the first popular astronomical periodical ever attempted in any language." In the same edition as this ad is an editorial comment on astronomical activity in Pittsburgh: "Mr. John A. Brashear of Pittsburg had the astronomical instinct in him, (as one has jocosely said,) and worked on glass reflectors while still a foreman in one of the larger rolling mills in the smoky city. He has now taken up the manufacture of reflecting telescopes, as a business, and has many very complimentary letters from astronomers in different sections of our country, to whom he has sent his instruments."

pled with the many long hours of toiling away in his optical shop precipitated a nervous breakdown.

Afterward, he began thinking about working full time as an instrument builder, particularly after Langley offered him a large commission to silver a heliostat mirror to study the

Samuel Pierpoint Langley (1834-1906)   William Thaw Sr. (1818-1889)

Allegheny Observatory, Pittsburgh, PA, around 1916

Figure 78: Brashear's benefactors. Samuel P. Langley, polymath astronomer and pioneer of aeronautics, was director of the Allegheny Observatory and encouraged Brashear in his optical production. Langley later headed the Smithsonian Institution; his name graces a NASA center, a US Air Force base, and several naval vessels and public schools. Philanthropist William Thaw Sr. funded Brashear's transition to full-time optical work and is memorialized by Brashear's 30-inch aperture, *f*/18.8 Thaw Refractor, in the Allegheny Observatory, 1916, bottom, courtesy Pittsburgh Press. John and Phoebe Brashear's remains are buried in the Observatory.

absorption effects of Earth's atmosphere. In 1880, Langley's longtime benefactor, the wealthy philanthropist William Thaw (**Figure 78**), paid for a new workshop next to Brashear's house. A third workshop was built in Allegheny in 1886: it was a wood structure, replaced in 1895 with a brick structure

"Standard" Brashear Spectroscope

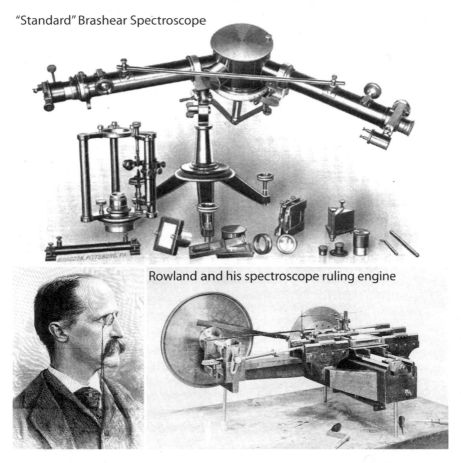

Rowland and his spectroscope ruling engine

Figure 79: Brashear's line of spectroscopes. As Brashear's optical factory became more successful, he assembled a catalog of standard products, including spectroscopes. One complete unit is shown at top, from Brashear Company's 1911 catalog, where he offered eight standard spectroscopes and a variety of gratings. Brashear also offered larger gratings for professional observatories and found a partner who could do the microscopic ruling on his optical substrate. Henry Augustus Rowland (lower left) developed such a machine (lower right) for ruling gratings on a mirror. Brashear would prepare a precise concave or flat speculum mirror and send it to Rowland in Baltimore at the Johns Hopkins University. There, Rowland would precisely engrave up to 14,438 lines per inch with his engine, owing to his unique technology involving a revolutionarily precise screw mechanism. They jointly prepared many such gratings that were "sought by every physical laboratory in the world."

that Brashear paid for. No longer would he have to labor in the Pittsburgh steel mills. The rest of his life would be devoted to the occupation he loved most: optical work.

Before long, Brashear's reputation, like the Clarks', was established and his esteemed role in astronomy assured. Two renowned scientists would be well served by Brashear, and vice versa. In 1881, Charles S. Hastings, an American physicist at Johns Hopkins University, known for his work in optics, commissioned Brashear to make a prism from glass left over from that used to fashion the objective of the Lick 36-inch refractor. Brashear, who was not fully versed in the mathematics of astrophysics, relied on Hastings' help in this respect to complete the work. But this was far from Brashear's most important contribution. Brashear, with his son-in-law and partner, James B. McDowell, went on to collaborate with Hastings to manufacture a number of large research telescopes, including the 30-inch Keeler Memorial Reflector at Allegheny and the 72-inch reflector at Dominion Astrophysical Observatory.

Pleased with Brashear's work on the Lick prism, Hastings recommended Brashear to Henry A. Rowland, also a Johns Hopkins physicist, who is chiefly remembered as being one of the first scientists to design successful diffraction gratings in the early 1880s.

Rowland had improved the design of the "ruled engine," a device that guided a diamond point across a speculum metal surface to produce thousands of parallel ruled lines with a fixed separation of as little as one thousandth of a millimeter. In 1882, Rowland discovered that a concave grating could act as a focusing lens, thus eliminating the use of glass lenses with their unwanted absorption at ultraviolet wavelengths. Rowland approached Brashear to manufacture and distribute several hundred concave gratings to physical and chemical laboratories, as well as astronomical observatories. By January 1901, the sales had garnered more than $13,000, over $365,000 in today's dollars. But the sales did not stop there. In the years that followed several thousand more gratings were sold — sending profits through the roof. Brashear

JOHN A. BRASHEAR COMPANY, LTD.
PITTSBURGH, N. S., PENNA., U. S. A.

Figure 80: Brashear at the top of his optical game. John A. Brashear (1840–1920) established a long career making premium optics. In his most productive years, he produced telescopes in this large factory (as depicted in an engraving from the Brashear Company 1911 catalog), a far cry from his backyard shed in **Figure 76**. Brashear produced his largest objective in this Pittsburgh optical shop (below) resting his arm on the 72-inch blank destined for the Dominion Astrophysical Observatory near Victoria, B.C. The telescope saw first light in May 1918, photograph courtesy National Research Council of Canada.

Standing: James Keeler (astronomer)   Reginald Fessenden (engineering professor)   John Brashear
Seated: Lucien Scaife (steel magnate)   William Hamilton (casket magnate)   John Walker (steel magnate)

Figure 81: Man about town. Known as "Uncle John," Brashear is embraced by adoring children, courtesy Carnegie Library. Below, a younger Brashear, back row right, hobnobs with Pittsburgh's leaders of industry (philanthropists) and academia, courtesy Jack Koester.

continued to be the sole source of gratings after Roland's untimely death in 1901.

Astronomers, teachers, and young people whom he inspired to study the stars held him in high regard. Many affectionately referred to him as "Uncle John" for his educational and philanthropic efforts. He served as acting director of the Allegheny Observatory from 1898 to 1900 and acting chancellor of the Western University of Pennsylvania, which is today the University of Pittsburgh. It was upon his initiative and efforts that $300,000 was raised to build and equip the newly relocated Allegheny Observatory. At its dedication on August 28, 1912, Brashear reflected on his starry nights on the riverbank: "I resolved then that whenever an opportunity offered, I would have a place where all the people who loved the stars could enjoy them."

Brashear died on April 8, 1920, and his ashes were interred in a crypt below the Keeler Telescope at Allegheny Observatory, along with those of his wife. The inscription on the crypt's plaque is a paraphrase of a line in the famous poem *The Old Astronomer To His Pupil* by the English poet and novelist Sarah Williams.

We have loved the stars too fondly to be fearful of the night.

A BRIEF HISTORY OF MAPPING LARGE-SCALE STRUCTURE IN THE UNIVERSE

Coma Berenices offers a unique view beyond our galaxy perpendicular to the plane of the Milky Way, through the thinnest part of the Galaxy toward the North Galactic Pole (**Figure 82**, right panel). An interpretation of this rich field is offered in **Figure 83**, with cones at the top presenting structures and objects in distance and the map at the bottom overlaying them on the flat page. Most structures are irregular, and the ellipses and grey bands presented here only sketch the massive, diffuse structures, sometimes described as "foam." Much of this large-scale structure has been mapped only in the last 40–50 years.

By the late 1920s, Edwin Hubble's distance-redshift relation provided a way of estimating extragalactic distances from

LOOKING TOWARD COMA BERENICES THROUGH THE MILKY WAY

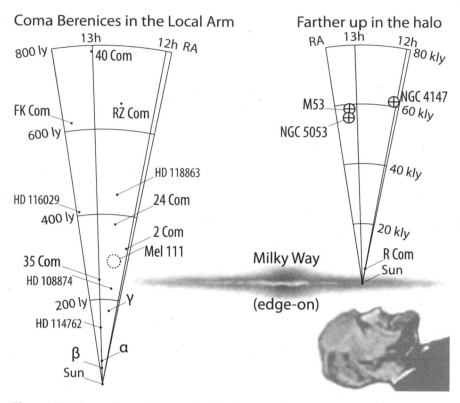

Figure 82: Coma Berenices: galactic view. Looking in a perpendicular direction from the disk of the Milky Way (left), Coma is involved in only one-half of a spiral arm before giving way to extragalactic space. A big gap (right) affords a view through the disk, where the three featured globular clusters orbit, a little more than halfway to the edge of the halo.

spectroscopic measurements, and astronomers avidly turned their attention to mapping the skein of galaxies they were observing. Gerard de Vaucouleurs made an early attempt to document the local structure in 1953, recognizing that our own Local Group of galaxies and the Virgo Cluster are part of a distinct larger structure, now called the Local Supercluster. Thirty-four years later, R. Brent Tully and J. Richard Fisher published their *Nearby Galaxies Catalog and Atlas,* comprehensive out to a recession velocity of 3,000 kilometers/second (about 130 million light-years). Tully and Fisher documented well-understood

LOOKING THROUGH COMA BERENICES: THE EXTRAGALACTIC VIEW

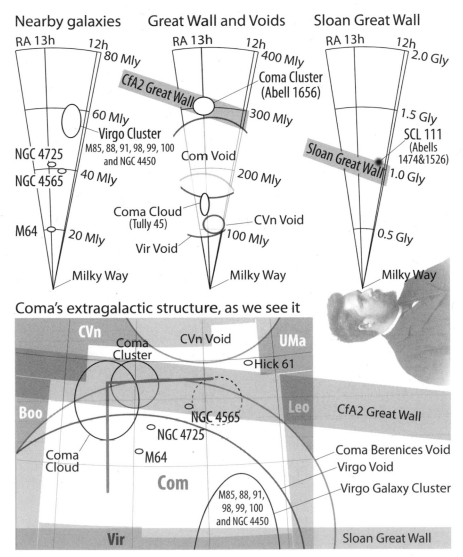

Nearby galaxies

RA 13h 12h
80 Mly
60 Mly
Virgo Cluster
M85, 88, 91, 98, 99, 100
and NGC 4450
NGC 4725
NGC 4565 40 Mly
M64 20 Mly
Milky Way

Great Wall and Voids

RA 13h 12h
400 Mly
CfA2 Great Wall
Coma Cluster
(Abell 1656)
300 Mly
Com Void
200 Mly
Coma Cloud
(Tully 45)
CVn Void
100 Mly
Vir Void
Milky Way

Sloan Great Wall

RA 13h 12h
2.0 Gly
1.5 Gly
SCL 111
(Abells
1474&1526)
Sloan Great Wall 1.0 Gly
0.5 Gly
Milky Way

Coma's extragalactic structure, as we see it

CVn
Coma Cluster
CVn Void
UMa
Hick 61
Boo
Leo
NGC 4565
NGC 4725
CfA2 Great Wall
Coma Cloud
M64
Coma Berenices Void
Com
Virgo Void
M85, 88, 91, 98, 99, 100 and NGC 4450
Virgo Galaxy Cluster
Vir
Sloan Great Wall

Figure 83: Coma Berenices: extragalactic view. Known objects and larger structures are presented in distance cones at the top and superimposed on a map below; it is complicated as we know a lot about what is in this 20° x 20° clear window into the extragalactic universe. Max Wolf (middle right) found the complexity in the Coma galaxy cluster and his sightline helps explain the figure.

structures like the Virgo Galaxy Cluster and proposed many new structures like the Coma Galaxy Cloud. De Vaucouleurs had proposed a closer group, the Coma I Cloud, including NGC 4725, which Tully later grouped into his massive Coma-Sculptor Cloud. Other researchers see less evidence for these being gravitationally bound large-scale structures; hence, verification continues.

Anthony Fairall analyzed the available redshift data in his 1998 compendium *Large-Scale Structures of the Universe* out through 10,000 kilometers/second (440 million light-years). He noted large areas that appeared to be devoid of galaxies, and so labeled these empty regions "voids"(mapped in the central cone). Visualizing the universe as a series of voids (roughly spherical empty spaces) is conceptually simpler than complex intersecting networks of filaments and walls. One of the more famous voids, the Boötes Void, was later found to not be as barren of galaxies, owing to sampling choices in the original discovery. Fairall's maps included the CfA2 Great Wall of galaxies, by Geller and Huchra, 1989, containing the Coma Galaxy Cluster.

Later, the Sloan Digital Sky Survey (SDSS) offered rich spectroscopic data out beyond 1 billion light-years, leading to the recognition in 2003 of the Sloan Great Wall of galaxies. Perhaps twice as large as the CfA2 Great Wall, this new structure incorporated several previously identified superclusters of galaxies, including those proposed by Jaan Einasto and colleagues from statistical analysis of estimated positions of Abell and Zwicky Galaxy Clusters. The Sloan Wall barely overlaps Coma Berenices; it includes faint Abell clusters 1474 and 1526, which are members of Einasto supercluster SCL 111, also called the Coma-Virgo Supercluster.

Rendering the three-dimensional structure of the universe on the flat page is a challenge and, moreover, creates a visual distortion that our imaginations are tasked to overcome. Tully and Fisher's *Nearby Galaxies Atlas* offers spectacular color cartography of selected nearby regions, though it remains an intellectual exercise to apprehend in three dimensions. The atlas section of Fairall's *Large-Scale Structures of the Universe* takes a different approach, mapping the structure with concentric hemispheres, each flattened on the page. Research literature is filled with blobby density structures captured in three-dimensional cubes and projected onto the page. Several visualization application programs offer the ability to fly through the structure, a dazzling experience though a challenge to navigate and set filters and scenes. Further, the International Astronomical Union has not established uniform naming for the large-scale structures, so we use the working names proposed by researchers, some in agreement with other researchers and some not. **Figure 83**, like all such attempts, is a compromise, designed around the observer's approach of visualizing the immensely deep third dimension in the dome of the night sky.

GALAXY CLASSIFICATION SYMBOLS IN BRIEF

This synopsis pertains to the galaxy classification types presented in the following **Tables 1** and **2**. We encourage readers to review the "Galaxy Classification" section in volume 1 for a more complete primer, or refer to the reference cited below.[*]

There are four broad galaxy classes apparent in this table: elliptical (E), lenticular (S0), spiral (S), and irregular (I).

Spiral and lenticular galaxies are organized into two families: ordinary spirals (SA, SA0) and barred spirals (SB, SB0), with intermediate objects (SAB, SAB0).

There are two main varieties of spiral and lenticular rings: (r) and (s). The (r) indicates the galaxy exhibits an inner ring while the (s) variety is a pure spiral, where the arms spring from a central bulge or the ends of a bar. Transition types (i.e., galaxies with broken inner rings) are denoted as (rs).

An underline beneath one of the letters in (rs), or beneath a subclass (A and B), is similar to a "weighted mean" and indicates that a galaxy is "more this than that." Hence (rs) means the galaxy is more (r) than (s); and (rs) implies the galaxy's variety is more (s) than (r). If a bar is a weak oval or of low contrast, it is classified SAB; if it is well defined but only slightly more so than an SB, it is designated SAB.

---

[*] Reference: *The de Vaucouleurs Atlas of Galaxies*, Ronald J. Buta, Harold G. Corwin Jr., and Stephen C. Odewahn (Cambridge University Press, 2007).

Elliptical galaxies range from "early" (E0 or spherical) to "late" (E7 or nearly lenticular), but not in the evolutionary sense. As Hubble himself wrote, these terms "are used to denote relative position in the empirical sequence without regard to temporal implications." Elliptical and lenticular galaxies may also be classed as a mixed variety using a slash /, as in E2/S0.

The various galactic stages for lenticular (S0) systems are distinguished as early (-), intermediate (°), and late (+), though again not in an evolutionary sense. The spiral sequence signified by a, b, c, d, also represents early-to-late stages. Transition stages are: ab, bc, and cd. Magellanic-type galaxies are labeled m, and highly irregular galaxies as Im. As the spiral form morphs into an irregular exhibiting a weak spiral arm similar to that in the Large Magellanic Cloud, the sequence extends from Sdm to Sm.

Roman numerals represent a galaxy's luminosity class (van den Bergh 1960) and is analogous to the luminosity class scheme for stars: I (supergiant galaxy), II (bright giant galaxy), III (giant galaxy), IV (subgiant galaxy), and V (dwarf galaxy). Intermediate varieties are I-II, II-III, III-IV, and IV-V.

Galaxies deemed peculiar, i.e., those that exhibit unusual features that precluded their being classified in the conventional sense, are flagged as pec. A colon (:) indicates an uncertain stage whereas ? denotes a doubtful feature. The notation sp — for spindle — incorporates the edge-on variety of spiral galaxy into the classification scheme. A d that comes at the beginning of a classification string indicates the galaxy is a dwarf. Similarly, a c preceding the classification denotes a compact galaxy.

Table 1: Coma Cluster (Abell 1656) Brighter Member Galaxies

Name	RA h m s	Dec ° ' "	V mag	SB	Size (')	PA	Type
CGCG 160-035	12 57 01.6	+29 03 45	14.6	13.4	0.9 x 0.45	24	SB(s)0° pec
CGCG 160-073	13 00 30.8	+28 20 47	13.9	13.2	1.0 x 0.6	5	SAB(rs:)0⁻
CGCG 160-141	13 07 13.2	+28 02 49	14.8	13.2	0.5 x 0.5		SA(rs)bc II
CGCG 160-247	13 00 16.5	+27 58 03	15.2	12.6	0.5 x 0.2	27	SB?0°: sp
IC 835	12 56 52.3	+26 29 16	14.2	12.9	0.6 x 0.6		SA(rs)ab
IC 842	13 00 39.5	+29 01 10	13.9	13.2	1.2 x 0.5	57	SA(r)bc I-II
IC 843	13 01 33.6	+29 07 50	13.6	12.9	1.2 x 0.5	131	S0°

Table 1: Coma Cluster (Abell 1656) Brighter Member Galaxies (Cont.)

Name	RA h m s	Dec ° ' "	V mag	SB	Size (')	PA	Type
IC 3900	12 55 41.3	+27 15 03	14.0	12.7	0.9 x 0.4	177	SB0°:
IC 4040	13 00 37.9	+28 03 27	15.2	13.4	0.7 x 0.3	153	SAb: II-III
IC 4045	13 00 48.7	+28 05 27	13.9	12.5	0.6 x 0.4	115	E2/S0
IC 4051	13 00 51.5	+28 02 34	13.6	12.9	0.8 x 0.6	49	E5
IC 4088	13 01 43.4	+29 02 41	13.8	13.4	1.5 x 0.5	89	SA(rs)b I-II
MCG +5-30-109	12 52 09.0	+27 28 38	14.6	13.8	0.8 x 0.6	96	SB(rs)0/a
MCG +5-30-111	12 52 16.2	+27 31 59	15.9	14.4	0.7 x 0.4	132	SAd: III-IV
MCG +5-30-116	12 53 16.1	+27 05 40	13.9	13.3	0.9 x 0.7	141	SB(rs)0°
MCG +5-31-18	12 56 51.2	+26 53 56	14.6	13.7	0.7 x 0.6	3	SA(rs:)0+
MCG +5-31-23	12 57 09.4	+27 27 59	14.5	13.2	0.6 x 0.6		SB(s)0⁻
MCG +5-31-36	12 57 54.5	+27 29 20	15.6	14.1	0.6 x 0.5	53	SBb
MCG +5-31-37	12 58 01.6	+27 29 23	14.9	13.6	0.7 x 0.5	87	SB(rs)ab
MCG +5-31-45	12 58 18.2	+29 07 44	14.6	13.6	1.0 x 0.5	29	SA(r)a
MCG +5-31-46	12 58 30.2	+28 00 53	14.1	13.7	0.9 x 0.9		E0
MCG +5-31-74	12 59 47.2	+27 42 37	15.9	14.9	1.1 x 0.4	165	SB?(r:)0/a: sp
MCG +5-31-95	13 00 52.1	+28 21 58	13.8	12.5	0.7 x 0.4	18	SB(rs:)0°
MCG +5-31-106	13 02 04.2	+29 15 12	14.5	12.9	0.9 x 0.3	159	S0°: sp
MCG +5-31-132	13 06 36.4	+27 52 23	15.3	14.2	0.9 x 0.5	126	Sa: pec sp
MCG +5-31-133	13 06 38.2	+28 50 54	14.7	13.7	0.9 x 0.5	177	SB(s)d: III-IV
NGC 4787	12 54 05.5	+27 04 07	14.4	13.2	1.2 x 0.3	2	SB(s:)0+
NGC 4788	12 54 16.0	+27 18 14	14.4	13.0	0.8 x 0.4	141	SAB(rs)0+
NGC 4789	12 54 19.0	+27 04 05	12.1	13.1	1.9 x 1.5	171	SA0⁻
NGC 4793	12 54 40.6	+28 56 19	11.6	13.0	2.8 x 1.5	50	SAB(rs)c III
NGC 4798	12 54 55.2	+27 24 45	13.2	13.1	1.2 x 0.9	30	SA(s)0+
NGC 4807	12 55 29.1	+27 31 17	13.5	13.1	1.0 x 0.8	21	E2:
NGC 4807A	12 55 30.6	+27 32 39	15.2	12.6	0.5 x 0.2	123	SAB0+
NGC 4816	12 56 12.2	+27 44 44	12.8	13.1	1.3 x 1.1	84	E0:
NGC 4819	12 56 27.9	+26 59 15	13.2	13.0	1.2 x 0.8	160	SB(rs)a
NGC 4821	12 56 29.1	+26 57 25	14.2	13.0	0.7 x 0.6	12	SA0°
NGC 4827	12 56 43.5	+27 10 44	12.9	13.2	1.4 x 1.1	48	E3:
NGC 4828	12 56 42.9	+28 01 14	14.2	13.3	0.7 x 0.7		SA(rs)0°
NGC 4839	12 57 24.4	+27 29 52	12.8	14.3	4.0 x 1.9	65	E4/S0
NGC 4840	12 57 32.8	+27 36 37	13.8	13.2	0.9 x 0.8	95	SA(s)cd III
NGC 4841A	12 57 32.0	+28 28 37	12.8	13.4	1.6 x 1.0	124	E2 pec
NGC 4841B	12 57 33.9	+28 28 56	12.6	12.3	1.0 x 0.7	134	E1 pec

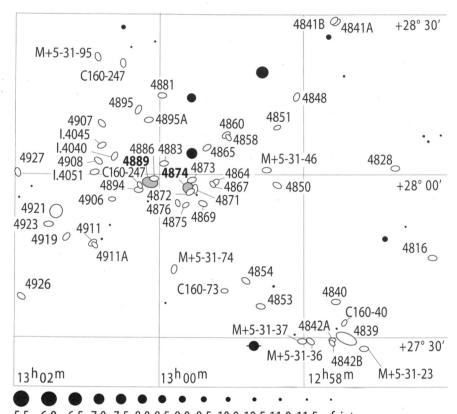

Wil Tirion / Barry Rappaport / Will Remaklus   Willmann-Bell, Inc. Copyright 1987- 2018

Figure 84: The core of the Coma Galaxy Cluster, Abell 1656. This approximately 1-degree scale map is the central area of the cluster and includes the field detailed in Max Wolf's image in **Figure 68**. Grayed galaxies with bold labels are the two core galaxies of the cluster. Galaxies presented in this figure and the next (wider map) are listed in **Table 1**. Cluster members lie in the general area where the recessional velocity is 6,925 km/s. Galaxies that diverge significantly from this value are either in the background or foreground of Abell 1656.

Table 1: Coma Cluster (Abell 1656) Brighter Member Galaxies (Cont.)

Name	RA h m s	Dec ° ' "	V mag	SB	Size (')	PA	Type
NGC 4842A	12 57 35.9	+27 29 36	14.0	12.0	0.4 x 0.4		E0/S0
NGC 4842B	12 57 36.1	+27 29 05	15.1	12.0	0.3 x 0.2	42	SA0⁻
NGC 4848	12 58 05.6	+28 14 33	13.7	13.3	1.6 x 0.5	158	SAB(rs)b: sp
NGC 4849	12 58 12.7	+26 23 49	12.9	13.6	1.7 x 1.3	175	E3
NGC 4850	12 58 21.8	+27 58 04	14.2	12.9	0.7 x 0.5	63	SAB(rs)0⁺

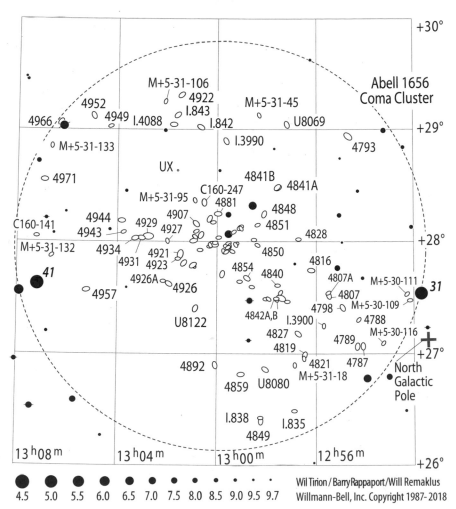

Figure 85: The Coma Galaxy Cluster, Abell 1656. The scale of this map is approximately 4 degrees. It represents the conventional size of the whole galaxy cluster, with labels omitted from the busy central region, presented in the previous figure. Both figures present galaxies brighter than magnitude 16. Wolf's plate, **Figure 69**, identified many fainter galaxies. These galaxies are also included in **Table 1**.

Table 1: Coma Cluster (Abell 1656) Brighter Member Galaxies (Cont.)

Name	RA h m s	Dec ° ' "	V mag	SB	Size (')	PA	Type
NGC 4851	12 58 21.7	+28 08 55	15.0	12.8	0.5 x 0.3	112	SAB(rs)0/a
NGC 4853	12 58 35.2	+27 35 47	13.6	12.8	0.8 x 0.7	81	SA(r)0/a
NGC 4854	12 58 47.4	+27 40 29	13.9	13.7	1.1 x 0.8	57	E2/S0

Table 1: Coma Cluster (Abell 1656) Brighter Member Galaxies (Cont.)

Name	RA h m s	Dec ° ' "	V mag	SB	Size (')	PA	Type
NGC 4858	12 59 02.1	+28 06 56	15.2	13.3	0.5 x 0.4	36	SB(rs)b II-III
NGC 4859	12 59 01.8	+26 48 56	13.6	13.6	1.4 x 0.8	95	(R')SA(r)0/a
NGC 4860	12 59 03.9	+28 07 25	13.5	13.3	1.0 x 0.8	126	E1
NGC 4864	12 59 13.3	+27 58 33	14.0	13.5	0.9x 0.9	162	E0
NGC 4865	12 59 19.9	+28 05 03	13.7	12.8	0.9 x 0.5	123	E5
NGC 4867	12 59 15.3	+27 58 15	14.5	12.8	0.5 x 0.4	36	E5
NGC 4869	12 59 23.4	+27 54 42	13.8	13.1	0.8 x 0.7	69	E0
NGC 4871	12 59 30.0	+27 57 23	14.1	12.6	0.7 x 0.4	177	(R')SB(s)0°
NGC 4872?	12 59 34.1	+27 56 49	14.4	12.8	0.6 x 0.4	123	(R)SB(r̲s)0+
NGC 4873	12 59 32.8	+27 59 01	14.1	12.9	0.7 x 0.5	105	E3
NGC 4874	12 59 35.7	+27 57 33	11.7	13.1	1.9 x 1.9		E0/S0⁻,cD
NGC 4875:	12 59 37.9	+27 54 26	14.7	12.2	0.4 x 0.3	123	SAB(r̲s)0°
NGC 4876	12 59 44.4	+27 54 45	14.4	12.6	0.5 x 0.4	18	E5
NGC 4881	12 59 57.8	+28 14 48	13.6	13.6	1.0 x 1.0		E0
NGC 4883	12 59 56.0	+28 02 05	14.4	12.9	0.6 x 0.5	97	SB(s)0°
NGC 4886	13 00 04.5	+27 59 15	13.9	12.8	0.6 x 0.6		E0
NGC 4889	13 00 08.1	+27 58 37	11.5	13.3	2.9 x 1.9	80	E3,cD
NGC 4892	13 00 03.5	+26 53 53	14.0	12.9	1.3 x 0.3	13	SB(r?)0/a: sp
NGC 4895	13 00 17.9	+28 12 08	13.2	13.2	1.8 x 0.6	153	SB?(r?)0°: sp
NGC 4895A	13 00 09.1	+28 10 13	15.0	13.7	0.7 x 0.4	99	E3/S0
NGC 4898	13 00 17.9	+27 57 21	13.7	13.3	1.1 x 0.8	100	E4/S0 pec + E4
NGC 4898ne	13 00 18.1	+27 57 24	15.0	12.9	0.6 x 0.3	135	E4
NGC 4898sw	13 00 17.7	+27 57 19	14.1	12.6	0.8 x 0.4	100	E4/S0 pec
NGC 4906	13 00 39.8	+27 55 26	14.4	13.2	0.7 x 0.6	40	E1
NGC 4907	13 00 48.8	+28 09 30	13.6	13.5	1.1 x 1.0	42	SB(rs)b I-II
NGC 4908	13 00 54.5	+28 00 34	13.2	13.3	1.2 x 0.9	105	E4/S0
NGC 4911	13 00 56.1	+27 47 27	12.8	12.9	1.2 x 1.1	127	SAB(rs)b I-II
NGC 4911A	13 00 54.1	+27 47 01	15.3	12.9	0.4 x 0.3	42	SAB:0/a
NGC 4919	13 01 17.6	+27 48 33	14.1	13.6	1.1 x 0.7	140	SAB(r̲s)0°
NGC 4921	13 01 26.1	+27 53 10	12.2	13.9	2.5 x 2.2	165	SB(r̲s)ab I
NGC 4922	13 01 24.9	+29 18 40	13.0	13.2	1.3 x 1.0	129	S0⁻ pec + I0:
NGC 4922sw	13 01 24.5	+29 18 30	13.2	13.2	1.4 x 0.9	137	S0⁻ pec
NGC 4922ne	13 01 25.3	+29 18 50	14.3	13.8	1.0 x 0.8	123	I0: pec
NGC 4923	13 01 31.8	+27 50 51	13.7	13.1	0.8 x 0.8		SA0⁻
NGC 4926	13 01 53.7	+27 37 28	13.0	13.2	1.2 x 1.1	57	SA0⁻
NGC 4926A	13 02 07.9	+27 38 54	14.2	12.8	0.6 x 0.5	90	SB(s)a

Table 1: Coma Cluster (Abell 1656) Brighter Member Galaxies (Cont.)

Name	RA h m s	Dec ° ' "	V mag	SB	Size (')	PA	Type
NGC 4927	13 01 57.6	+28 00 21	13.7	12.8	0.8 x 0.6	15	SAB0⁻
NGC 4929	13 02 44.4	+28 02 43	14.1	13.7	1.0 x 0.9	52	E1
NGC 4931	13 03 00.9	+28 01 57	13.5	13.5	1.7 x 0.7	78	S0 sp
NGC 4934	13 03 16.2	+28 01 50	14.4	13.0	1.1 x 0.3	104	SA?(r:)0⁺: sp
NGC 4943	13 03 45.0	+28 05 03	14.4	13.2	0.7 x 0.5	111	SA:(rs)0°:
NGC 4944	13 03 50.0	+28 11 09	12.9	12.7	1.7 x 0.6	89	SA?(s:)0⁻: sp
NGC 4949	13 04 17.9	+29 01 46	14.9	13.5	0.8 x 0.4	108	SAB(rs)0⁺:
NGC 4952	13 04 58.4	+29 07 20	12.4	13.1	1.8 x 1.1	23	E4/S0
NGC 4957	13 05 12.4	+27 34 11	13.0	13.2	1.2 x 1.0	100	E2
NGC 4966	13 06 17.3	+29 03 47	13.3	12.4	1.0 x 0.5	143	SB(rs)b: pec II
NGC 4971	13 06 55.0	+28 32 53	13.5	13.4	1.0 x 1.0		SB(rs̲)0⁺
UGC 8069	12 57 11.4	+29 02 42	14.2	13.8	1.4 x 0.6	21	SB(r?)0°: pec sp
UGC 8080	12 58 02.4	+26 51 34	14.0	13.1	1.0 x 0.5	56	(R)SAB̲(r)0/a
UGC 8122	13 00 49.9	+27 24 21	14.0	13.7	1.2 x 0.7	160	(R)SA(r)0⁺

Table 2: Galaxies in the general area of Com featured galaxies

Name	RA h m s	Dec ° ' "	V mag	SB	size (')	PA	Type
IC 771	12 15 13.2	+13 11 04	13.9	12.2	0.6 x 0.4	98	SB(s)cd III:
IC 781	12 20 03.3	+14 57 42	13.3	13.0	1.0 x 0.8	45	dS0(4)
IC 783	12 21 38.8	+15 44 42	13.8	13.6	1.2 x 0.8	141	SA(rs)0/a:
IC 783A	12 22 19.6	+15 44 01	14.5	12.9	0.5 x 0.5		dE4,N
IC 792	12 27 08.8	+16 19 32	14.0	13.6	1.6 x 0.5	59	SA(rs̲)bc II
IC 796	12 29 26.3	+16 24 17	13.1	12.7	1.3 x 0.6	145	S0/a pec
IC 797	12 31 54.8	+15 07 27	12.9	12.9	1.3 x 0.9	108	SAB(s)cd: III
IC 800	12 33 56.7	+15 21 17	13.4	13.8	1.5 x 1.1	157	SB(s)d III
IC 3044	12 12 48.5	+13 58 34	13.5	13.8	1.9 x 0.8	68	SAB(s)dm IV
IC 3059	12 14 55.2	+13 27 41	14.2	14.9	1.7 x 1.3	0	SB(s)m V
IC 3061	12 15 04.4	+14 01 44	13.6	13.3	2.2 x 0.4	122	SA?(s)c: sp II-III
IC 3062	12 15 05.4	+13 35 41	13.9	12.9	0.8 x 0.6	6	SAB(rs)c I-II
IC 3065	12 15 12.6	+14 25 58	13.6	12.8	0.9 x 0.6	0	SA0⁻
IC 3077	12 15 56.3	+14 25 59	14.1	13.4	0.9 x 0.7	0	dS0(4)
IC 3091	12 16 29.2	+14 00 45	14.0	13.6	1.3 x 0.6	126	SB0°: pec.
IC 3094	12 16 56.0	+13 37 32	13.9	12.2	0.5 x 0.5		SA(rs)bc: III-IV:
IC 3096	12 16 52.4	+14 30 53	14.3	13.7	1.4 x 0.5	96	SB?m: sp IV-V

Table 2: Galaxies in the general area of Com featured galaxies (Cont.)

Name	RA h m s	Dec ° ' "	V mag	SB	size (')	PA	Type
IC 3109	12 17 44.1	+13 10 16	14.7	13.1	0.5 x 0.5		SA(s)c I
IC 3313	12 25 36.4	+15 49 48	14.2	13.5	0.8 x 0.8		dE2
IC 3344	12 26 32.4	+13 34 44	14.6	13.1	0.8 x 0.3	48	dS0(5)
IC 3355	12 26 51.1	+13 10 31	14.9	14.2	1.2 x 0.5	172	Im pec IV-V
IC 3365	12 27 11.5	+15 53 50	13.8	13.8	1.7 x 0.7	72	SA(s)m IV
IC 3392	12 28 43.3	+14 59 58	12.2	12.8	2.3 x 0.9	40	SA(rs)0/a
IC 3432	12 30 27.8	+14 09 37	14.6	13.0	0.7 x 0.4	54	SB(r)cd pec III:
IC 3476	12 32 41.9	+14 03 01	12.7	13.7	2.0 x 1.4	30	SB(r̲s̲)dm pec IV
IC 3478	12 32 44.2	+14 11 46	13.3	13.1	1.1 x 0.9	105	dSA0(0)
IC 3501	12 33 51.6	+13 19 21	13.9	13.2	0.7 x 0.7		dE0
IC 3522	12 34 45.7	+15 13 15	14.7	14.4	1.4 x 0.6	95	IB:m sp V
IC 3530	12 34 49.3	+17 48 51	14.0	13.9	1.2 x 0.9	162	SAB̲(s)0⁻
IC 3583	12 36 43.7	+13 15 26	12.7	13.5	2.2 x 1.1	0	I:Bm sp IV
M88	12 31 59.2	+14 25 14	9.6	13.0	6.9 x 3.7	140	SA(r̲s̲)b I-II
M90	12 36 49.8	+13 09 47	9.5	13.4	9.5 x 4.4	26	SAB(r̲s̲:)ab I-II
M91	12 35 26.4	+14 29 47	10.2	13.4	5.4 x 4.3	150	SB(rs)b I-II
M98	12 13 48.3	+14 54 02	10.1	13.6	9.8 x 2.8	155	(R')SAB(rs)ab II
M99	12 18 49.6	+14 24 59	10.0	13.3	5.4 x 4.7	51	SA(s)c I-II
M100	12 22 54.9	+15 49 20	9.4	13.4	7.4 x 6.3	30	SAB(s)bc I
MCG +3-31-75	12 13 09.0	+16 17 49	13.9	12.4	0.7 x 0.4	135	SA(r)b II
MCG +3-31-94	12 17 27.3	+17 39 02	13.8	12.8	0.8 x 0.5	135	E2/S0
MCG +3-32-3	12 20 14.3	+17 20 48	13.9	12.0	0.5 x 0.4	174	SA(r̲s̲)bc II
NGC 4164	12 12 05.5	+13 12 20	14.7	12.9	0.6 x 0.3	111	E2
NGC 4165	12 12 11.8	+13 14 47	13.5	13.3	1.2 x 0.8	160	SA̲B̲(r)ab: III
NGC 4166	12 12 09.6	+17 45 25	13.1	13.1	1.2 x 1.0	20	SB(r)0/a
NGC 4168	12 12 17.3	+13 12 19	11.2	13.2	2.8 x 2.3	120	E1
NGC 4186	12 14 06.5	+14 43 33	13.8	13.4	1.0 x 0.8	60	SA(rs)ab
NGC 4189	12 13 47.3	+13 25 29	11.7	13.1	2.4 x 1.7	85	SAB(r̲s̲)c II-III
NGC 4193	12 13 53.6	+13 10 23	12.3	13.0	2.2 x 1.0	93	SB(s)bc II-III
NGC 4206	12 15 16.8	+13 01 26	12.2	14.0	6.2 x 1.0	0	SA:(s:)bc:
NGC 4212	12 15 39.4	+13 54 05	11.2	13.0	3.2 x 1.9	75	SA(r̲s̲)c III
NGC 4216	12 15 54.4	+13 08 58	10.0	12.8	8.1 x 1.8	19	SAB(s:)b sp II
NGC 4222	12 16 22.5	+13 18 26	13.3	13.7	3.3 x 0.5	56	Scd: III? sp
NGC 4237	12 17 11.4	+15 19 26	11.6	12.6	2.1 x 1.3	108	SA(rs)bc II-III
NGC 4239	12 17 14.9	+16 31 53	12.8	12.9	1.4 x 0.7	120	E5
NGC 4262	12 19 30.6	+14 52 40	11.6	12.7	1.9 x 1.7	120	SB(s)0°

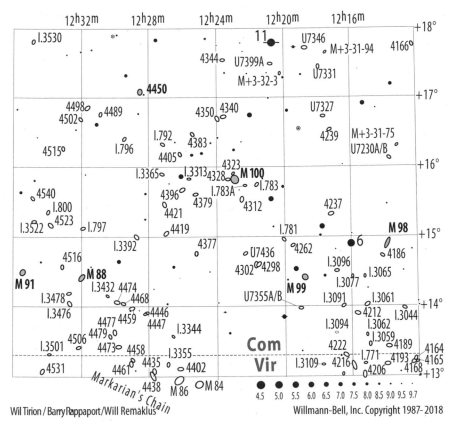

Figure 86: Galaxies in the general area of featured Coma Berenices galaxies. This approximately 5-degree scale map shows a rich field of galaxies brighter than magnitude 15. Grayed galaxies with bold labels are featured objects in this chapter. **Table 2** lists all of the Coma Berenices galaxies in the above map.

Table 2: Galaxies in the general area of Com featured galaxies (Cont.)

Name	RA h m s	Dec ° ' "	V mag	SB	size (')	PA	Type
NGC 4298	12 21 32.8	+14 36 22	11.3	13.1	3.2 x 1.8	140	SA(rs)c III-IV
NGC 4302	12 21 42.4	+14 35 57	11.6	13.3	5.5 x 1.0	178	Sc: sp III?
NGC 4312	12 22 31.4	+15 32 16	11.7	13.3	4.6 x 1.1	170	SA(rs)a: sp
NGC 4323	12 23 01.8	+15 54 20	13.9	13.2	0.9 x 0.6	140	dSB(s)0°:,N
NGC 4328	12 23 20.0	+15 49 13	13.0	13.1	1.3 x 0.9	90	dSA0-(0),N
NGC 4340	12 23 35.3	+16 43 21	11.2	13.0	3.0 x 2.0	102	SB(r)0+
NGC 4344	12 23 37.5	+17 32 27	12.3	13.3	1.7 x 1.6	90	SA?(r)0°
NGC 4350	12 23 57.9	+16 41 36	11.0	12.4	3.0 x 1.4	28	SA:0⁻: sp
NGC 4377	12 25 12.3	+14 45 44	11.9	12.7	1.7 x 1.4	177	SAB(rs)0°

Table 2: Galaxies in the general area of Com featured galaxies (Cont.)

Name	RA h m s	Dec ° ' "	V mag	SB	size (')	PA	Type
NGC 4379	12 25 14.8	+15 36 27	11.7	12.8	1.9 x 1.6	105	SB(s)0⁻
NGC 4383	12 25 25.5	+16 28 12	12.1	12.7	1.9 x 1.0	28	Sa? sp pec
NGC 4396	12 25 59.0	+15 40 17	12.6	13.7	3.3 x 1.0	125	SA(s)d: sp III-IV:
NGC 4402	12 26 07.6	+13 06 46	11.7	13.2	3.9 x 1.1	90	Sab: sp
NGC 4405	12 26 07.2	+16 10 52	12.0	12.6	1.8 x 1.1	20	SAB:(rs)a:
NGC 4419	12 26 56.4	+15 02 51	11.2	12.4	3.3 x 1.1	133	SB?(rs:)a sp
NGC 4421	12 27 02.5	+15 27 41	11.6	13.3	2.7 x 2.0	20	SB(s)0/a
NGC 4435	12 27 40.5	+13 04 44	10.8	12.5	2.8 x 2.0	13	SB(s:)0°:
NGC 4438	12 27 45.7	+13 00 32	10.2	13.6	8.5 x 3.2	27	SA?(s?)0/a pec
NGC 4446	12 28 06.8	+13 54 42	13.9	13.6	1.1 x 0.8	106	SA(rs)c I-II
NGC 4447	12 28 12.5	+13 53 57	14.0	13.3	0.9 x 0.7	105	SAB(rs)0⁺
NGC 4450	12 28 29.6	+17 05 06	10.1	13.2	5.2 x 3.9	175	SA(s)ab I-II
NGC 4458	12 28 57.6	+13 14 31	12.1	13.1	1.7 x 1.6	45	E1
NGC 4459	12 29 00.0	+13 58 43	10.4	12.7	3.5 x 2.7	110	SA0⁻
NGC 4461	12 29 03.0	+13 11 02	11.2	12.8	3.5 x 1.4	9	SAB(rs)0°
NGC 4468	12 29 30.9	+14 02 57	12.8	13.1	1.4 x 1.1	73	SA(r)0°:
NGC 4473	12 29 48.9	+13 25 46	10.2	12.8	4.5 x 2.5	94	E5
NGC 4474	12 29 53.5	+14 04 07	11.5	12.7	2.4 x 1.4	80	S0°: sp
NGC 4477	12 30 02.2	+13 38 11	10.4	13.1	3.8 x 3.5	9	SB(r)0⁺
NGC 4479	12 30 18.1	+13 34 40	12.4	13.0	1.5 x 1.3	24	SB(s)0°
NGC 4489	12 30 52.3	+16 45 32	12.0	13.0	1.7 x 1.5	165	SA(r)0⁻
NGC 4498	12 31 39.5	+16 51 10	12.2	13.3	2.9 x 1.1	133	SB(rs)d III
NGC 4502	12 32 03.2	+16 41 14	13.9	13.3	1.1 x 0.6	40	SA(s)dm III-IV
NGC 4506	12 32 10.5	+13 25 11	12.7	13.2	1.6 x 1.1	110	SAB(rs)a: pec?
NGC 4515	12 33 05.0	+16 15 56	12.3	12.6	1.3 x 1.1	9	SAB0⁻
NGC 4516	12 33 07.5	+14 34 30	12.8	13.2	1.7 x 1.0	7	SB(rs)0°:
NGC 4523	12 33 48.0	+15 10 06	14.1	15.4	2.0 x 1.9	45	SAB(s)m IV-V
NGC 4531	12 34 15.9	+13 04 31	11.4	13.3	3.1 x 2.0	155	SA(r)a
NGC 4540	12 34 50.8	+15 33 05	11.7	12.7	1.9 x 1.5	40	SAB(s)cd III-IV
UGC 7230a	12 13 37.7	+16 07 10	14.9	14.9	1.4 x 0.9	5	SB(rs)cd pec
UGC 7230b	12 13 39.6	+16 07 31	16.4	14.3	0.6 x 0.3	7	SB(rs)d: pec
UGC 7327	12 17 37.7	+16 43 39	14.9	13.6	1.7 x 0.2	91	Sc: sp II-III?
UGC 7331	12 17 53.5	+17 26 32	13.6	13.5	1.5 x 0.7	0	(R')SAB(rs)b
UGC 7346	12 18 41.8	+17 43 07	14.6	16.2	2.2 x 2.2		dS0
UGC 7355A/B	12 19 03.5	+13 58 54	14.9	15.0	1.5 x 0.9		SABm IV-V + dSA0:
UGC 7399A	12 20 48.8	+17 29 14	13.6	14.0	1.7 x 1.0	85	dE/S0

Corona Australis

Corona Australis, the southern crown, which follows immediately the curved tail of Scorpius, is nevertheless sufficiently far north to be included in the original forty-eight groups of Ptolemy who assigned thirteen stars to it.

— E. J. Hartung

Corona Australis is squarely a summer constellation in the Northern Hemisphere, crossing the meridian in early August between 9 and 10 p.m. From latitude 30° north, the central portion of the constellation climbs to a maximum altitude of about 20°, roughly the same as the stars comprising the Scorpion's stinger, which lies due west. One is apt not to notice this frail grouping, however, given its proximity to the billowy star clouds and clusters of the Milky Way. It forms a curving arc of mostly 4th- and 5th magnitude stars, putting it pretty much in the background, though it is a pleasing sight in 7x50 binoculars, with the main arc of stars just fitting in the field of view.

There are no legends related to Corona Australis. Aratus does not name the constellation, but references it as a circlet of

Corona Australis, the Southern Crown	
Abbreviation: **CrA**	Pronunciation: **cuh-ROE-nuh aw-STRAL-iss**
Genitive: **Coronae Australis**	Pronunciation: **cuh-ROE-nee aw-STRAL-iss**
Midnight culmination: **June 30**	
Size on the sky: **127.7 square degrees**	
Bright stars: **None**	
Bright nonstellar objects: **None**	
Popular asterisms: **The Lemon Slice**	
Note: Double star Gamma (γ) Coronae Australis considered "superb" by John Herschel; region contains magnificent Corona Australis molecular cloud.	

Figure 1: Corona Australis, the Southern Crown. Celestial mapper Johannes Hevelius presented this small arc of stars as a contemporaneous crown, tangled in the forelegs of the centaur-archer, Sagittarius. Hevelius' atlas, *Firmamentum Sobiescianum sive Uranographia*, published in 1690, added several new constellations to our concept of the sky, most of which endure in our current maps.

stars below the forefeet of Sagittarius. To the Greeks it was not a crown but a wreath, though myth says nothing about to whom it belonged. Ian Ridpath, in *Star Tales*, suggests it may have fallen from the Archer's head. Julius D. W. Stahl, in *The New Patterns in the Sky*, tells us that islanders living in the Torres Strait, which separates New Guinea from the Cape York Peninsula of Australia, envisioned a canoe made from stars in the tail of Scorpius and Corona Australis. The canoe belonged to the creation deity Tagai. In southern skies, Tagai is seen standing in the canoe holding in his left hand a spear formed by the Southern Cross, and in his right a fruit called *Eugenia* (a botanical berry) formed by the stars of Corvus the Crow. The Boorong

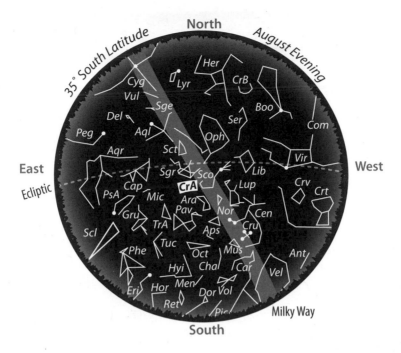

Figure 2: Corona Australis located on the celestial sphere.

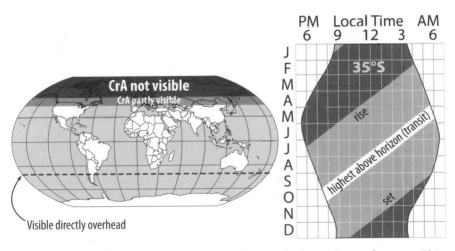

Figure 3: Seeing Corona Australis from the Earth throughout the year. This constellation is visible from 2/3 of our planet, biased to the Southern Hemisphere. The hourglass figure on the right shows the time at which Corona Australis appears highest in the sky across the months of the year and the duration of night at 35° S latitude. Transit times may be used at any latitude.

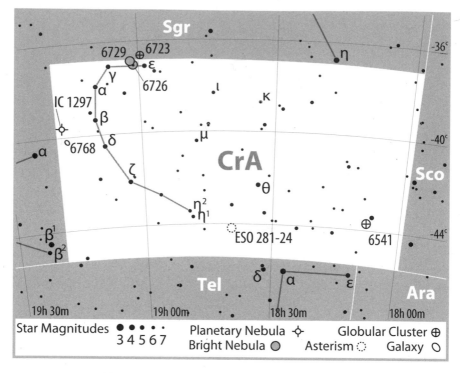

Figure 4: Corona Australis featured objects.

people of southeastern Australia saw Corona Australis as a boomerang thrown by Totyarguil (represented by the star Altair in Aquila the Eagle). Indeed, Corona does have a shape similar to that well-known airfoil. Totyarguil was a colorful mythological character who was killed by a Kelpie (Australian sheep dog) while bathing.

Corona Australis had its little moment of controversy in 1932, when the International Astronomical Union published a list of constellation names with alternative four-letter abbreviations. Readers may recall that the IAU established the constellations' names and three-letter abbreviations at its very first General Assembly in 1922. These, as well as the official boundaries of the constellations, were published in 1930 in two definitive references by Eugène Delporte, *Délimitation scientifique des constellations* and *Atlas Céleste*. Apparently, however, some IAU members demanded four-letter abbreviations in cases where saving space was unnecessary. In this list,

---

Corona Australis Featured Objects, North to South

NGC 6726/6727 and NGC 6729: reflection and emission nebulae in molecular cloud (**page 284**).

R and T Coronae Australis: galactic objects in front of NGC 6729 (**page 284**).

Gamma (γ) Coronae Australis: eclipsing binary of W UMa type (**page 278**).

Epsilon (ε) Coronae Australis: eclipsing binary (**page 283**).

Alfecca Meridiana, Alpha (α) Coronae Australis: rapid rotator: may possess circumstellar disk (**page 275**).

Kappa (κ) Coronae Australis: attractive fixed double star (**page 283**).

Beta (β) Coronae Australis: K giant star (**page 277**).

IC 1297: planetary nebula with elusive central star (**page 295**).

NGC 6768: binary galaxy (**page 301**).

NGC 6541: very old globular cluster (**page 297**).

ESO 281-24: probable asterism (**page 293**).

Corona Australis was respelled as Corona Austrina, with the abbreviation Cor A. Although the IAU repealed the list in 1955, the name Corona Austrina appeared in the official constellation list as late as 2008 (as did the obsolete constellation Argo). This has since been rectified.

Corona Australis lies along the shore of an ocean of deep-sky wonders in neighboring Scorpius and Sagittarius, but it has at least one thing going on within its borders: a major molecular cloud running east to west in its NW quadrant, along the border with Sagittarius. A favorite of imagers, the cloud is opaque in some places, but here and there stars shine through and reflect off the nebulosity.

NOTABLE STARS IN CORONA AUSTRALIS

Alfecca Meridiana, Alpha (α) Coronae Australis
Rapid rotator; may possess circumstellar disk

The Southern Crown's alpha star shares its magnitude value (4.1) with Beta CrA, but Alpha, at least, has a proper name:

Alfecca	Alpha (α) CrA)	RA 19ʰ 09ᵐ 28.3ˢ Dec −37° 54′ 16″
Meridiana	HD 178253	Mag 4.1 SpType A2V
Star		

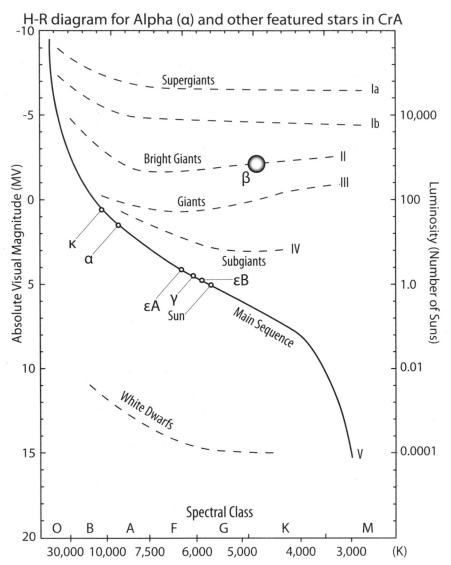

Figure 5: Alpha (α) Coronae Australis and other featured stars on a Hertz-sprung-Russell diagram.

Alfecca Meridiana. Once again, however, we are presented with the convolutions of stellar etymology. The name actually reflects the appellation of the alpha star in the Northern Crown, which has the alternate spelling of Alphecca. In medieval Arabic that name, applied to the entire constellation, means to separate or break. Perhaps Alphecca may be a reference to the Northern Crown's shape, which is a broken circle of stars. The word "Meridiana" is curious as such a name usually refers to the Sun's position on the meridian at noon ("ad meridiem"), though an alternate translation of ad meridiem is "to the south." At any rate, for observers in the Northern Hemisphere, the star's name may indicate the direction in which it may be found.

Alfecca is an ordinary A-class hydrogen-burning dwarf star located some 40 parsecs (130 light-years) in the direction of the Corona Australis molecular cloud. It has a radius a little over twice that of the Sun and is about 30 times more luminous. Like many A-class stars it is a rapid rotator, spinning at 180 kilometers per second. What makes this star a bit more exceptional is that it exhibits an infrared excess, indicating the possible presence of a circumstellar disk. It's a borderline case, as various investigations have detected the excess but have had difficulty separating out its signal from contamination by the molecular cloud. High-resolution mid-infrared observations (Moerchen et al., 2010) estimate that if there is unresolved emission arising from dust in a disk, it should have temperatures of at least 246 K. (Note that room temperature is considered to be about 298 K.) The color temperature of this excess emission corresponds to that of dust particles emitting like blackbodies in the region of the asteroid belt (1–3 AU). The star's mass of 2.5 times solar, and its estimated age of 255 million years, place it halfway through its main-sequence lifetime.

Beta (β) Coronae Australis

K giant star

There is even less to say about Beta. Its magnitude, as mentioned previously, is on par with Alfecca Meridiana. Perhaps it

Beta (β) Corona Australis Star	HD 178345 HIP 94160	RA 19^h 10^m 01.7^s Dec −39° 20′ 27″ Mag 4.1 SpType K0II/IIICNIb

comes in second because it is an orange giant, class K, and hence may appear a tad fainter than the blue-white alpha star. On the other hand, Beta is far more luminous than Alfecca, over 700 times solar. The radius comes in at 43 times that of the Sun, and the effective temperature is around 4,575 K. James Kaler notes that the mass is probably 5 $M_\odot$, and that it is presently stably fusing helium as a red "clump star" (for its position on the H-R diagram with other similarly evolved stars). It began life some 100 million years ago as a hot class B star. As it proceeded from the main sequence toward the higher luminosities of giant stars, cyanogen bands increasingly strengthened as lower atmospheric pressures fostered the molecule's formation, (hence the CN prefix in its spectral classification). The distance is around 145 parsecs (470 light-years).

Gamma (γ) Coronae Australis
Close visual binary star

A much neglected binary, Gamma Coronae Australis has been mentioned in the literature just 39 times in over 167 years, and there is little in the way of dedicated research. No doubt, though, amateur astronomers have observed it far more than that. John Herschel discovered the binary in 1834 and described it as "superb." His measured separation (1.2″) has changed little since (1.4″), but the position angle has changed over time so that a proper orbit of 122 years has been determined. E. J. Hartung describes it as a "fine bright object, neatly resolved in a 7.5 cm and a good pair to watch at intervals."

The distances cited in various studies range between 11 and 60 parsecs. Most, however, fall between 16 and 18 parsecs. That cited by the Extended *Hipparcos* Compilation is 17.3 parsecs (56 light-years), so this star can be considered a neighbor. At that distance, the pair has a mean separation of 33 AU; the high orbital eccentricity brings them as close as 22 AU and as

Gamma (γ) Coronae Australis	HD 177474J	RA 19h 06m 25.1s Dec –37° 03′ 48″
	HIP 93825	Mag 4.5 + 6.4 SpType F8V+F8V
Double or Multiple Star		PA 338° Sep 1.40″ Epoch 2017

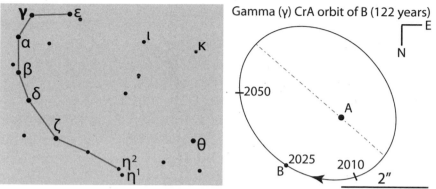

Figure 6: Gamma (γ) Coronae Australis, a close binary star. A bright star near the northward side of the crown, Gamma's orbit has been well-understood for a century.

far apart as 43 AU. Gamma CrA A (HD 177474) has a luminosity of 3.7 $L_\odot$, which works out to a radius of 1.7 $R_\odot$ and a mass of 1.3 $M_\odot$. The combined mass is 2.4 times solar and the temperature is about 6,200 K. Kaler tells us that these parameters may be up for grabs, as the pair cannot be fitted comfortably by stellar theory. The class and temperature, he says, are not known with precision. Although both components are often cited as F8 dwarfs, Gamma CrA A has been listed cool as G0 with a radius slightly over solar. Maybe it's time more concerted research was dedicated to this star.

Epsilon (ε) Coronae Australis

Eclipsing binary of W UMa type (contact binary)

Epsilon is in the northernmost arc of the Southern Crown asterism, tucked between 5th-magnitude HD 175362 (V686) and its associated reflection nebula, and another reflection nebula to the NW (IC 4812), which lies along the edge of the Corona Australis Molecular Cloud. The star is a contact binary of the W Ursa Majoris type, and the brightest of its kind in the Southern

Epsilon (ε) Coronae Australis Eclipsing Binary	HD 175813 HIP 93174	RA 18ʰ 58ᵐ 43.3ˢ Dec –37° 06′ 26″ Mag 4.7–5 SpType F2V Period 0.59 day (14.1 hours)

ε CrA system parameters and light curve

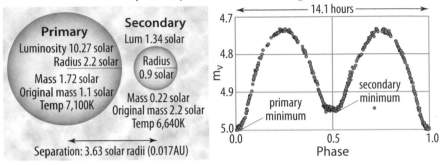

Figure 7: Epsilon (ε) Coronae Australis system physical description and light curve. The two stars that make up the system are described using parameters from Yildiz, 2014. The stars' shapes are not the crisp spheres shown in this simplified schematic, as they are actually quite distorted by their mutual gravitational interaction and loss of mass to the complex environment. As they orbit each other rapidly, the total brightness varies predictably, shown in the right panel that plots data from Tapia, 1969, using a 16-inch reflecting telescope with a refrigerated photomultiplier over five nights at Cerro Tololo. **Contemplative observing:** With the naked eye, find Epsilon CrA. Consider that this is a very close double star that slightly varies in magnitude over 14.1 hours. Know that over their nearly 3-billion-year lifespan, the smaller secondary has lost 90% of its mass, a small portion of that mass now a part of the larger primary.

Hemisphere. W UMa stars are intriguing systems, consisting of two stars so near each other they fill their Roche lobes to overflowing and are in physical contact, forming a lopsided hourglass-shaped system with one bulb of the hourglass larger than the other.* The true separation is 0.017 AU, or a little over 2.5 million kilometers. The orbital inclination of 74° creates a two-phase total eclipse in which the fainter component passes in front of the brighter one, followed by the brighter component passing in front of the fainter one. Such a system is classified an A-type contact binary. (A system in which the less massive star

---

* A Roche lobe is the region of space surrounding a star within which its atmosphere remains gravitationally bound. In a contact binary system, the Roche lobes of both stars "overflow," and their outer atmospheres create a common envelope.

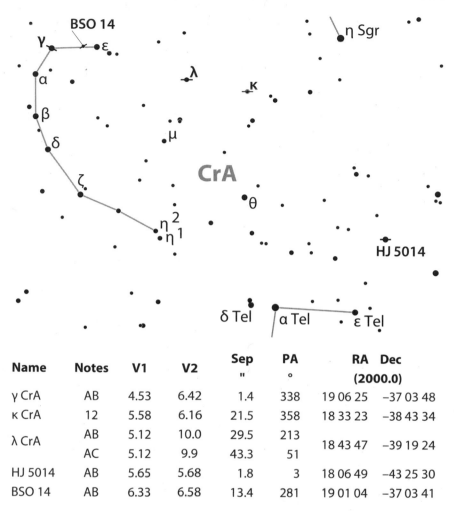

Name	Notes	V1	V2	Sep "	PA °	RA Dec (2000.0)	
γ CrA	AB	4.53	6.42	1.4	338	19 06 25	−37 03 48
κ CrA	12	5.58	6.16	21.5	358	18 33 23	−38 43 34
λ CrA	AB	5.12	10.0	29.5	213	18 43 47	−39 19 24
	AC	5.12	9.9	43.3	51		
HJ 5014	AB	5.65	5.68	1.8	3	18 06 49	−43 25 30
BSO 14	AB	6.33	6.58	13.4	281	19 01 04	−37 03 41

Figure 8: Corona Australis double stars for beginners. This is a set of easy double stars in Centaurus, presented in the style of William Olcott's 1909 *In Starland with a 3-inch Telescope.*

is more luminous is called a W-type.) The light varies continuously over a period of 0.59 days (14.2 hours) and exhibits nearly equal minima.

Gerard Kuiper coined the term "contact binary" in a 1941 *Astrophysical Journal* paper on the Beta Lyrae system, and the term has been synonymous with W UMa stars ever since. Kuiper qualified the configuration of such a system as one in which "not mere contact exists, but a common envelope as well." Of course, he was referring to Beta Lyrae, which is a semi-detached binary in which one of the components fills its Roche lobe but the other does not. Still, his paper developed quantitative morphological ideas and presented early insights into the mechanics and stability of close binary systems. In 1955 Zdenek Kopal, another pioneer in the study of close binary stars, made the distinction among detached systems (in which both stars are close but smaller than their Roche lobes), semidetached, and contact binaries. He was the first to suggest that the majority of close binary stars with spectral types from late A to early K (which includes the W UMa systems) may be contact binaries.

The Epsilon CrA parameters, based on a study of the properties of the system and estimated mass-transfer rate (Yildiz 2014) are presented in **Figure 7**. The "original mass" is an estimate of the stars' masses when the stars were created nearly 3 billion years ago. The secondary was originally slightly more massive than the primary, but over this period, a third of the system's mass was lost to the surrounding environment. Note that the masses of 1.72 $M_\odot$ and 0.22 $M_\odot$ endow Epsilon CrA with one of the highest mass ratios known among contact binaries. Also, the given radii do not indicate contact, because the two stars are so distorted.

Epsilon's variability was suspected in 1949 and confirmed by Cousins and Cox (1950) in the course of the Royal Observatory's "Bright Star Programme" at the Cape of Good Hope.[*] A photometric study of the star (Knipe 1967) produced the first continuous light curve at two wavelengths, 4,300 and 5,280 angstroms. The spectral type shared by the components is often cited as early F2 or F3, though some sources place it as late as F5 or as early as F0. Measurements of the stars' radial velocities (Goecking and Duerbeck, 1993) show extreme differences and indicate that the principal star (the one showing the least motion) is eight times more massive than the secondary. Spectra indicate that the rotation period corresponds with the orbital period. Their spin is rapid enough to create significant

---

[*] The Bright Star Programme, which began in 1945, provided accurate photographic magnitudes for about 800 stars south of the equator. It concluded in the early 1950s.

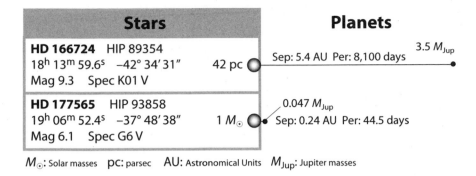

Stars	Planets
HD 166724 HIP 89354 18^h 13^m 59.6^s –42° 34′ 31″ 42 pc	Sep: 5.4 AU Per: 8,100 days 3.5 M_{Jup}
Mag 9.3 Spec K01 V	
HD 177565 HIP 93858 19^h 06^m 52.4^s –37° 48′ 38″ 1 $M_\odot$	0.047 M_{Jup} Sep: 0.24 AU Per: 44.5 days
Mag 6.1 Spec G6 V	

$M_\odot$: Solar masses   pc: parsec   AU: Astronomical Units M_{Jup}: Jupiter masses

Figure 9: Two stars with planets in Corona Australis.

magnetic activity, which in turn produces star spots that supplement the overall variation as they wheel about a common center of gravity.

The distance generally cited is 30 parsecs, or 98 light-years. Kaler notes that Epsilon is a high-velocity star, moving along at about 60 kilometers per second, indicating this is not an inherent member of the solar neighborhood but one that happens to be passing through.

Kappa (κ) Coronae Australis
Attractive fixed double star

Little Kappa Coronae Australis lies outside the crown, 5.2° WSW of Epsilon. This is one of the finest fixed double stars in the constellation. The components, κ¹ and κ², are so similar in magnitude they look like twins. John Herschel made the first satisfactory measurement of this star in 1836. His position angle (359.8°) has changed very little (358° in epoch 2013), but the separation has slipped from 30 arcseconds to 21.5. Considered a line-of-sight double (the two have very different distance estimates), the pair nonetheless makes a pleasing composition against the dusty starry background. The separa-

Kappa (κ) Coronae Australis Double or Multiple Star	DUN 222A/B HD 170867/8	RA 18^h 33^m 23.0^s Dec –38° 43′ 12″ Mag 5.6 + 6.1 SpType B9V+A0III PA 358 Sep 21.5″ (Epoch 2016)

tion also makes it an easy object for small telescopes. One might even give it a go using 10x50 or 8x56 binoculars. Being so similar in magnitude, they may appear oblong or as a figure eight. Sissy Haas, in *Double Stars for Small Telescopes*, deems it a "showcase pair."

The alternate designation, DUN 222A/B, is a little confusing as DUN 222A is identified with κ^2 and DUN 222B with κ^1.

R and T Coronae Australis

See NGC 6729.

GALACTIC OBJECTS IN CORONA AUSTRALIS

The Corona Australis Molecular Cloud
Reflection and emission nebulae in molecular cloud

NGC 6726/6727 and NGC 6729

The Southern Crown's most striking deep-sky offering is a broad field of bright and dark nebulosity 38.5 arcminutes NE of Epsilon Coronae Australis, or 28.5 arcminutes ESE of the globular cluster NGC 6723 in Scorpius. Deep images of this area and points east reveal the bright nebulosity lies at one end of a dusky interstellar tail of obscuring material trailing well into Sagittarius. It goes by many names in the literature, depending on its various stellar and nonstellar components, but as a whole it is referred to as the Corona Australis Molecular Cloud (CAMC). The brightest portion of the nebula consists of two nodules of nebulosity in an oblong configuration oriented NNE to SSW. The northernmost nodule is NGC 6727 and the southern one is NGC 6726.

Like an offshore island, the bright/dark mass of NGC 6729 lies some 5 arcminutes to the SSE, within which smolder the Herbig Ae/Be stars R and T Coronae Australis. R is near the northeastern apex of the bright bell-shaped portion of the nebula seen in images, while T, 1.2 arcminutes to the SE, might be described as the bell's clapper. Both stars are very young, with

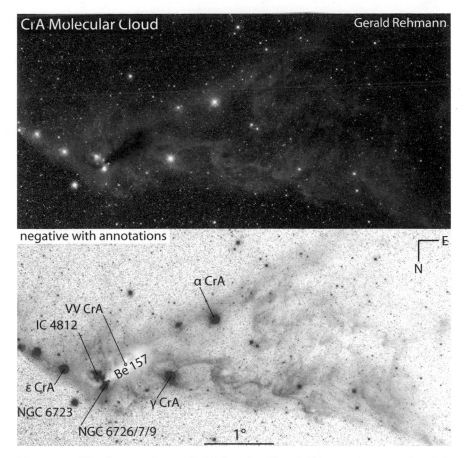

Figure 10: The Corona Australis Molecular Cloud. This massive, complex Galactic object (image courtesy ccdguide.com) is about 8 degrees across and contains many objects of interest, including several discussed in this chapter. **Contemplative observing:** Look at the upper part of the Southern Crown stars Epsilon, Gamma, and Alpha with the naked eye or widefield binoculars. Consider that active variable stars, a dark nebula (Be 157), and a massive cloud of molecules stretch like windblown smoke eastward from this arc of stars.

estimated ages (Herbig 1960) of between 10^5 to 10^7 years. Thanks largely to the brightness fluctuations of R (magnitude 10 to 14.3) and T CrA (11.6 to 14.3), NGC 6729 is a variable nebula. As with Hubble's Variable Nebula in Monoceros, observers and imagers may notice changes in its appearance over time. The nebulosity may appear "fluffier" at one interval, particularly on the SE end, while during the next it may appear

NGC 6726/6727 GN 18.58.3 Bright Nebula	RA 19ʰ 01ᵐ 42ˢ Dec –36°53′ 00″ Mag – Size 9′ x 7″ Type Reflection
NGC 6729 PP 87 Bright Nebula	RA 19ʰ 01ᵐ 55.8ˢ Dec –36°57′ 34″ Mag – Size 1′ x 1′ Type Emission/Reflection

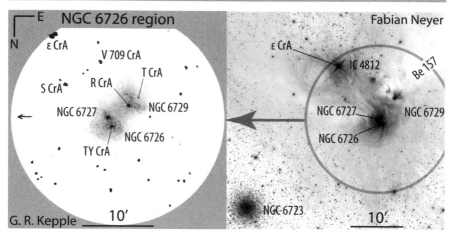

Figure 11: The NGC 6726 region. An eyepiece impression compared to an astrophotograph at right, courtesy ccdguide.com. The field includes globular cluster NGC 6723, dark nebula Be 157, and many variable stars, annotated.

more shrunken, with T CrA more clearly exposed. Visually, the brightest portion of the nebula is about 30 arcseconds in diameter; in images, it is well over an arcminute across.

In binoculars, one may also notice a northern version of the Coal Sack south and east of NGC 6729, where dense regions of dust obscure background stars. The entirety of the region spans an area, by our reckoning, roughly 50 x 15 arcminutes or more. This large expanse is often cataloged as Be 157 in star atlases. If, however, we refer to the source catalog for this object, "A Catalogue of Bright Nebulosities in Opaque Dust Clouds" compiled by Swedish astronomer Claes Bernes (1977), we see that he gives number 157 a diameter of only one arcminute. Moreover, its coordinates (1950) center it atop V 709 CrA, an Orion-type variable star with a magnitude range of 11.3 to 11.6. Surrounding this star is a small reflection nebula (which is how Bernes classifies it), which, indeed, is about an arcminute in diameter. It lies adjacent to a mass of obscuring dust immediately to the east, the beginning of the "Corona Australis Coal Sack," if you will. A SIMBAD search for this object, with the search term formatted "[B77] 157," yields coordinates for a "bright nebula" at $19^h 01^m 30^s, -37° 02' 00''$. As plotted in the Aladin Sky Atlas, these coordinates take you very near V 709 CrA. Clearly, Be 157 does not refer to the vast region of starless sky immediately to its south and east, but to the reflection nebula surrounding V 709 CrA. It appears this dark nebula has no formal name to speak of, though we note that some amateur astronomers refer to it as DN Be 157 (DN standing for "dark nebula").

The dark, sooty region west of the bright portion of NGC 6729 marks the densest cloud core in the region, with extinctions up to an astonishing 45 magnitudes. This cloud has several identifiers: *condensation A* (Rossano 1978), FeSt 1-445 and FeSt 1-447 (Feitzinger and Stüwe, 1984), and DoH 2213 (Dobashi et al., 2005). SIMBAD recognizes it as both CrA and R CrA cloud.

Another stellar inhabitant of the CAMC is S CrA, a magnitude 11 T Tauri star 9.3 arcminutes west of the NGC 6729 complex, shining within a Pleiades-like skein of interstellar dust. It has a 12th-magnitude companion at 1.4 arcseconds in PA 157° (epoch 2005). The spectral types are G0V and K0V. Some 6 arcminutes south of S CrA (or 28 arcminutes east of Epsilon CrA), we find a remarkable pair of side-by-side stars seemingly involved in still denser Pleiades-like drapery, designated IC 4812. The slightly brighter eastern component, HD 176270 (magnitude 6.4), lies 13 arcseconds WNW of HD 176269 (magnitude 6.7). Both are pre-main-sequence stars and are virtual twins, with spectral types of B8V and B9V, respectively. Moreover, both are spectroscopic binaries. The position angle and separation of the main components (epoch 2013) are similar to their first measurements in 1837, so this is likely a proper motion pair. The designation as listed in the *Washington Double Star Catalog* is BSO 14 (Brisbane Observatory).

Both NGC 6726 and NGC 6727 are immersed in overlapping nebulosity, which depending on aperture is visible as a double halo of greater or lesser extent. The outer edges are tenuous and streaky. In telescopes of 15 inches or greater, both nebulae are about 2 arcminutes across and contrast sharply with the surrounding field. Images reveal an even greater expanse, with nebulosity extending at least 8 arcminutes in diameter.

Visual observers will immediately notice a double star near the center of the 6726/6727 complexes. This is actually a multiple system, HD 176386, though only two components are readily visible: the brighter A component (magnitude 7.3) and the fainter C component (magnitude 9.5). Component C is the Herbig Ae/Be star TY CrA, an irregular variable with fluctuations from magnitude 9.4 to 9.8. The separation of the AC pair is 57.6 arcseconds in PA 23°. Component B (magnitude 13.4) is closer in, with a separation of 4 arcseconds from the primary at PA 137° (epochs 2016 and 2001, respectively) and pretty much involved in the glare of the primary. Both AB and AC have remained virtually unchanged since measured in 1927 and 1913, respectively. The C component is also an eclipsing double-lined binary. We will return to this system below.

German astronomers Albert Marth and Johann Friedrich Julius Schmidt are credited with independently suspecting the variability of NGC 6729, but Schmidt also noticed the variability of R, T, and S CrA. In popular literature, Schmidt usually gets the credit for the discovery of all three nebulae in 1861, while he was the director of the Athens Observatory in Greece. Schmidt is recognized mainly for his intense and detailed study of the lunar surface, but he is also esteemed for his thousands of measurements of variable stars, which is how he came across these objects. Beginning in 1911, NGC 6729 was photographically monitored. A comparison of photographs made between this year and 1913 unequivocally showed that the nebula was variable and that its variability was related to the star located at the northwestern apex of the comet-like nebulosity, R CrA.

Not part of the molecular cloud and its nebulosities, but nonetheless conspicuous, is the globular cluster NGC 6723, half a degree NW of the NGC 6726-6727 pair. We profile this object in a later section.

In general, molecular clouds are the coldest, densest, and most massive forms of interstellar matter and are sites of current star formation. They contain mostly molecular hydrogen, but also carbon monoxide and dust. Typical investigations seek to understand how fragments comprising tens of thousands of solar masses are able to condense from molecular clouds. Physical processes that are known to be important are gas pressure, gravitation, and magnetic fields. Energy inputs include winds and radiation from young stars, whereas energy sinks include gas cooling and radiative shock waves. These effects combine to affect the relationship between density and velocity dispersions at various scales, which may lead to fragmentation. There is still much to be learned about this process.

The CAMC complex is one of the nearest regions with ongoing and recent intermediate- and low-mass star formation, although for many years it posed an anomaly: it had all the features of a star-forming region but appeared to contain very few young stars. Over the years, a series of infrared surveys gradually lifted the curtains of dust and revealed a robust population of embedded infrared sources and a multitude of young stellar objects (YSOs), some of which are Class I (those that are just beginning to shine through their dusty domains). Beginning in the 1970s, seven Herbig-Haro (HH) objects were discovered in the cloud. In one case (HH 100), a reflection nebula was detected but no observable source of the illumination was found (Strom et al., 1974). In images, this object appears as a dusky wisp 1.5 arcminutes SW of NGC 6729. A 1984 survey (Taylor and Storey) revealed a compact cluster of about a dozen young stars (~1 Myr) around R CrA, and thus showed for the first time that the CAMC harbored a population of protostars (Class 0/I). Many of these have subsequently been detected via X-ray and radio wavelengths. The cluster was aptly christened the "Coronet" (small crown). At least five brown dwarf candidates were sifted out in 1997 (Wilking et al.). A comprehensive survey (Wang et al., 2004, **Figure 12**) not only confirmed the earlier detections but also turned up 12 new HH objects, mainly surrounding R CrA and VV CrA, that were probably created by outflows from these young objects. Other HH objects found in

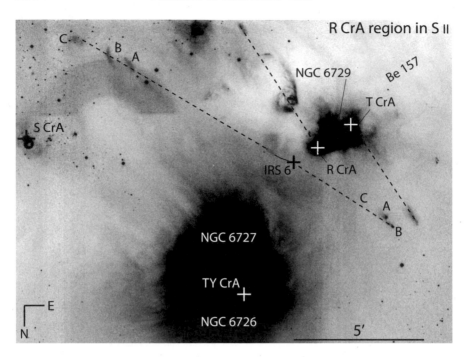

Figure 12: Possible optical outflows in the R CrA region. Wang et al., 2004, studied the nest of variable stars in the CrA Molecular Cloud. Looking at the radiation of a narrow band of sulfur emission (S II), they detected what appears to be outflows (dashed lines) from some of these active objects (crosses). More research is necessary to confirm this, though they assigned preliminary ABC labels to some of the knots. IRS 6 is a nebulous infrared source discovered by Wilking et al., 1997. Wang's work confirmed a number of sources in this chaotic region, and discovered others, several marked here. **Contemplative observing:** View this small field with the largest telescope you can. Know that this region is a chaotic place with many dynamic forces, some driven by a clutch of variable stars.

the region likely arise from outflows from S, T, and Ty CrA. The HH flows in the R CrA region indicate star formation in the cloud's core has been ongoing over the past 10^5 to 10^6 years.

VV CrA is of some interest. It is a binary T Tauri star (magnitude 14) located some 25 arcminutes SE of the complex in the middle of the dark cloud, and apparently all by itself. The separation is about 2 arcseconds in PA 44° (epoch 2001) and the companion is highly reddened. Indeed, images render a ruddy, slightly elongated object. When discovered in 1985, the companion dominated the near-infrared emission of the system, despite being invisible at shorter wavelengths. The companion, referred to as VV CrA NE, has since faded and now the visible component (VV CrA SW) is presently the brighter source at all wavelengths. The causes of both the high obscuration and the secondary's variability remain unknown, though two possible scenarios have been put forth for the former phenomenon (Smith et al., 2009). Either VV CrA NE is inclined such that we view it, or attempt to do so, through its circumstellar disk, or perhaps the primary's disk is the source of the obscuration. In any case, the variability may be caused by variations in the dust density of the environment, leading to changes in extinction. It is also possible that the former brightness of VV CrA NE was the result of a stellar outburst similar to that of FU Orionis, which is a pre-main-sequence eruptive variable. Intriguingly, both components host hot disks, but only one is visible at optical wavelengths. Models of the system (Scicluna et al., 2016) suggest a combined stellar mass of 1.7 $M_\odot$ and an age of 3.5 million years.

Another binary star of interest is TY CrA, briefly mentioned above. Infrared observations (Friedemann et al., 1996) detected excess far-infrared emission, indicating a massive accretion disk around the star. Eclipsing double-lined binaries like this are important because they can be used to derive the mass of both components directly from Kepler's third law. In turn, they can be used to test and calibrate pre-main sequence stellar models, thus honing our understanding of star formation in general (Neuhäuser and Forbrich, 2008). The primary's mass specs out at 3.16 $M_\odot$, while the secondary is 1.64 $M_\odot$. TY CrA was among the first intermediate-mass stars from which hard X-ray emission was detected (Koyama et al., 1996).

Dense molecular clouds of high visual extinctions and whose interiors are opaque to external radiation harbor a rich stew of molecular species. The CAMC is no exception. Millimeter-wavelength maps of molecular line and continuum emission (Lindberg and Jørgensen, 2012, **Figure 13**) detected emissions of formaldehyde (H_2CO), methanol (CH_3OH), cyanoacetylene (HC_3N), cyclopropenylidene (c-C_3H_2), cyanide (CN), hydrogen cyanide (HCN), and silicon monoxide (SiO). These occur on scales from 3 to 60 arcseconds (400 to 8,000 AU

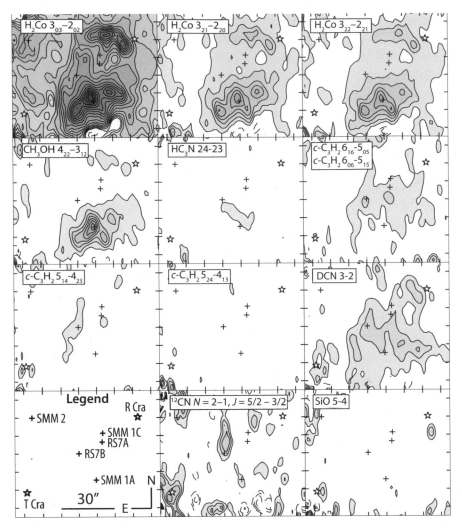

Figure 13: Radio observations of NGC 6729 region near R CrA. Two radio telescopes, the Submillimeter Array (SMA) and the Atacama Pathfinder Experiment (APEX), measured radio emissions from seven molecules heated by stars (courtesy Lindberg and Jørgensen, 2012). The richest signal is from the organic molecule H_2CO, formaldehyde, top row. The crosses are locations of previously known young stellar objects (YSOs), theoretically considered to be the source of the heating. As there is little correlation with the YSOs, it appears that R CrA (star symbol upper right in each frame) may be the source of the heating. It is remarkable that we are able to map concentrations of molecules in interstellar space by measuring their faint radio emanations caused by stars heating molecules to perhaps 50 K.

at 130 parsecs). Most of the H_2CO emission was found to arise from two elongated ridges, 6,000 AU and 1,500 AU long. The inferred temperatures of the H_2CO emission are no less than 30 K and more likely between 50 and 60 K. Such temperatures are too high to be ascribed to internal heating from the low-mass YSOs in the region. Moreover, the shape and location of the ridges with respect to the YSOs suggest that this region is strongly subjected to external, not internal, heating. However, R CrA, acting as an external heating source upon the envelope, could explain the temperatures. The morphology of the H_2CO-luminous ridges is comparatively symmetrical around the YSOs, which might indicate that the ridges are parts of a spherical shell around the low-mass YSOs.

CAMC is located about 18° below the Galactic plane and, hence, is not part of the Gould Belt. The 3-D space motions of the cloud's T Tauri stars suggest it formed via a high-velocity cloud impact onto the Galactic plane. In such a scenario, the high-velocity cloud may be destroyed, forming a lower-velocity cloud in its place. Alternately, the star formation in the cloud may have been triggered by the expansion of the Upper-Centaurus-Lupus (UCL) superbubble. The UCL is a subgroup of the Scorpius-Centaurus Association, which includes many of the hot, massive stars comprising the constellations Crux, Centaurus, Lupus, and Scorpius. (For more, see the Scorpius-Centaurus Association in Centaurus in Volume 5.) The cloud's complex has been found to be moving away from the UCL with a velocity of 7 kilometers per second. At that velocity, it would have been located near the UCL's center about 14 million years ago (Mamajek and Feigelson, 2001).

ESO 281-24

Probable asterism

This curious object is both perceived and identified as an open cluster, but it is more likely an asterism of unrelated stars. ESO 281-24 caught our eye while we were perusing some of the observing literature by amateur astronomers in South Africa and Australia. It is not often mentioned in most popu-

ESO 281-24	MWSC 2971	RA 18ʰ 40ᵐ 01ˢ	Dec –44° 12.0′
Asterism		Mag –	Size 5′
		~10 stars BT*Vm 9.6	Type II-III 1p

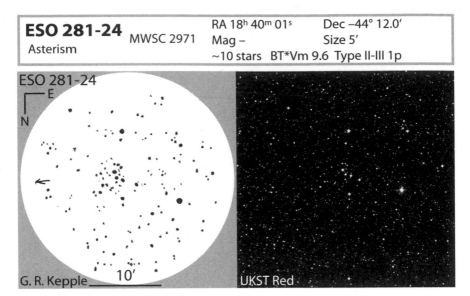

Figure 14: ESO 281-24. An eyepiece impression (left) compared to a survey photograph.

lar astronomy literature or software programs, though it is plotted in the *Uranometria 2000.0 Deep Sky Atlas*. The WEBDA open cluster database does not list it, but if you enter it into WEBDA's "Clusterix" online software program, which is designed to separate an open cluster's stars from the stellar background, you get a message stating "ESO 281-24 does not contain data needed for membership estimation." In other words, nobody knows how many stars are genuine members. After a little personal research, it is our opinion that none are. This is an asterism, which some observers appreciate while others looking for more stunning deep-sky fare do not. Those in the latter group may feel free to skip to the next object.

Due to the lack of observational parameters, the size, approximate number of stars, and cluster type are based on our own assessment.

The general area of ESO 281-24 is 1.7° WSW of Eta¹ CrA; more specifically, it is 7.3 arcminutes WSW of 7.3-magnitude HD 172144, a yellow-white F8 subgiant that stands out in the field. We recommend moderate magnification at first. Look for a tiny string of stars in a row, "pointing" at HD 172144. When you think you have it centered, crank it up to at least 200x. Four main stars form a "belt" extending almost 3 arcminutes SW to NE. One of the stars is slightly out of line from the other three, so the eye may see the entire assembly as a shallow arc of stars. A 10th-magnitude star (TYC 7927-179-1) floats 2.6 arcminutes to the north, and numerous 11th- to 13th-magnitude stars are strewn about the field.

The four belt stars are (SW to NE) TYC 7914-1781-1 (brightest), TYC 7914-1357-1, TYC 7927-913-1, and TYC 7927-53-1. Their visual magnitudes are 9.6, 11.2, 10.2, and 10, respectively. Based on parallax measurements made by the *Gaia* space astrometry mission, these four stars lie at significantly different distances; they also have different proper motions, hence, this is not a coherent cluster. Most open clusters have true diameters of no more than five parsecs. Of the four belt stars, the two nearest each other in space — 913-1 and 53-1 — are still nearly 30 parsecs apart, based on distances calculated from the *Gaia* parallaxes.

Other than HD 172144, none of the other stars mentioned have been assigned spectral types. Going out on the proverbial limb, we suspect that TYC 7914-1357-1 may be a giant or supergiant based on its ruddy hue and its considerable distance (1,700 parsecs) based on its *Gaia* parallax.

IC 1297

Planetary nebula with elusive central star

We find IC 1297 1.5° ESE of Beta (β) Coronae Australis, or 15.7 arcminutes WSW of 7.4-magnitude HD 180546, an RRAB Lyrae star with an irregular light curve and large amplitude. In their *Observing Handbook and Catalogue of Deep-Sky Objects*, Christian Luginbuhl and Brian Skiff remark that in a 15-centimeter telescope, the planetary is indistinguishable from a magnitude 10.5 star. We agree; at just 24 arcseconds in extent, it is nearly lost in the field, except for its pale blue hue and diffuse edges. In an 11-inch at high magnifications an approximate magnitude 15 star lies 30 arcseconds to the NNW. The inner disk appears slightly duskier than the rim, endowing the nebula with a torus-like appearance. An O III filter brings

IC 1297 Planetary Nebula	PN G358.3-21.6 PK 358-21.1 Hen 2-431	RA 19h 17m 23.4s Dec -39° 36' 46" Mag 10.7 Size 24" Central star *Vm 14

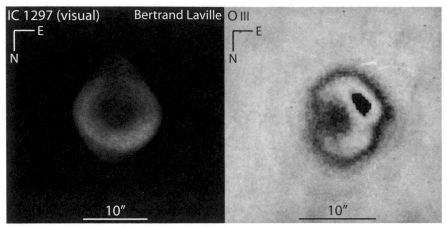

Figure 15: IC 1297. This small planetary nebula is depicted in a high-power eyepiece impression (left) compared to an early narrowband CCD image from Cerro Tololo, courtesy Aller et al., 1986. Image credit: Brad Schaefer.

this out still more, with the northern part of the torus appearing more pronounced. Short exposures bring out an icy blue color, and the hard inner edge gives way to an extremely tenuous outer aureole. If the exposure is not too deep, a faint star may just be seen offset from center to the SSE by about 9 arcseconds, giving the nebula an elongated, diamond-ring appearance. The central star, RU CrA, is a slow irregular variable with a magnitude range of 9.8 to 12.4. It can be glimpsed in good sky conditions, though not all observers report seeing it, probably owing to its variability. Having expended its hydrogen, the star is unstable, contracting and expanding as well as expelling its outer atmosphere, creating the planetary nebula that we now observe.

In the Perek-Kohoutek *Catalogue of Galactic Planetary Nebulae*, the authors echo George Herbig's conclusion that the planetary and the variable star are not coincident. A subsequent investigation, however (Bond 1976), found that they were identical, although the variations from 9.8 to 12.4 magnitudes were considered to be of instrumental origin. This conclusion was later contested (Aller et al., 1986). An *International Ultraviolet Explorer* spectrum was obtained with the strong O V λ1371 line, which is seen as a P Cygni wind-outflow feature in a number of planetary nebulae and accompanied by strong continuum features of stellar origin. However, it showed no trace of a central star, which made this object unique among planetaries. Subsequent analysis of *IUE* archival high-dispersion data did reveal a spectrum rich in nebular and stellar features. The terminal wind velocity measured from the O V λ1371 P Cygni profile was 3,670 ± 150 kilometers per second.

IC 1297 has appeared in numerous surveys, but little dedicated research has been done on this curious object. It is considered a high-excitation "double-ring" planetary nebula, a fainter analog to NGC 7662, the "Blue Snowball" Nebula in Andromeda. It exhibits an inner oval or broken ring with a 6.5-arcsecond radius surrounding a nearly round outer disk about 11 arcseconds in radius. In some deep images, a slight protrusion emerges from the inner ring on the north side, and it may possess a lane passing diagonally across the ring.

Just 36 arcminutes SSW is the magnitude 12 elliptical galaxy NGC 6768, which we profile later.

NGC 6541
Very old globular cluster

This very fine globular cluster may be found in the constellation's southwestern corner, 5.6° east of the visual double star Theta (θ) Scorpii and just within the edge of the Milky Way. Italian astronomer Niccolo Cacciatore discovered NGC 6541 on March 19, 1826, at the Palermo Observatory; James Dunlop independently discovered it several months later. Wolfgang Steinicke, in his *Observing and Cataloguing Nebula and Clusters*, notes that Cacciatore's description, that the object was "visible in the telescope in spite of moonlight and distinguishable in the cross-wire eyepiece," suggest Cacciatore found the cluster using the observatory's 3-inch azimuthal refractor. Dunlop, who observed the globular five times, was more expansive in his *Catalogue of Nebulae and Clusters of Stars in the*

NGC 6541 GCI 86	RA 18ʰ 08ᵐ 02.4ˢ Dec −43° 42′ 53″
Globular Cluster C 1804-4371	Mag 6.3 Size 2.4′
	Bt*Vm 12.1 Conc class III

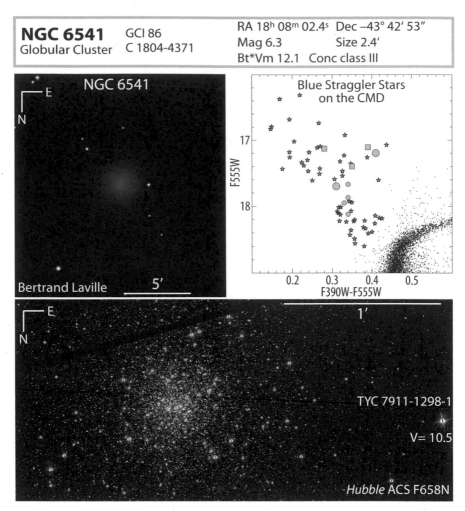

Figure 16: NGC 6541. This visually small globular cluster is depicted in a high-power eyepiece impression (upper left) compared to a high-resolution *Hubble Space Telescope* photograph below. An extract of the *Hubble*-derived color magnitude diagram (upper right) shows the blue straggler stars (BSS) in the central region of the cluster, spilling to the upper left from the turnoff point, courtesy Fiorentino et al., 2014. Imaging over time identified nine SX Phoenicis-type variable stars, plotted as circles (F pulsators) and squares (F0 pulsators), with regular BSS marked as five-pointed stars. **Contemplative observing:** Observe this faint remote globular with a large telescope and high magnification. Consider that this object spans a much greater area than it appears — out to a radius of over 7 arcminutes. What we see is the nucleus of a much larger globular cluster.

Southern Hemisphere:

> A very bright round highly condensed nebula, about 3' in diameter. I can resolve a considerable portion round the margin, but the compression is so great near the centre, that it would require a very high power, as well as light to separate the stars; the stars are rather dusky.

Hartung writes, "The combination of this globular cluster and its starry field is most beautiful; it is well condensed, round and resolved into gleaming stars, the outliers run up to 6' across." Luginbuhl and Skiff note that the cluster is visible in 3-centi-meter apertures as a "well-concentrated spot." In a 25-centimeter, the cluster is partially resolved and extends to 5 arcminutes in diameter. In larger telescopes at about 125x, the central region appears slightly more extensive and more defined, with a tight core of about 50 arcseconds, at which point stars begin radiating outward in a series of irregular chains. These soon fall off at a radius of some 3 or 4 arcminutes. A magnitude 10 star lies 1.7 arcminutes to the east. Deep images render a burned-out center that pretty well "absorbs" the magnitude 10 star, but the field, as Hartung describes, emerges dense with powdery stars.

NGC 6541 is categorized as an inner halo globular, one that is near the Galaxy's center. Chemical abundance studies of such globular clusters are problematic due to large interstellar reddening, but efforts beginning in the 1970s saw some headway. An early color-magnitude diagram (Alcaino 1979) found the cluster to be similar to the metal-poor M13 in Hercules, with a steep giant branch, a group of blue horizontal branch stars, and the presence of an asymptotic giant branch. Only one variable star was noted at the time, a long-period variable near the cluster's center with a variation of about 3.5 magnitudes. Multicolor CCD photometry for more than 3,000 stars in NGC 6541 (Alcaino et al., 1997) found that the main-sequence turnoff occurred around magnitude 19, with the horizontal branch extending over 3 magnitudes. It was determined that the difference between the magnitude of the horizontal branch and the turnoff magnitude could be as great as 3.7 magnitudes. Four blue straggler candidates were also found. Again, the metallicity was compared to M13, but also M79 in Lepus. The color magnitude diagrams, however, indicated great age, as much as 17 billion years! Today, an age of 13.2 billion years is often cited in the literature.

Subsequent photometry using the *Hubble Space Telescope* showed a well-defined blue horizontal branch, consistent with its low metallicity and age (Lee and Carney, 2006). More recently (Fiorentino et al., 2014), *HST* was used to probe the cluster's central region in search of variable blue straggler stars (BSSs). The observations enabled the discovery of three W Ursae Majoris and nine SX Phoenicis stars with average mass values of 1.06 $M_\odot$, which is significantly in excess of the main sequence turn-off mass (~0.75 $M_\odot$). In color-magnitude diagrams, BSSs are bluer and brighter than the main-sequence turnoff stars, often more than 2 magnitudes brighter. Hence, these stars mimic a young stellar population with masses larger than normal cluster stars.

Data obtained with the *Fermi Gamma-ray Space Telescope* revealed a possible gamma-ray source within the tidal radius of NGC 6541 (Tam et al., 2011). The offset from the core was about 9 arcminutes. Based on a distance of 7 kiloparsecs, the gamma-ray luminosity of the source was estimated at about 3.7×10^{34} ergs. The source was probably the coalescence of a close, low-mass X-ray binary, cataclysmic variable, or millisecond pulsar.

Slewing 1.7° WSW of NGC 6541 takes you to another globular, NGC 6496 on the border with Scorpius. A number of observing guides list this as being in Corona Australis, but technically it is more squarely in Scorpius. One would think it should appear brighter at magnitude 8.6, but its concentration class (XII) indicates a loose conglomeration of faint stars, the brightest being magnitude 14.3. Many of the brighter stars in the field are probably not members. According to observing notes in *The Night Sky Observer's Guide*, in 12- to 14-inch telescopes, NGC 6496 appears as "a faint, diffuse, 3-arcminute diameter patch peppered with threshold stars." As opposed to NGC 6541, this is a young (~ 10 Gyr), metal-rich globular cluster that hosts at least five to six long-period variables.

| NGC 6768 Galaxy | ESO 337-18 LEDA 62997 | RA 19ʰ 16ᵐ 32.5ˢ Dec –40° 12′ 33″ Mag 12 SB 12.5 Type E Size 1.2′ x 1.1′ PA 36 |

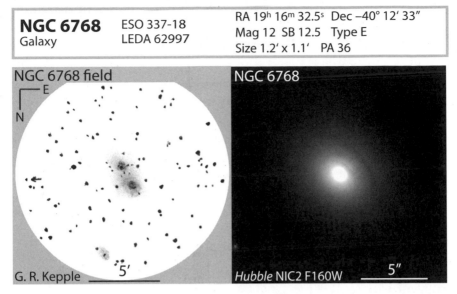

Figure 17: NGC 6768. An eyepiece impression of the field (left) compared to a high-resolution *Hubble* image of the galaxy's core.

EXTRAGALACTIC OBJECTS IN CORONA AUSTRALIS

NGC 6768

Binary galaxy

It should come as no surprise that Corona Australis, being in close proximity to the dusty Milky Way, is not brimming with bright galaxies. The ones that do abide within its borders are small and faint. NGC 6768 is one of the brighter ones. It lies exactly halfway on a line between Rukbat (Alpha Sagittarii) and Beta CrA, or about 36 arcminutes SSW of IC 1297. Although it has appeared in a number of catalogs and broad surveys, there are no dedicated studies. SIMBAD lists only 20 references to the galaxy since 1850. It is considered a binary system since it shares space with ESO 337-17 (40-arcsecond diameter, magnitude 14), which lies 1 arcminute to the SSW. Both galaxies have similar velocities and redshifts, and images (of which there are few) show overlapping haloes. NGC 6768 (but not ESO 337-17) was discovered by John Herschel in 1834; he deemed it vF, S, R, pslbM, or "very faint, small, round, and pretty suddenly brighter in the middle." In telescopes between 15 and 18 inches in aperture at high magnifications, NGC 6768 is exactly that: small, faint, and round, though in images it has a slight ovoid shape. ESO 337-17 may be glimpsed (barely) with averted vision. According to Steve Gottlieb, the pair is no problem in a 30-inch, with NGC 6768 sporting a bright, relatively large core.

In the *ESO/Uppsala Survey of the ESO (B) Atlas* (Lauberts 1982), both galaxies are classified as S0; NED and SIMBAD classify NGC 6768 alone as E4. Harold Corwin agrees with the S0 classification, but would extend it to S0⁻: pec, noting that both coronae are disturbed by the interaction. The distance is about 77 megaparsecs.

The pair lies about 5 arcminutes south of two other galaxies, ESO 337-16 (blue magnitude 15) and 2MFGC 14846 (blue magnitude 16.3). (The 2MFGC prefix stands for *2MASS Flat Galaxy Catalog*.) ESO 337-16 is a nearly face-on spiral and the latter is an edge-on system of unknown type. Judging by their velocities and redshifts, ESO 337-16 is the more distant of the two, but all four share similar redshift space. They are also very small systems, with NGC 6768 being the largest at 1.2' x 1.1'.

A chain of very small, faint "ghost" galaxies extends from the brighter pair to the east and ENE as well as to the SE. Most are magnitude 13 and fainter, but we can envision an enterprising imager placing all four of the bright galaxies on the northwestern edge of the frame and making a deep exposure of the "blank" field to the east and SE.

Yet another galaxy that may be of interest to observers with large-aperture telescopes is IC 4808, an SA(s)c-type spiral which lies 2.8° NE of Eta CrA, practically on the Telescopium border. The magnitude is listed variously as 12.3 to 13. It is highly inclined, about 2 arcminutes across its major axis, with a bright nucleus and, in images, patchy arms. At best, it will appear as a soft oval oriented NE to SW in a 15-inch telescope at 200x. A magnitude 10.3 star (TYC 8374-1692-1) lies 5 arcminutes to the SE.

This, too, is a neglected galaxy in the literature, though there is a very fine image in the Carnegie-Irving Galaxy Survey. The mean NED distance is 53 megaparsecs.

LOOKING TOWARD CORONA AUSTRALIS THROUGH THE MILKY WAY

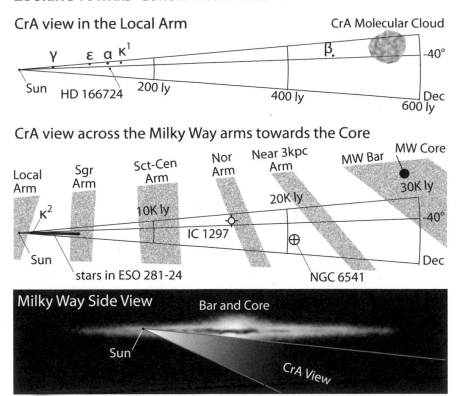

Figure 18: Corona Australis Galactic view. Corona Australis looks through some of the densest parts of our galaxy, from bright objects in the Local Arm (top) across the four arms that lie between us and the Milky Way core (center panel). The asterism ESO 281-24 appears to be a coincidental alignment of stars in the Local and Sagittarius arms, not a gravitationally bound cluster. Planetary nebulae emerge from stars, most densely in the Galaxy's arms, and globular clusters may appear anywhere in the halo, which is reflected in the placement of these two objects, though perhaps also a product of the figure's simplification of the irregular arm structures. Note that the view out of the Galaxy angles slightly "south" of the Milky Way (bottom panel), clipping the outer regions of the bar. Determining the structure of the Milky Way has been a long quest; this middle panel summarizes one consensus around a particular set of observations and measurements developed in 2008 and is likely not the final word.

LOOKING THROUGH CORONA AUSTRALIS: THE EXTRAGALACTIC VIEW

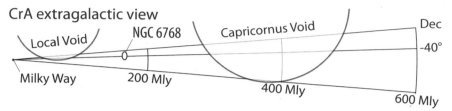

Figure 19: Corona Australis: extragalactic view. As CrA is heavily obscured by the Milky Way, we know little about the extragalactic structure seen in this direction. There are about 100 bright galaxies cataloged in this constellation, though we feature only one of the brightest, NGC 6768 and its companion. There are only three faint Abell Galaxy Clusters that do not appear to be a part of any currently known superclusters, and only one of their redshifts has been measured; all are well to the right of this figure. Anthony Fairall proposed two galaxy voids (regions of galaxy underdensity) intruding into CrA from the north: the well-studied Local Void and what he proposed as the Capricornus Void, though his evidence suggests that it is centered in Sagittarius, just to the north of Corona Australis. The International Astronomical Union has not established a uniform naming standard for large-scale extragalactic structures, so we summarize from disparate sources.

Figure Acknowledgments

Many astronomers, researchers, observatories, institutions, and publishers have generously granted their permission to reproduce or adapt their artwork in the figures in this book. Where possible, the full acknowledgment of the source appears in the artwork itself or the caption; where this approach is not practical, the full acknowledgment appears in this appendix. For images labeled POSS I, UKST, Arp Atlas, Hubble Legacy Archive, and Carnegie-Irvine Galaxy Survey, see statements at the end of this appendix.

Chamaeleon

Figure 5: NASA & ESA. Acknowledgments: Kevin Luhman (Pennsylvania State University) and Judy Schmidt.

Figure 5: Boulanger, F. et al., "CO and IRAS observations of the Chamaeleon molecular clouds," *A&A*, 332, 273 (1998). Reproduced with permission © ESO.

Figures 8 and 9: UKST.

Figure 9: Grady, C. A. et al., "The Environment of the Optically Brightest Herbig Ae Star, HD 104237," *ApJ*, 608, 809 (2004). © AAS. Reproduced with permission.

Figures 9 and 10: Feigelson, Eric D. et al., "The ε Chamaeleontis Young Stellar Group and the Characterization of Sparse Stellar Clusters," *ApJ*, 599, 1207 (2003). © AAS. Reproduced with permission.

Figure 10: López Martí, B. et al., "Proper motions of young stars in Chamaeleon. I. A Virtual Observatory study of spectroscopically confirmed members," *A&A*, 552, 46 (2013). Reproduced with permission © ESO.

Figures 12 and 15: UKST.

Figure 15: Bureau, M. et al., "The Shape and Figure Rotation of the Dark Halo of NGC 2915," *AJ*, 118, 2158 (1999). © AAS. Reproduced with permission.

Figure 15: Hubble Legacy Archive.

Figure 16: UKST.

Circinus

Figure 5: Weiss, Werner W. et al., "The roAp star α Circinus as seen by BRITE-Constellation," *A&A*, 588, 54 (2016). Reproduced with permission © ESO.

Figure 9: Bally, John et al., "Multiple CO Outflows in Circinus: The Churning of a

Molecular Cloud," *AJ*, 117, 410 (1999). © AAS. Reproduced with permission.

Figures 10, 11, and 12: UKST.

Figure 13: Hubble Legacy Archive.

Figure 14: UKST.

Figure 14: Vasquez, R. A. et al., "A detailed study of the open cluster PISMIS 20," *A&A*, 111, 85 (1995). Reproduced with permission © ESO.

Figure 18: Mingo, Beatriz et al., "Shocks, Seyferts, and the Supernova Remnant Connection: A Chandra Observation of the Circinus Galaxy," *ApJ*, 758, 95 (2012). © AAS. Reproduced with permission.

Figure 18: Greenhill, L. J. et al., "A Warped Accretion Disk and Wide-Angle Outflow in the Inner Parsec of the Circinus Galaxy," *ApJ*, 590, 162 (2003). © AAS. Reproduced with permission.

Figure 18: Hubble Legacy Archive.

Columba

Figure 10: UKST.

Figure 11: Hubble Legacy Archive.

Figure 12: Han, Sang-Il et al., "The Presence of Two Distinct Red Giant Branches in the Globular Cluster NGC 1851," *AJ*, 707, 190 (2009). © AAS. Reproduced with permission.

Figures 13 and 14: UKST.

Figure 15: Carnegie-Irvine Galaxy Survey.

Figure 15: Domgörgen, H. et al., "What perturbs NGC 2188?" *A&A*, 313, 96 (1996). Reproduced with permission © ESO.

Figure 15: Domgörgen, H. et al., "On the ionization of the diffuse ionized gas: spectroscopy of NGC 2188," *A&A*, 322, 391 (1997). Reproduced with permission © ESO.

Figure 17: UKST.

Figure 18: Hubble Legacy Archive.

Figure 18: Véron-Cetty, M.-P. and Véron, P., "NGC 1808: a nearby galaxy with a faint Seyfert nucleus," *A&A*, 145, 429 (1985). Reproduced with permission © ESO.

Figures 18 and 19: Carnegie-Irvine Galaxy Survey.

Figure 20: Salak, Dragan et al., "Gas Dynamics and Outflow in the Barred Starburst Galaxy NGC 1808 Revealed with ALMA," *ApJ*, 823, 68 (2016). © AAS. Reproduced with permission.

Figure 21: UKST.

Figure 23: Carnegie-Irvine Galaxy Survey.

Figure 23: Hubble Legacy Archive.

Figure 24: Carnegie-Irvine Galaxy Survey.

Coma Berenices

Figure 7: Gray, David F. et al., "The Rotation of the G0 Dwarf β Comae," *ApJ*, 475, 303 (1997). © AAS. Reproduced with permission.

Figure 9: POSS I.

Figure 10: Courtesy the Archives, California Institute of Technology.

Figure 11: Pace, G. et al., "The Wilson-Bappu effect: A tool to determine stellar distances," *A&A*, 401, 997 (2003). Reproduced with permission © ESO.

Figure 12: Wilson, O. C. and Vainu Bappu, M.K., "H and K Emission in Late-Type Stars: Dependence of Line Width on Luminosity and Related Topics," *ApJ*, 125, 661 (1957). © AAS. Reproduced with permission.

Figure 14: POSS I.

Figure 15: Hackman, T. et al., "Flip-flops of FK Comae Berenices," *A&A*, 553, 40 (2013). Reproduced with permission © ESO.

Figures 16 and 17: Korhonen, H. et al., "Study of FK Comae Berenices. V. Spot evolution and detection of surface differential rotation," *A&A*, 476, 881 (2007). Reproduced with permission © ESO.

Figure 18: Huenemoerder, D. P. et al., "A spectroscopic and photometric study of FK Comae in 1989," *ApJ*, 404, 316 (1993). © AAS. Reproduced with permission.

Figure 22: Rovithis, P. and Rovithis-Livaniou, E., "Photoelectric observations and minima times for RZ Comae Berenices," *A&A Supp*, 58, 679 (1984). Reproduced with permission © ESO.

Figure 25: Guerrero, C. A. et al., "Stellar Multiplicity of the Open Cluster Melotte 111," *AJ*, 150, 16 (2015). © AAS. Reproduced with permission.

Figure 27: Sarajedini, Ata et al., "BVI CCD photometry of NGC 5053: The most metal-poor galactic globular cluster," *AJ*, 109, 269 (1995). © AAS. Reproduced with permission.

Figure 28: Palma, Christopher et al., "On the Distribution of Orbital Poles of Milky Way Satellites," *ApJ*, 564, 736 (2002). © AAS. Reproduced with permission.

Figures 32 and 33: Chun, Sang-Hyun et al., "A Wide-Field Photometric Survey for Extratidal Tails Around Five Metal-Poor Globular Clusters in the Galactic Halo," *AJ*, 139, 606 (2010). © AAS. Reproduced with permission.

Figure 37: Braun, Robert et al., "Counterrotating gaseous disks in NGC 4826," *ApJ*, 420, 558 (1994). © AAS. Reproduced with permission.

Figure 40: Heald, G. et al., "The Westerbork Hydrogen Accretion in LOcal GALaxieS (HALOGAS) survey. I. Survey description and pilot observations," *A&A*, 526, 118 (2011). Reproduced with permission © ESO.

Figure 41: Kormendy, John et al., "Detection of a Pseudobulge Hidden Inside the "Box-shaped Bulge" of NGC 4565," *ApJL*, 715, 176 (2010). © AAS. Reproduced with permission.

Figure 43: Wevers, B. et al., "Neutral hydrogen observations of the interacting galaxies NGC 4725 and NGC 4747," *A&A*, 140, 125 (1984). Reproduced with permission © ESO.

Figure 48: Haynes, Martha P. et al., "NGC 4254: An Act of Harassment Uncovered by the Arecibo Legacy Fast ALFA Survey," *ApJ*, 665, 19 (2007). © AAS. Reproduced with permission.

Figure 49: POSS I.

Figure 52 : CFHT/Coelum – J.-C. Cuillander and G. Anselmi (2014).

Figure 52: Vollmer, B. et al., "Kinematics of the anemic cluster galaxy NGC 4548. Is stripping still active?" *A&A*, 349, 411 (1999). Reproduced with permission © ESO.

Figure 55: Rozas, M. et al., "Internal turbulence, viriality, and density bounding of the most luminous H II regions in the spiral galaxy M 100," *A&A*, 338, 15 (1998). Reproduced with permission © ESO.

Figure 56: Ofek, E. O. et al., "The Environment of M85 Optical Transient 2006-1: Constraints on the Progenitor Age and Mass," *ApJ*, 674, 447 (2008). © AAS. Reproduced with permission.

Figure 60: Nehlig, F. et al., "Effects of environmental gas compression on the multiphase ISM and star formation. The Virgo spiral galaxies NGC 4501 and NGC 4567/68," *A&A*, 587, 108 (2016). Reproduced with permission © ESO.

Figure 61: POSS I.

Figure 62: Hubble Legacy Archive.

Figures 63 through 65: Arp Atlas.

Figures 68 and 69: Reference plates B164a and B165a. This work made use of the Heidelberg Digitized Astronomical Plates (HDAP), which was produced at Landessternwarte Heidelberg-Königstuhl under grant No. 00.071.2005 of the Klaus Tschira Foundation.

Figure 70: Gregory, S. A., "The Coma/A1367 supercluster and its environs," *ApJ*, 222, 784 (1978). © AAS. Reproduced with permission.

Figure 71: Ramella, Massimo et al., "Groups of galaxies in the Center for Astrophysics redshift survey," *ApJ*, 344, 57 (1989). © AAS. Reproduced with permission.

Figure 72: Gu, Meng et al., "A Novel Approach to Constrain the Mass Ratio of Minor Mergers in Elliptical Galaxies: Application to NGC 4889, the Brightest Cluster Galaxy in Coma," *ApJ*, 733, 34 (2013). © AAS. Reproduced with permission.

Figure 72: Feretti, L. and Giovannini, G., et al., "High resolution radio observations of NGC 4874," *A&A*, 182, 15 (1987). Reproduced with permission © ESO.

Figure 74: Van Dokkum, Pieter et al., "A high stellar velocity dispersion and ~100 globular clusters for the ultra-diffuse galaxy dragonfly 44," *ApJL*, 828, 6 (2016). © AAS. Reproduced with permission.

Figure 75: Heidelberg University Library, Astronomische Ansichtskarte Nr. 8. Photographisches Fernrohr der Königstuhl-Sternwarte, Bild-ID 86852.

Figure 75: Heidelberg University Library, Max Wolf, Bild-ID 86954.

Figure 84: POSS I.

Corona Australis

Figure 12: Wang, Hongchi et al., "Optical Outflows in the R Coronae Australis Molecular Cloud," *ApJ*, 617, 1191 (2004). © AAS. Reproduced with permission.

Figure 13: Lindberg, J. E. and Jørgensen, J.K., "Strong irradiation of protostellar cores in Corona Australis," *A&A*, 548, 24 (2012). Reproduced with permission © ESO.

Figure 14: UKST.

Figure 15: Aller, Lawrence H. et al., "Spectrum and chemical analysis of the dou-

ble-ring planetary nebula IC 1297," *ApJ*, 311, 930 (1986). © AAS. Reproduced with permission.
Figure 16: Hubble Legacy Archive.
Figure 16: Fiorentino, G. et al., "Blue Straggler Masses from Pulsation Properties. I. The Case of NGC 6541," *ApJ*, 783, 34 (2014). © AAS. Reproduced with permission.
Figure 17: Hubble Legacy Archive.

Detailed copyright statements for Digitized Sky Survey Images (POSS I and UKST), *Atlas of Peculiar Galaxies*, the Hubble Legacy Archive, and the Carnegie-Irvine Galaxy Survey:

POSS I: Use of this starfield image reproduced from the Digitized Sky Survey (c) AURA is courtesy of the Palomar Observatory and Digitized Sky Survey created by the Space Telescope Science Institute, operated by AURA, Inc. for NASA and is reproduced here with permission from AURA/STScI.
UKST: The "Second Epoch Survey" of the southern sky was made by the Anglo-Australian Astronomical Observatory (AAO) with the UK Schmidt Telescope. Plates from this survey have been digitized and compressed by the STScI. The digitized images are copyright ©1993–2004 by the Anglo-Australian Observatory Board, and are used with permission.
Atlas of Peculiar Galaxies (1966), Halton Arp, Mount Wilson and Palomar Observatories. Published by the California Institute of Technology, Pasadena, California 91109, used with permission.
Hubble Legacy Archive (HLA) images are based on observations made with the NASA/ESA *Hubble Space Telescope* and obtained from the Hubble Legacy Archive, which is a collaboration between the Space Telescope Science Institute (STScI/NASA), the Space Telescope European Coordinating Facility (ST-ECF/ESA), and the Canadian Astronomy Data Centre (CADC/NRC/CSA) and are released via the HLA website, http://hla.stsci.edu/.
Carnegie-Irvine Galaxy Survey images are from an online repository, used with permission. The following papers document the research:
Ho, L. C. et al., "The Carnegie-Irvine Galaxy Survey. I. Overview and Atlas of Optical Images," *ApJS*, 197, 21 (2011).
Li, Z.-Y. et al., "The Carnegie-Irvine Galaxy Survey. II. Isophotal Analysis," *ApJS*, 197, 22 (2011).

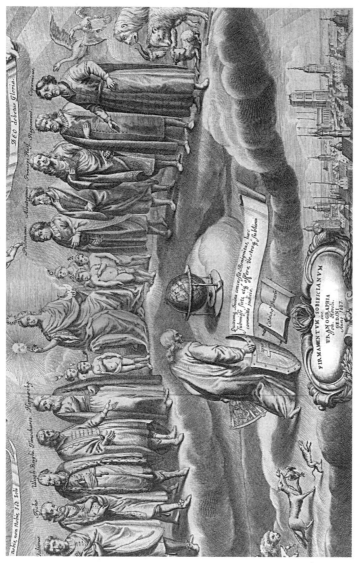

Johann Hevelius offers his atlas to a celestial pantheon. A detail from the frontispiece to Hevelius' *Firmamentum Sobiescianum sive Uranographia*, 1690, courtesy the U. S. Naval Observatory, depicts the astronomer accompanied by symbols of his newly proposed constellations, including Scutum (shield), Sextans (sextant), Lacerta (lizard), Canes Venatici (hunting dogs), and others; not all stood the test of time. Accepting his work are notable astronomers including Ptolemy and Tycho Brahe led by the seated Urania, flanked by symbols of the existing constellations and children representing the planets.

Index